THE BODY AT WAR

The body at war

The story of our immune system

SECOND EDITION

John Dwyer

J M DENT
London

© John Dwyer 1993

First published in Great Britain in 1993 by
J M Dent Ltd
The Orion Publishing Group
Orion House
5 Upper St Martin's Lane
London WC2H 9EA

Set in 10/11pt Palatino by Graphicraft Typesetters, Hong Kong
Printed by Kim Hup Lee Printing, Singapore

A catalogue record for this book is available from the
British Library

ISBN 0 460 86199 9

Contents

Introduction

WRITERS of books nearly always thank their families profusely in the introduction. So common is the practice that when an author fails to do it, one must suspect that there is no family to thank. If I ever thought such dedications were politic rather than deserved, the writing of this book has taught me otherwise. When one is fully occupied by a demanding career, finding time to write a book is very difficult. While for the author the writing may be a labour of love, for his family it is a demonstration of love, for the time that is normally shared with them is given to writing. For two years my family have lived with the great excuse: 'I must work on the book'. To my wife Catherine and my children Justin, Gabrielle and Christopher, then, my love and sincerest thanks for letting me produce this work.

Grateful as I am to my family, the book is not dedicated to them; it must be dedicated to my patients. For thirty years the sick and the weak have been teaching me how healthy and strong is the human spirit. I specialise in caring for people with chronic diseases. Their courage, patience and ability to structure quality into a life that at first glance has only quantity, is inspiring. I feel privileged to have been able to work in the field of immunology with such patients. Many of their stories are told in the pages that follow. This is therefore their book. Finally, I must thank the famous photographer Lennart Nilsson and Boehringer Ingelheim for permission to use their wonderful electron microscope photographs coloured by computer that allow us to actually look at the body at war.

John M. Dwyer
1988

Preface to the
second edition

THIS second edition of *The Body at War* is
being completed as I leave Budapest after a most successful Eighth
World Immunology Congress. Scientific excitement generated by
advances in the discipline of immunology was matched, as I'm sure
you can imagine, by the joy that was almost palpable among our
Eastern European colleagues meeting us for the first time and
knowing that their personal and academic freedom was secure.

Of course, the heady atmosphere of Hungary remains tempered
by the realisation on the TV screens of the world that millions are
having their immune systems compromised by starvation and even
lives full of terror.

We are fortunate that the first edition of *The Body at War* is well
and truly out of date. Our knowledge of just how the human immune system works continues to accelerate as the tools of the
molecular biologist allow us to pursue fundamental questions, until
recently shrouded in mystery. In many areas, as we will see, the
potential for immunological understanding and techniques to improve the quality of life for millions is being realised. Young men
and women, interested in a career in science, are increasingly turning
to immunology and indeed 90 per cent of the scientists who ever
worked in this field are doing just that today.

Nothing associated with the writing of this book has given me
more pleasure than the receipt of letters indicating that it was the
reading of *The Body at War* that led someone towards a career in
science with a special interest in immunology.

In this edition, we can discuss antigen presentation in a manner impossible in 1988. We know just about everything that there is to know about AIDS, except how to stop the spread of this dreadful disease and cure those infected with the responsible virus. All the important new information is presented here.

To put modern knowledge of immunology in perspective, I have added a chapter on the history of thoughts about the immune phenomenon. Progress in our knowledge of the subject has required a complete rewriting of the chapter on chronic fatigue syndrome and the introduction of the concept of 'tallergy' into our discussion of allergic diseases.

To those who wrote to point out mistakes in the first edition and to suggest changes which might make the subject more approachable, I am indeed grateful. The subject matter remains complex but to me more fascinating than ever. It is my sincere hope that, despite the inclusion of additional information, this book will still be found approachable by biological novices wishing to explore new concepts in their enthusiasm for an understanding of how their body works—an essential pre-requisite if more and more of us are to enjoy for a lifetime *the body at peace*.

John M. Dwyer
March 1993

Prologue

IMAGINE that you could stroll with me through a country fairground in Gloucester, England, in the summer of 1794. Here we are, a hundred miles to the northwest of London, and naturally we are intensely curious as we take our first close look at our cousins of 200 years ago. Our first impressions are less favorable than we might have expected. To be frank, our ancestors could do with a good bath and some eau de cologne. They are smaller than the average person in our own time, and many look sickly, even malnourished. We look at the faces, study the body gestures and peer into the eyes of these people as we try to learn something about their spirit.

We are struck by their poor complexions. At first we wonder if 60 to 70 per cent of these people have had bad acne, judging by all those scarred, disfigured faces.

In a side paddock, an uproarious competition is under way. Urged on by the crowd, a group of milkmaids is racing against the clock to fill buckets with fresh milk, squeezing with gusto on the udders of protesting cows. The eager young faces of these excited, energetic girls are beautiful; they have fair complexions and the disfigurements noted earlier among the general throng are not noticeable here. Why is it, we ask, that these girls have such beautiful skin?

This question has been exercising the mind of Dr Edward Jenner, a doctor in Gloucestershire, for many years. Jenner's eye for beauty, his skills in observation and his deductive mind combined to provide us with a great medical discovery that not only answered this question but saved millions of people from disfigurement or premature death.

To understand better what has been going on in Jenner's mind, we need to leave the merriment of the fair and travel just two miles to the south to meet one of Dr Jenner's patients. Twelve-year-old Billy Smythe is healthy enough, although he could do with a little more meat on his bones. He does not look much different from the other farm children who help their parents work the squire's land. However, if you look closely at Billy, you will notice that there is a slightly unnatural glow about his face. If you were to inquire, he would admit that he does not feel 100 per cent well.

All day long he has been aware of a headache and a few back pains but has told himself they are not worth worrying about, especially when you think of what happened to cousin Emily. Two weeks ago to the very day, she was playing in his house and seemed full of strength and good humor, even dancing around the kitchen table with him while his father played the fiddle. She had a rather long coughing fit after the dancing, but she certainly had not seemed sick. But now he has heard she is 'deathly sick'.

Emily died six days after her fever started. Billy lasted only two days longer.

Poor Emily, poor Billy. Just like millions of frail humans before them, they fell victim to a tiny brick-shaped foe they would never see. Billy's cousin Emily delivered him into the hands of the enemy. When she coughed over him, millions of the tiny invaders were propelled swirling into the air around Billy's face. Only breath was needed to vacuum into his lungs and thence his bloodstream tiny organisms that would destroy him. They took up residence in his liver and lymph nodes (glands), multiplied again and again inside his own cells, only to burst forth to invade the lining of his blood vessels and his skin. Fevers and muscle aches racked his tortured body. Blisters appeared on his skin to give way to deep, pusfilled ulcers, from which the infectious agent jumped to lie on clothes, on bed linen and even in the dust on the floor. In these places it awaited a new victim. Those infected by this ruthless enemy became so weak so quickly that other enemies could jump into the lungs and produce a pneumonia, causing the victim to suffocate slowly.

Not everybody engaged in this life-and-death struggle with the unseen enemy lost the battle. Some won, lived to tell the tale and fought further battles with more enemies. Their scarred faces proclaimed their victory over the enemy that came to be known as the smallpox virus.

With this background, we can understand why Jenner was so fascinated with the exceptional resistance to smallpox displayed by many milkmaids. They did not have to fight and perhaps lose the battle with this disease and as a result many stood out from the crowd as beauties.

Jenner had correctly surmised that the reason why the milkmaids did not contract smallpox had something to do with the disease that they *did* get. The cows of the day frequently suffered from weeping ulcers on their udders and milkmaids handling these infected parts contracted a not very prolonged or serious illness popularly known as 'cowpox'. A 'pox' in those days was anything that caused discrete ulcerated sores on the skin. Jenner did not know why, but observed that infection with cowpox, a minimally disfiguring condition, offered protection against smallpox.

After much professional and public debate he convinced the people in his area to let him scratch into the skin of children who had not had smallpox some of the material he harvested from the cows' ulcers. He had heard about the process of inoculation, that is, the introduction into the healthy body, usually the skin, of material obtained from a patient with a disease to try to protect one from that disease. A widely travelled Englishwoman, Lady Mary Wortley Montagu, had brought back from the Middle East tales of dangerous customs practised by the Turks and many others in the region that appeared to protect many from smallpox. In fact, we know that the Chinese as early as the fifth century BC were practising inoculation.

For centuries medical men, from physicians to magicians, had known that the crusted scab that formed over a healing smallpox ulcer on the skin could be protective. Unfortunately, it could also kill. If this dry crust was scratched into the skin (in China it was inhaled into the lungs) one of two things would happen to a patient who had never had a smallpox infection. An ugly ulcer might form at the site of the inoculation and the patient might suffer from fevers, headache and general malaise for a few days and then recover splendid health, protected from smallpox forever. On the other hand, the results of the inoculation might lead to a full-blown attack of smallpox with scarring or death. (Given the danger associated with the procedure, it is an interesting comment on the sexist nature of Turkey in the sixteenth century that fathers insisted on their daughters being inoculated to protect their beauty.)

To comprehend why so many people went ahead and took the risk involved in such inoculation, one has to understand the odds that were being faced. In many areas 20 per cent would actually contract smallpox from the inoculation itself, but without it the figure for smallpox victims frequently exceeded 75 per cent of the population. Of the latter group, at least 60 per cent could be expected to die.

In all ancient medicine nothing was more revered than the property of the 'pox dust'. Physicians of all persuasions harvested it diligently and stored it as if it were gold. Unlike the majority of ancient medications, this one really worked.

A few years ago I was invited by the United States Agency for International Development to visit several countries in West Africa to advise on a number of matters. Unable to walk away from the problems that I encountered on that first visit, I have returned on many occasions since to work on various projects.

On one visit to Bamako, the capital city of Mali, I attended a large meeting of the Malian Medical Society organised for no other reason than to allow the country's minister of health to talk tribal physicians into surrendering their smallpox dust to health authorities.

The World Health Organisation had masterminded a military offensive against smallpox and, as a result of worldwide vaccination efforts, had been able to declare that smallpox was defeated. Vaccination procedures could stop. Two potential sources for the reintroduction of this disease remain, however. Some modern laboratories have live virus stored away for research efforts, and some thousands of traditional doctors in Africa and elsewhere have tons of pox dust in which, sleeping quietly but full of virility, are billions of smallpox viruses.

After some debate it was clear that the traditional doctors would not do as they were asked. Smallpox had been here forever and would be here forever and nothing would make them surrender their most powerful medicine. The west African landscape remains covered with biological timebombs.

Without any knowledge that there were micro-organisms that could cause disease, Dr Jenner nevertheless reasoned that cowpox disease (remember that there was no concept of infection) changed one's body so that smallpox could not occur. That is why the milkmaids and many farmers who contracted cowpox were spared from smallpox. To honor Jenner's pioneering work with cowpox (the technical name for which is *vaccinia*) we call all those materials that when injected into the body produce protection from a specific illness, vaccines. The procedure for introducing these materials into the body is known as vaccination.

What exactly happened when Dr Jenner scratched the protective pus into the backside of those no doubt protesting young children all those years ago? How were the children's immune systems stimulated and armed with weapons that could kill the smallpox virus? How does knowledge of such mechanisms relate to problems we still encounter today, such as eczema, AIDS, poison ivy, cancer, sensitivity to bee stings, disorders in pregnancy and bone marrow transplants? We are about to explore the answers to these and many other questions.

Today most people are interested in how their body works and perhaps even more interested in why it may not work. This is a very healthy attitude. But too much of what is presented as authoritative is just plain wrong. A recent irresponsible statement in a tabloid newspaper reported that a clinic in the west of the United States could cure cancer in AIDS victims by the daily administration of caffeine enemas. Desperate people, seeking hope as much as cure, flock to such clinics, only to be robbed before they die.

Most medical publications for lay people, even if correct, are so patronising that the simplifications offered must ultimately be unsatisfying to any intelligent reader who wants to understand *why*. It is with this understanding that this book has been written. While it may help people to enjoy better health, its primary purpose is to inform and to illustrate how entertaining and even fascinating the study of the body's workings can be.

With this in mind I will not insult the reader with over-simplification or avoidance of complex details; even the 'mumbo jumbo' that is the terminology of our science will be included. I want to piece together for you one of the most, if not the most, fascinating of all biological jigsaw puzzles and help you find the excitement that I feel you will enjoy when you understand and say, 'Isn't that incredible!'

Our exploration of immunology, of course, must not be slow, tedious and unrewarding. This is not in any way a textbook; rather, my intention is to model this book on the symphonies of Sibelius. As the climax of the symphony arrives, fragments of self-contained melody come together and suddenly such a flood of luscious melody is released that the heart sings and the soul stirs. While I cannot guarantee that anyone reading this book will enjoy such an experience, I am building my 'symphony' with fragments that will lead us to that sustained melody that is a full understanding of the role of the immune system in daily life.

In so many areas—from allergies to arthritis, from transplantation to viral disease, from T cells to bereavement—the immunologist is involved. I want to show you the excitement that is immunology, the future that is immunology, and make you familiar with that complex but approachable system in whose integrity rests the body's ability to avoid so many diseases.

PART 1

THE WAR AND THE WARRIORS

1

Why we need an immune system

In the fall of 1972, I met an intelligent and worried mother. She told a distressing tale, as puzzling as it was intriguing. Now twenty-eight years of age, she had given birth to three children. The first, a boy, had been perfectly well and developed normally until he was thirteen months old. At that time the young family to which he belonged lived in rural Illinois. When the baby developed his first bout of high fever and irritability, his mother was not unduly concerned; she did not panic when their family doctor took a few hours to come to the house. However, the physician soon recognised that the baby's condition was worrisome: the child was toxic. Alarmed, he arranged for his admission to the nearest hospital, which was a good fifty miles from his home.

Meningitis was suspected and then confirmed when streptococcal bacteria of a particular type known as *pneumo-coccus* were found in the child's spinal fluid. Despite massive doses of appropriate antibiotics, he died twelve hours after admission. An autopsy revealed overwhelming sepsis but no clues as to why this previously healthy child should have become sick and died within twenty-four hours. A tragedy of course, lots of unanswered questions certainly but, consoled the family doctor, 'These things happen occasionally, bacteria can be deadly. You are young and time and your future children will help ease this pain.'

The next baby born to this couple was a girl, who arrived a year after the loss of their first child. Indeed, it was true that time and this beautiful infant did ease that earlier pain, for a while, at least.

She was in perfect health and when she was fifteen months old, the family moved to Detroit. When, out of the blue, the child developed the onset of a high fever and listlessness, the now sensitised parents immediately rushed her to the emergency room of a university hospital.

She was admitted for observation and her condition rapidly deteriorated. Meningitis was diagnosed, together with pneumonia. The parents must have felt desperate as the all too easily remembered scenario unfolded before them yet again. The same bacteria that had killed their son were found in their daughter's spinal fluid. Again, antibiotics were administered in large doses but were useless against the rapidly multiplying bacteria. Once more, these parents lost their baby within twenty-four hours of the onset of the illness. An autopsy was performed but showed no obvious abnormalities; the baby had simply been overwhelmed by the virulent organisms.

Another consulting physician in another hospital office did his best to answer the parents' anguished questions. How could this have happened to two babies, both appearing to be so healthy in their first year of life? 'It may be coincidence,' said the Detroit pediatrician, 'but it is also possible that there is a genetic defect in. your children. Perhaps your babies do not have normal immune systems. They certainly seem to have been unable to present any defence with which to fight these invading bacteria.'

After much anguish, the parents decided on a third attempt at parenthood. A second beautiful and healthy baby girl entered their lives. When this most precious of children was nine months of age, the mother brought her to my clinic and told me the story.

'I know you are going to say the baby looks normal and has had no serious problem and therefore there is nothing to worry about at this stage, but this was true of my other children as well,' she said. 'Please take my baby and find out if she does have a weakness that will stop her from fighting bacteria. Don't let this baby be taken away from me.'

Needless to say, all of us in the clinic were moved by this story and the anguish that the mother was clearly experiencing. She had read extensively and knew that she wanted all the defence mechanisms that act in concert to constitute our 'immune system' checked for hidden, even subtle imperfections.

To the best of our ability we obliged. We contacted the hospitals where the first two children had died. No help was obtained from Illinois, but Detroit told us that they had in retrospect checked the second baby's serum to determine if normal amounts of antibodies (bacteria-fighting chemicals that we will discuss in detail a little later) had been present in normal amounts. No abnormalities were found.

We tested the third baby's blood and secretions for antibodies. We immunised the child with a new vaccine against pneumococcal bacteria. We challenged her white blood cells in our test tubes and in every test that we performed, the baby appeared to be perfectly normal.

Six weeks later the mother, holding her baby close to her, heard the words she wanted to hear from this immunologist: 'I don't know what was wrong with the babies that you lost, but this little one is in perfect condition and has responded well to the new vaccine that we gave her. I am confident that her immune system is working well. Please put the past behind you, relax and enjoy her.'

Four months later, the mother called to tell me that her baby was dead. The news devastated me more than any other professional loss.

The story of the third loss had been identical to that of the other two, with a distraught mother failing to save her child, despite early and competent medical attention.

I have begun my introduction of immunology at this low point for a number of reasons. Firstly, the cases we have discussed allow one to emphasise the lethal potential of the microbial enemies with which we are all constantly battling. Indeed, every day many people, for various reasons, are overwhelmed by infections and die within twenty-four hours. These cases which so baffled us in 1972 also illustrate how rapidly this youngest of clinical specialities is moving. For today, presented with such a story, a correct diagnosis would immediately be suspected, readily established and life-saving therapy provided.

The three children described could not make certain types of antibodies needed to help defend them from certain types of bacteria. The word 'immune' is derived from the Latin word meaning safe. The Romans used it to mean 'protected from taxes' while we use it to mean safe from infection. The immune system is a protective apparatus that defends us from that moment when we begin to move down the birth canal to that equally dramatic moment when we need no further biological help. It seems to me logical to begin discussing immunity by explaining from what it is exactly that we need protection. The body's answer appears to be 'everything'. We human beings recognise our bodies as sacrosanct, and do not allow anything foreign to remain in our microenvironment. The only exception we make involves certain bacteria and fungi that live on our inner surface—the lining of our intestinal tract. Strictly speaking these organisms are not 'inside' us and indeed they are attacked viciously if they penetrate the delicate mucous membrane, a sort of inner skin, that protects us from mouth to anus. These organisms are tolerated because they offer us a service and do us no harm. They help us with both digestion and the production of vitamins.

If we will not tolerate anything foreign in our bodies then we must have a way of knowing the difference between the millions of components that make up our own special body (self) and anything else (non-self). The ability to make this distinction represents the essence of the biological miracle of immunity. We must therefore explore the mechanisms by which the body manages this most demanding of tasks.

Non-self can be divided into two categories that represent problems of very different magnitude. Non-self can be passive; that is, the invading foreignness might not be actively dangerous at all and it certainly will not actively attack us. A splinter in the finger and even someone else's transplanted kidney would come into this category. Our body will vigorously reject them both; useful in the case of the splinter, not so good with the kidney.

On the other hand, many examples of the non-self that our immune system encounters are very dangerous indeed, as we have already seen. The best examples include those viruses, fungi, bacteria and parasites that invade and will kill us if we do not kill them. In such cases, urgent action is necessary. Often we are dealing with an adaptable and in that sense 'intelligent' foe that knows its immunology. For example, many viruses can deliberately induce changes in our body that will suppress our immune system's capacity to fight.

One further enemy engages our immune system and therefore needs discussing. This one comes from within. Just as personality can change under various influences from delightful to disturbing, so that we may no longer equate the person we see today with the one we knew ten years ago, so bodily structures can change in just such a way. The biological equivalent to this change in personality is known as cancer. A woman with cancer in her breast has changed. The cells that may kill her are very like normal breast cells but there is a subtle and potentially lethal difference. These cancer cells, now out of control, were derived from normal breast tissue. If she (via her immune system) does not kill them, she may die because of what these genuinely malignant cells can do to normal tissues.

As we will explore in detail in a later chapter, the available evidence strongly suggests that in many cases of cancer our immune system efficiently recognises the departure of these cells' behavior and appearance from the normality of self and consequently destroys them. But in a number of situations in which certain types of cancer take hold, it appears that the immune system might have failed to realise what was going on and in this sense has let us down by exposing us to the ravages that will follow.

Throughout this book, the term *antigen* is used to refer to anything in our body that engages our defensive forces. Usually that something will be 'non-self'—but not always, as we will see.

Our sophisticated protective mechanisms do such a remarkable job on a day-to-day basis that, for most of us, antigens that enter our body are rapidly handled without their presence disturbing our health at all.

As we have seen, some antigens are downright hostile while others, though perhaps painful (such as splinters), are harmless. Before we meet the dangerous antigens that challenge our immune system—that is, the living microbial organisms that infect us and damage one or more parts of us, producing disease—there is one basic biological unit we must discuss in detail, otherwise all that follows will be unintelligible. That basic unit is the cell.

The cell is the basis of all living organisms, from plants to people. Cells are three-dimensional structures, most of which are spherical to cuboidal in shape and made up of walls or membranes that enclose an array of complicated internal machinery. Imagine that you have blown up a red balloon not with air but with water. Having distended the balloon you now drop a few small pieces of wood into the fluid inside the balloon before sealing the mouthpiece securely. Such an arrangement gives you a crude mental image of a living cell; expandable membranes surrounding a fluid space that contains specific and functionally crucial structures. Next, imagine placing twenty such balloons next to each other on the floor. On each, build a column of balloons by balancing twenty on top of each other. You now have a wall of 400 balloons (and a secure job with the Barnum and Bailey circus). Obviously, for such a precarious structure to hold together so that balloons do not bounce down the corridor, discharging their contents onto expensive carpets as their fragile membranes burst, the membranes must be glued together so that each touches the balloon above, below and to each side. If this is done, the result is a wall of balloons moving slightly, capable of swinging this way and that as pressures are applied. Now, start walking backwards from this remarkable achievement. As your wall recedes, the individual balloons begin to lose definition, and eventually you will think that you see a solid red wall.

Every tissue and organ in our body is composed in this fashion: billions of balloons glued together to form us. We have balloons of many different colors in our cellular repertoire. Blue balloons may enable us to see, red ones can make urine and purple ones make us feel passionate. In other words, clusters of cells all involved in the one function operate in concert as an organ. There is one fundamental difference, however, between the way that we would build a wall of balloons and the way Nature constructs a wall of cells. Instead of blowing up millions of individual balloons and aligning them neatly as a bricklayer might build a wall, Nature makes cells divide to form two, then four, then eight, then sixteen and so on— a mathematical process known as geometric expansion. Each of us

Figure 1. From one cell to a specialised organ

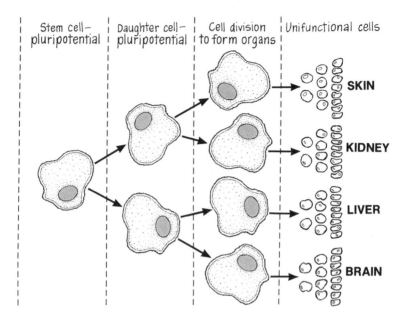

starts as one cell that divides time and time again, in fact almost infinitely, to supply us with all the cells needed for the body's various functions.

At some point the products of cell division begin to change. This controlled differentiation allows the various components of the body machinery to develop and interact. (Figure 1.) Using this sort of imagery by analogy, look at the back of your hand. Your skin looks like an homogeneous layer. Looking at the same skin with the aid of a microscope is like walking closer to our wall of balloons. When you get close enough, the individual cellular elements become clear. While there is no doubt about the fundamental truth of Alan Sherman's words of wisdom, 'You need your skin to keep your insides in', skin, that most useful of tissues, heats and cools us and acts as a first line of defence to keep micro-organisms out of our body. The oily secretions of the skin, the urine secreted by the kidney, the saliva secreted by the cells of our salivary glands bear witness to the fact that the cells of the different tissues or organs are factories performing some specific service to that mighty cellular conglomeration we call 'us'.

Now, the balloon analogy is far too simple of course. Our cells do contain much water but it is saturated with a myriad of chemicals.

Instead of pieces of wood floating around in a disorganised fashion, the bits and pieces of the cells' inner machinery are highly organised indeed. Every cell in our body is in fact a factory, many being required to produce a number of products as well as reproduce themselves.

The facet of cellular life of most relevance to our discussion is the way in which cellular happenings are organised. Headquarters in a cell is known as the 'nucleus'. It is from the nucleus that instructions come that when obeyed give a cell its special characteristics. Stored within every nucleus in every cell are all the instructions or blueprints needed to run our complex bodies. We refer to individual sets of instructions as genes which, as we will see, are collections of chemicals that provide a translatable message to the cell's machinery. It is likely that more than 400 000 blueprints are stored in every cell, and between them they must provide everything from our most sensitive and intelligent thought to the knee-jerk reflex. Of course, in any given cell only a limited number of the available blueprints are being used simultaneously.

This fundamental biological fact gave rise to the storyline in the famous Ira Levin novel *The Boys from Brazil*, which concerned cloning. Theoretically, if you can obtain and preserve one cell from any individual, you have all the coded material that generated all the functions of that particular body. One cell preserved from Hitler was used to reproduce the monster in this fortunately still fanciful book.

Human genes are composed of the most famous of all chemical structures, deoxyribonucleic acid, which is such a mouthful that it's universally referred to as DNA. DNA is a double-stranded helix structure. If you think of two pieces of wire twisted around and around each other, like hair that has been plaited, you'll get the idea. Each strand of DNA is composed of what at first appears to be a random arrangement of four chemicals that repeat themselves along the strand. The chemicals are members of one of two molecular families known as purines and pyrimidines. For the sake of simplicity they are referred to as 'bases'. The names of the four chem icals are guanine, cytosine, adenine and thymine. Each base on one strand of DNA lines up with a specific partner on the other, with guanine always opposite cytosine and adenine always opposite thymine. Now, segments of the helix containing a variable number of these base pairs supply a translatable message, and such a sequence is called a gene. It's a bit like the barcode on the jar of coffee in the supermarket. The magic wand waved over the bar sequences translates the code.

There are 46 chains of double-stranded DNA in the nucleus of most human cells. Mature red blood cells don't contain any genetic

Figure 2.   Genes, DNA and chromosomes

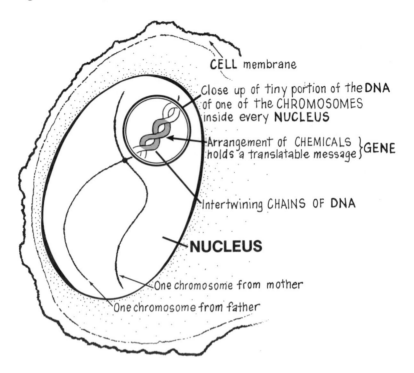

CELL membrane

Close up of tiny portion of the **DNA**
of one of the CHROMOSOMES
inside every **NUCLEUS**

Arrangement of CHEMICALS }
holds a translatable message } **GENE**

Intertwining CHAINS OF **DNA**

NUCLEUS

One chromosome from mother

One chromosome from father

information for they have no plans for reproducing themselves, and the cells that combine to form new life, sperm cells and egg cells from the ovary, have only half the normal number of chromosomes. Each chain of double-stranded DNA and the genes contained therein are inherited from either mother or father, each supplying 23 of the chains which pair off in the nucleus. A particular chain of double-stranded DNA is called a chromosome, and we thus have 46 chromosomes and 23 chromosomal pairs in each cell. Each pair of chromosomes is fused at one point. (Figure 2.)

If you think of the nucleus of a cell as a computer, then each chromosome can be likened to a hard disk containing hundreds of programs (genes). A cell in our kidney making urine is only playing the relevant programs. One can imagine the chaos that would follow if this were not the case.

In the last year or two, courts around the world have been examining the usefulness and reliability of the technique known as 'DNA typing' (also known as 'DNA fingerprinting'). Can this technique be used as a means of definitely linking an individual to the scene of a crime? Judges can only advise members of a jury to rely on such advances in technology once they have been convinced by the scientific community that any problems associated with this testing have been overcome. Well, the state of this particular art has become so advanced that convictions relying on the use of such technology are becoming more commonplace.

DNA typing is a particularly powerful law enforcement weapon in cases of rape because it has the potential to exonerate a suspect or to place him at the scene of the crime. It is of course useless in rape cases, such as those that have received so much publicity involving William Kennedy-Smith and Mike Tyson, in which intercourse is conceded to have occurred and the only real issue is consent. However, the following cases illustrate just how useful the technology can be.

In the summer of 1990, a young woman on vacation in Vermont stopped at a rest area along a major highway. As she emerged from a rest room, she was grabbed from behind, handcuffed and gagged; her head was covered with a pillow-case. Terrified, she was forced into the back of a trailer truck which left the area immediately. Half an hour later, the truck stopped and one Randolph Jakobetz entered the back of the trailer and 'proceeded to brutally and repeatedly rape and sexually assault his victim'. Four hours later, he released the unfortunate woman in the Bronx, New York; she immediately sought help at a local hospital.

At the trial, DNA typing performed by FBI scientists was introduced into evidence. A blood sample had been obtained from the defendant, Mr Jakobetz, and the DNA profile found in his blood cells was compared with that obtained from a semen sample recovered by vaginal swab from the victim. All the remaining evidence was highly circumstantial. The DNA comparison provided a match and the trial judge accepted the opinion of the experts; the jury had every right to be convinced by the technology and they were so instructed.

In a similar case, an American Indian known as Two Bulls was charged with aggravated sexual abuse for the rape of a fourteen-year-old girl on the Pine Ridge Indian Reservation in South Dakota. The results of DNA testing of the blood of Two Bulls and semen samples obtained from the girl produced identical results and the court was assured that it would be extraordinarily unlikely for this match to occur purely by chance. At this stage Two Bulls pleaded guilty and was sentenced to 108 months in prison. His lawyers decided to appeal on the grounds that the judge had been too willing to accept the DNA testing as the gold standard. It is important that the court hearing the appeal rejected that argument, feeling that DNA typing technology was indeed reliable. The judge did emphasise reasonably enough that the prosecutors would have to establish that such testing was carried out in competent laboratories by real experts.

Now, all this genetic information needs to be organised in the cell, and indeed it is. We have already discussed the fact that genes are housed in the 'brains' of the cell, known as the 'nucleus'. Extraction of such structures from cells allows us to examine the genes therein. Now we are getting closer to the information needed to convict someone like Two Bulls.

You only have to look around you to see that your genetic package is virtually unique. Superficially, we do not look like each other and those physical differences are much more than skin deep. Thus, if you examine the structure of a piece of DNA from two individuals, quite definite differences are noted.

Imagine that you are out at a racecourse watching horses being placed in the stalls for the next race. The barrier may have twenty or so stalls for individual horses, and can be thought of in this analogy as chromosomes. The horses slotted into specific stalls are genes. The chance that, in two consecutive races, identical horses with identical jockeys wearing identical colours would occupy identical places within the stalls is remote indeed! Now, imagine that the barrier has 20 000 stalls and that a million horses are available for selection for the 20 000 places, a situation more akin to what happens in chromosomes. What chance is there that in two consecutive races we would encounter 20 000 identical horses all arranged in exactly the same order? It is not impossible, but the probability is extremely low; the prosecutor in the Jakobetz case was able to give the probability of such a thing happening as about one in 300 000 000.

DNA typing involves the collection of material that contains cells and therefore nuclei and therefore DNA. Seminal fluid contains cells. Extracting DNA and analysing the particular chemical structure of the genes therein (the particular horses) will lead to the particular horses in the stalls being displayed for all to see. As noted above, it is a bit like a very complicated barcode from the bottom of a jar of coffee in a supermarket. Cells taken from a suspect are subjected to such treatment, and the barcodes obtained from the suspect and the sample are compared. Thus, a new weapon system has been created with which to fight crime. It is hoped that such knowledge will deter some from committing crime.

This exciting technology is not only of use in forensic science. It can help us identify genetic defects that are responsible for disease, and will undoubtedly be of great assistance as we develop ways of introducing new genes to prevent or cure disease.

When we humans reproduce, we get the chance to create a unique genetic experiment by combining the gene package donated by mother and the gene package donated by father. Some random packages may create something uniquely wonderful (most parents believe this to be the case) or may produce something that's not so good; but such experimentation is essential if, in the natural order of things, we are to improve our species by coming up with packages of superior genes. We will be discussing in detail that group of cells playing the immunology 'program', but first we must examine those tiny, indeed usually invisible, microbes that would kill us if we didn't have an immune system. Let's take a look at some of our enemies.

Viruses

I once saw a large neon-lit advertising display in the yard of a car service centre that read, 'Virus is a word used by doctors to mean your guess is as good as mine'.

What motivated the manager to give the world this information remains unknown, but I imagine that this Californian businessman had once been laid low by a flu-like illness. His doctor probably said, 'Not much I can do for you, old man. It's just a virus. Go home, drink a lot of fluids and take it easy for a few days.'

This is admittedly frustrating, but with a few exceptions it is absolutely accurate advice. Viral infections are essentially private battles fought between the virus and the patient's immune system. Very few effective antiviral agents have been developed so that, except when treating some herpes-like viruses, doctors have very few specific remedies to offer. Antibiotics which may kill or damage bacteria or fungi do nothing to viruses. To date, most success in handling viruses has come from developing vaccines that stop infection in the first place. The inability of the medical profession to do very much about viruses, the difficulty associated with culturing these organisms and the frequently vague symptoms they produce tend to make people think that viruses are strange and mysterious things. This is not entirely true; we know as much about viruses as we do about bacteria; viruses however have developed far more sophisticated techniques for survival in the human body.

What are viruses? Looked at dispassionately from a non-human point of view, viruses are very clever and successful life forms (or near-life forms; they cannot survive on their own, as we will see). For a virus to grow and multiply, it must enter into the sacrosanct environment of specific cells that will become unwilling hosts. Viruses are therefore parasites, living off other organisms.

A virus is composed of genetic material in the form of DNA, sometimes single-stranded rather than double-stranded as in the

Figure 3. Viruses can insert genetic messages into host DNA

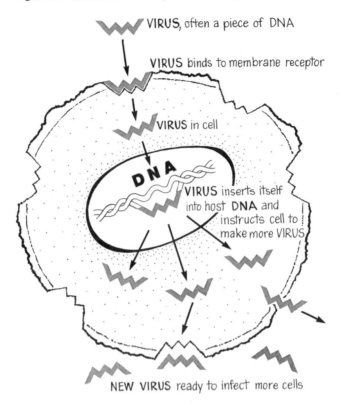

VIRUS, often a piece of DNA

VIRUS binds to membrane receptor

VIRUS in cell

DNA

VIRUS inserts itself
into host **DNA** and
instructs cell to
make more VIRUS

NEW VIRUS ready to infect more cells

case of human cells, or an alternative genetic chemical known as ribonucleic acid, or RNA. The only way that RNA differs from DNA is that the purine thymine is replaced by another one called uracil. Viruses carry 5–200 genetic messages with them and a number of these are instructions for reproducing themselves. Viruses composed of DNA or, as we will see in discussing AIDS, RNA viruses capable of translating their genetic messages *into* DNA can actually insert their programs into human DNA inside the nucleus of the cell, thus adding a new set of blueprints. RNA itself is a blueprint for a protein and can instruct the cell's machinery to manufacture a copy of the virus. In this way, a simple life form is capable of reproducing time and time again, often damaging the parasitised cell in so doing. (Figure 3.)

The cells so infected have no alternative but to produce the virus, although they have produced some defence mechanisms to combat it. The infected cell may die as it fills up with new viral particles and its membranes burst asunder as the virus explodes through the cell. So released, the virus simply moves into a nearby uninfected cell and another cycle is repeated. Even if a cell infected with a virus does not die, such damage can be done to the sophisticated control mechanisms that regulate cellular life that abnormal function and even a malignancy may develop—that is, a cancer cell may be born.

In most circumstances, all that stands between us and domination by viruses is our immune system. Its ability to recognise viral infection and deal with it is described later in this book, but clearly much of the complexity of our immune system has resulted from adaptations made to control viral infection. For now, let us simply emphasise the fact that viruses become part of us, and to destroy them we frequently have to destroy the cell that carries them. If you are unfortunate enough to get hepatitis B, your immune system may have to destroy many of your liver cells to get rid of the virus they are sheltering. If too much of the liver is infected, one may actually destroy oneself (as humans cannot survive without a liver) in attempts to destroy the virus.

Viruses are tiny; they cannot be seen under an ordinary microscope, and this is one of the reasons why their discovery took so long. In fact, these agents were presumed to exist for many years before they were cultured or seen. In 1898 some German scientists were seeking the cause of the disastrous foot-and-mouth disease that affects cattle. They were able to show that disease could be passed from one animal to another using a number of body fluids from infected animals that had been passed through filters known to block the passage of even the smallest bacterium. They called the infectious agent responsible an 'ultramicroscopic filterable virus'. Today, this class of infectious agent is simply called a virus, of which many different types are now known to exist. *'Virus'* is a Latin word meaning a poison that disturbs the soul. Viruses have different shapes and often a biologist looking at a virus can tell much about its properties simply because of its physical characteristics.

It is hard to imagine just how small an individual virion (viral unit) actually is. They range in size from 17 to 300 nanometers; a nanometer is one billionth of a metre (1 metre = 39.37 inches). As a further illustration, imagine that you put a needle in your skin and allow one drop of blood to emerge. In that drop of blood you would find about five million red blood cells. Each of these cells could very easily house a thousand virions.

When a virus is reproduced by the cell it has invaded, it is often wrapped in an envelope made of a combination of protein and fatty material. Most viruses thus live inside a capsule. This enables many viruses to live undamaged for extended periods of time outside the body. In replicating itself or in designing the envelope in which it will live, the virus programs in a complementary three-dimensional feature enabling it to interact with the specific membrane of the cell it wishes to invade. Quite unwittingly, certain cell membranes carry receptors on their surfaces for certain viruses. It is of great medical significance that viruses are choosy about their hosts. The viruses that cause influenza do not infect kidneys under any circumstances; the herpes viruses that cause so much genital suffering will not infect the liver.

Humans are certainly not the only victims of viral infection. Plants, insects and all animals can be infected by viruses. Certain viruses have learned how to invade bacteria, so you could be invaded by a bacterial enemy that has already been infected by a virus. A virus that likes plants, however, likes only plants. Viruses are so specifically designed to invade one cell type that those causing animal diseases rarely infect humans, and vice versa. If one removed the preferred host from the environment, a particular virus would cease to exist. However, we humans have not considered self-annihilation a very good remedy for the problem of viral infections.

How do viruses get into our body? When they are not in their favored hosts, they can be found lying on the floor, attached to a dust particle, resting in the soil or trapped on the fur of animals, etc. To enter our body they may find a break in the skin that might, for instance, follow an accident, the bite of an animal or insect, or the prick of a needle in the case of a drug addict. In the last case, infected fluid may be transmitted into the tissues and even the bloodstream.

By far the most common way the virus enters our body, however, is through direct contact with the infected secretions of another human. Many viruses can be found in the sexual secretions of an infected person and all the viruses which live in our respiratory tract can be transmitted from one person to another by direct contact, for example, kissing. We humans have our mouths open too much of the time for our good, you may say. Besides talking too much and eating too much, we can easily inhale viral particles floating in the air. Millions of viruses leave the nose with a good sneeze; many may enter the air when a room is dusted. Many people frequently put their hands to their faces or place fingers or fingernails into the mouth. Fingers are frequently covered with viruses and hands can become dangerous if unwashed. Thus, in most cases, viruses easily move from one body to another during close physical contact.

Viruses can also leave the body of a strong, immunologically experienced mother and cross the placenta into a fragile inexperienced fetus, doing a great deal of damage; this happens, for example, with the virus that causes German measles. Doctors may inadvertently give their patients viral infections when the instruments they use to peer into or penetrate the body are infected with viruses; even such meticulously sterile operations as corneal transplants that may give someone the gift of sight have occasionally ended in tragedy when the transplanted tissue was infected with viruses.

Now that we are dealing with viruses that have learned how to infect and kill the cells of the immune system (the disease AIDS, discussed later), we have been forced to realise once again what dangerous enemies viruses are. Certainly the last chapter of the book that will chronicle our battle with these challengers has not yet been written.

Bacteria

I first met Bill in the emergency room of a hospital. This 21-year-old white male was convulsing and sweating profusely as the result of an obvious fever. Having protected his tongue with a mouthguard, stopped his convulsions with Valium injected intravenously and improved his color by administering oxygen, we took a more detailed look at this very sick young man who was unknown to all the regular staff.

Bill was thin, not exactly emaciated but close to it, very dirty and the possessor of a five- to six-day-old beard. The rest of his physical examination revealed three findings of great significance to us. From his arms leaped the bruised, abused and punctured veins of the drug addict, an all-too-familiar sight. More unusual, however, were the sounds coming from his distracted heart, which was beating too rapidly and irregularly. Between the sounds of the rapid opening and closing of those heart valves that ensure the forward movement of blood as the heart contracts was big trouble. Instead of the silence that heralds the smooth onward rushing of the river of life, the sound of a turbulent waterfall vibrated through the stethoscope. As the blood moved from one chamber in the heart to another, irregularities on the normally smooth surfaces of the valves were distorting the powerful jet of blood in much the same way as a smooth column of water issuing from a partially opened tap may be deviated if a finger is placed in the stream.

The third sign that supplied the pattern-revealing piece of this complicated jigsaw puzzle was found on looking at Bill's hands. Under the nails of three fingers could be seen tiny red spots where miniscule blood vessels had ruptured and spilt their precious cargo into the nail bed.

Adding up all these clues, any medical sleuth could have guessed the nature of the events that had led to Bill's critical condition. Ten days earlier, he had bought some heroin with money that he had won in an instant lottery game. From a deprived background, unable to work, often in trouble with the law and hopelessly addicted to drugs, Bill must have thought that winning $1000 for a 50c expenditure was a signal from the gods that things were about to change. As it turned out, his good fortune nearly killed him. He bought some 'good stuff' and injected it into himself. Among hard-drug users, the syringe and needles necessary for the injections are often passed from one person to another, to be used time and time again with minimal attempts to keep the apparatus sterile. Often between uses an attempt will be made to rinse out the syringe with tap water, a totally unsatisfactory way to clean the needle. In such needles and syringes, many of the human's greatest enemies, including bacteria, can take hold and multiply.

Bacteria live practically anywhere. In Bill's case, some of the particular bacteria known as streptococci (strep for short) probably went from the skin of one person into the needle he used for the injection of his 'good stuff'. Once they found themselves injected into his bloodstream, the strep organisms multiplied themselves hundreds of times in twenty-four hours. Blood is an excellent source of both oxygen and glucose, both of which are necessary for bacteria to flourish.

Now, at this point of Bill's story, we must understand more about bacteria, knowledge of which is less than one hundred years old. In fact the first bacteria seen were those that cause leprosy. In a laboratory in Norway, not a country you are likely to link to leprosy, late in the nineteenth century, a certain Dr Hansen looked down his microscope at tissue from a patient with leprosy and saw not one but hundreds of thousands of the little organisms that cause this disease (that, by the way, is why leprosy is often referred to as Hansen's disease).

Bacteria are very different from the viruses we discussed previously, mainly because bacteria are complete life forms. Unlike viruses, they are not parasites and do not need an unwilling host to reproduce themselves. The bacteria that cause tetanus by secreting a toxin that can paralyse nerves live just as happily in the soil as they do inside the human body. Bacteria consist of one or more cells, each of which has its genetic information grouped in a nucleus-like structure. There has been some debate as to whether to refer to the area where genetic material is clustered in a bacterium as a nucleus, for there is no membrane surrounding the DNA as we find surrounding the genetic information in higher species. For our purposes, what is important is to understand that there are indeed genetic programs composed of DNA that tell a bacterium how to be a bacterium and reproduce itself. They are much bigger than viruses, although they are still far too small to be seen by the unassisted eye. Bacteria just eat and divide constantly; they do both better when the conditions are right. We culture bacteria by placing them in a dish in an incubator so that their favorite food source, temperature, humidity and gaseous environment are supplied. Under such conditions, bacteria soon reproduce themselves so effectively that colonies are produced and they can be seen on the surface of the culture dish.

Bacteria can do terrible things to us in at least three ways:

- As they multiply in the body, they may secrete poisonous chemicals (toxins) that disturb one or more bodily functions. Some may paralyse our nerves, while others block the ability of the cells in our intestinal tract to absorb water into our bodies (think of the terrible diarrhoea caused by the bacteria responsible for cholera).

- Bacteria can invade a tissue, for example in our lungs they may multiple so quickly that the staggering number of organisms that accumulate may interfere with the function of the organ, causing pneumonia.

- When our immune system mounts a vicious attack on the invading bacteria, innocent tissue (us) caught up in the mêlée may be damaged. Such tissue destruction results in an abscess, and the chemically digested remains of the bacteria and those parts of our cells inadvertently destroyed are called pus.

Let us get back to Bill who, as you remember, had just injected some of these creatures into his bloodstream. The bacteria, of course, were soon racing around his body with no corner inaccessible, because blood goes everywhere.

Now, if you have ever been in Geneva or other places where lakes can easily be studied as they fill up with water racing down from the mountains, you will have noticed that gates are used to control the flow of water. When the gates are fully opened a jet of water spurts through the centre of the opening at great speed but just at the side of that central force are patches of quiet water. That same effect occurs in the heart. Some bacteria may have their headlong tumble through the bloodstream stopped when they spin off to the side of the jet stream into the 'quiet' blood. When this happens, the bacteria concerned may seep onto the surfaces of the values of the heart, the gates that control the flow of blood. Here the bacteria may grow in a rich and nutritious atmosphere relatively undisturbed. As they do so they form colonies, just as they do in our culture dishes. They heap up on the valves and form outgrowths that look a little like the surface of cauliflower; for this reason they are known as vegetations. These vegetations will slowly lead to the destruction of the valves; we can hear this damage in the form of heart 'murmur' (often in reality a roar). If a disturbance in blood flow is severe enough, the turbulence may often be felt right through the chest wall if the hand is placed flat over the heart. It is just like putting the hand on the cover of a speaker blaring forth loud music.

Bill's heart was in trouble, but the disaster was only beginning. As the heart was no longer able to operate as a smoothly performing pump, some of those bacterial vegetations broke away from the heart valves and joined the bloodstream once more as it raced away from the heart. Now, however, the bacteria were travelling as clumps. One such clump shot up into the brain and, as it passed into some of the tiny blood vessels on the left-hand side of Bill's cerebral cortex, it became jammed, physically wedged in a tiny artery. Once more the bacteria were able to establish a colony and rapidly grow in the rich sugar-saturated environment of the brain. Eventually they formed a local abscess that damaged the brain tissue it self and led to convulsions and, at a later time (for Bill is still alive at this writing), a paralysis of most of the right side of his body. You may remember that the left-hand side of the brain con-trols the right-hand side of the body.

In a similar fashion, some of these bacteria broke away from the vegetations on the heart and ended up in vessels under the nail bed where the damage they produced in the blood could be seen through the window that is the cuticle. That is how we discovered what had happened to Bill. He required the services of a cardiac surgeon to replace his damaged heart valves, skilled and prolonged adminis-tration of antibiotics and much rehabilitative help. Unfortunately, he is partially paralysed and his intelligence is impaired, but he is alive and no longer addicted to drugs.

The bacterial enemy can live independently, multiply so rapidly and produce so much damage that special antibacterial processes must be generated to supplement the body's defensive mechanisms.

Bacteria have names usually derived from Graeco–Latin words. Most people have heard of staphylococci and strep tococci. At the suggestion of a Professor of Greek in Aberdeen a Scottish surgeon, Alexander Ogston, who was the first to associate these bacteria with pus more than a hundred years ago now, coined the highly appropriate name staphylococcus (Greek for a bunch of grapes). The name was used for one of the major forms of bacteria producing disease in humans. The other major bacteria known to be present in pus at that time were made up of chains of cells rather than clusters, and were thus given the name streptococcus. There are, however, thousands of species of bacteria and they come in all shapes and sizes. By looking at disease-causing bacteria for different physical properties, bacteriologists can name a particular bug and then physicians can apply treatment (usually antibiotics) known to be effective against a specific organism.

Some bacteria actually live inside the body's cells and, once there, they are protected from antibacterial forces floating around in our bloodstream. Such bacteria are referred to as intracellular pathogens and examples include those that produce the diseases tuberculosis and leprosy. As mentioned before, bacteria, though simple organisms, have enough DNA to run essential programs and respond to environmental pressures (for example, antibiotics) which threaten the species. Most bacteria possess about 1000 genes. Bacteria divide rapidly and they can exchange genetic information with adjacent organisms—a primitive form of sexual activity. As a result, new genetic packages and therefore programs can be produced constantly. Most will not advantage the bacterium but some will, and bacteria with better programs survive. When bacteria encounter a new antibiotic, furious genetic activity allows them to quite rapidly produce members of the family that are resistant to that antibiotic. They flourish and in such cases infection will continue and a breed of resistant bacteria will be launched into the world. Most of the bacteria that could be killed by penicillin when it was discovered almost fifty years ago are now resistant because bacteria actually contain genes which will produce an antidote to that antibiotic.

This ability to learn new and nasty tricks is a common feature of rapidly dividing organisms. If we humans become progressively more indolent, in a million years we may look quite different, but the evolutionary changes that may take away lazy legs will occur very, very slowly. On the other hand, bacteria can evolve (that is, significantly change) in very short periods of time. This clearly makes them all the more dangerous for us.

Here is an example of what I mean.

Mary Rogers was an infection control nurse at a large city hospital. Like most such institutions, hers was always busy and it was a daily battle for administrators to find sufficient beds for those in trouble, who presented to either the hospital's emergency room or were booked in for admission for surgery or investigation of a serious problem. Well aware of this, Mary was not looking forward to her meeting with Frank Kennedy, the Director of Medical Administration, as she had bad news for him.

As she sat in his office, she wasted no time in getting to the point. 'Frank, we will have to close Ward 6 immediately,' she told him firmly. 'MRSA I'm afraid,' she continued. Frank knew immediately what she meant. Ward 6 was the orthopaedic ward and a series of wound infections there had caused many people concern. Wounds created by violent trauma are often serious and slow to heal, and to have them become infected added much to the suffering and expense and the time a patient would be required to spend in hospital. Two days earlier, Mary had collected samples from a number of infected wounds and taken them to Jim Clinton in the bacteriology laboratory and explained her problem. Within twenty-four hours, he told her that all the wounds were contaminated with staphylococcus aureus (golden staph). Twenty-four hours after that, he told her that they were Methacillin-resistant staph, or MRSA.

Thus Mary knew that in Ward 6 very dangerous bacteria were spreading from patient to patient, despite every effort to stop this from happening. Culture plates placed on desk tops and bedside tables produced colonies of the troublesome bacteria, which being microscopically small and very light could float through the air and find a new home in a healing wound. These are indeed 'superbugs'. They have set their genes to the task of coming up with ways to outsmart one of our most useful anti-staphylococcal antibiotics—Methacillin. Changes that they have made to themselves allow them to resist the effects of the drug. MRSA are thus very difficult organisms to eradicate. Such organisms simply cannot be allowed to spread in a hospital, for obvious reasons; hence the need to close Ward 6 and allow time to thoroughly clean and decontaminate the whole area so that a fresh clean start could be made.

Recently, to help humanity scientists have been harnessing the remarkable ability of bacteria to multiply quickly and to produce large amounts of proteins. A bacterial cell, like any other, is a factory making whatever products its genes tell it to make. We can splice a gene carrying a specific message into a chromosome within a number of bacterial cells and change the production patterns of these cells so that they will produce something specific. Each cell will not produce much, of course, but when cells reproduce as fast as bacteria can, that is no problem. Billions of cells may soon be at work producing something specific for the genius who has mastered them. In such fashion, very large quantities of insulin that can be used by diabetics and growth hormone that can be used by children with stunted growth may be supplied in extremely pure form.

Fungi

Mary Beth was sixteen when I first saw her. She was in our intensive care unit, her arms heavily bandaged and tied to the frame of the bed. The night before, she had tried to commit suicide by slashing her wrists.

Unlike many wrist slashers, Mary Beth had really meant to kill herself and had very nearly succeeded. She had lost a great deal of blood and was still receiving a blood transfusion. She was wide awake and as I approached she looked at me with eyes that seemed drained of all feeling. Mary Beth had tried to kill herself because she felt herself to be ugly. Hers was an ugliness that made people shiver as they turned away in embarrassment at their obvious inability to hide their shock. What place was there in this world which so venerates beauty for a sixteen-year-old girl with her disfigurements?

Mary Beth's nose was swollen to twice the normal size; a black crust covered most of it. Pus from deep ulcers covered most of her face, and her top lip was swollen and twisted. I had seen a number of people similarly afflicted, suffering from an illness associated with severe breakdown of the immune system.

After receiving indifferent permission to examine the rest of her body, I noticed that she had trouble opening her mouth, but it was clear that the inside of her cheeks and her tongue were covered in a milky white substance. The rest of her body bore isolated ulcers in no particular pattern. Between the upper part of her legs her skin was an angry red color, as was her markedly swollen vulva. A profuse creamy discharge came from her vagina. Mary Beth was the victim of a fungal infection caused by an organism known as *candida albicans*; her disease is called chronic mucocutaneous candidiasis (*muco* = mucous membranes; *cutaneous* = skin). While she could defend herself from bacteria, she had no defence against fungi. Each requires a separate system of defence.

Everyone has come in contact with some fungi. Moulds are fungi; they can grow on a piece of old bread or crawl up a shower curtain. There are literally thousands of fungi, the great majority of which are totally harmless to humans. They are another ancient and well-adapted form of life. Fungi possess a simple membrane-bound nucleus which contains their genetic information and the walls of the organisms are made up of polysaccharides. Their appearance may vary from the single-celled forms of yeast to a mass of interlacing strands of cells. As is true of bacteria, not all fungi cause disease, in fact some can be positively health-giving. Fungi are added to improve the quality of food, such as cheese and yoghurt, and bread and fermenting drinks have been used for millennia.

More than two hundred species of fungi are known to cause disease in humans. In people with depressed immune systems fungal infections of the skin, intestinal tract, lungs and brain are only too frequent. Often fungi are geographically restricted: you will only get certain fungal diseases in certain areas of the world.

The fungus that was so troubling Mary Beth had been doing so since she was six weeks old. This particular fungus, which will be called *candida* for short, is the one your body knows best because everyone grows it in their intestinal tract. Since our bowels are full of bacteria (unavoidable when you think of what we put in our mouth), defence mechanisms have developed to ensure that the bacteria will not only harm us but also work in our favor. Bacteria make vitamins for us and break down proteins to help us digest and reassimilate the essential nutrients that we eat. But, as we have seen, they can get out of hand very easily and may grow so rapidly in our intestinal tract that they swamp our defence mechanisms. To prevent this, a number of strategies are in place. One uses *candida* by allowing it to grow in our intestines and compete with bacteria for essential nutriments. An ecological balance is maintained that prevents excessive growth of either the bacteria or fungus.

It is very common, especially with babies who have antibiotic treatment for, say, a chest or ear infection, to solve one problem while creating another. While clearing up the ear infection, the antibiotics may also kill off the bacteria in the gastrointestinal tract. The result is that fungus can spread up and down the intestinal tract. *Candida* may emerge in the mouth as a white coating on the tongue (commonly referred to as thrush); it may also emerge from the anus and cause discomfort to the skin of that area.

Because of the proximity of the anus to the vagina, it is very common for women to get severe vulval and vaginal infection with this fungus, which flourishes on the moist vaginal lining. For normal people, such an overgrowth causes a superficial infection, with discharge and itchiness being the major complaints. Seldom do our defences let the fungus penetrate our tissues to cause deep infections. However, if one's immune system is deficient, deep tissue infection occurs and serious problems may develop, such as those that affected Mary Beth.

We were able to help this brave woman which chemical extracts from the cells of normal individuals whose defence system knew how to handle the fungus that so troubled her. As her infections began to subside, her pessimism and depression were replaced by optimism and renewed courage. Today, she's a happily married working mother. One of her two babies was born with their mother's problem but we are fortunate in now having available drugs which are safe and effective against *candida albicans*. Little Ellen is growing up healthy and will never experience the pain and suffering endured for so long by her mother. We will return to the damage that fungi can do to individuals with a damaged immune system when we discuss the Acquired Immune Deficiency Syndrome.

Parasites

A few years ago I was driving a small, sadly deteriorated Renault through western Senegal en route to the capital, Dakar. On this particular Sunday afternoon, hot and very thirsty, I stopped the vehicle as I approached a tiny village hoping to find some roadside hut selling Coca-Cola. I was out of luck, however, as there were no vendors around and indeed no one was to be seen around any of the six or eight huts that comprised the hamlet. I stopped the car at the side of the road to drink some very hot mineral water and surveyed a desolate scene. Suddenly, from behind the huts in one of the barren fields, a man came into view leading what turned out to be a procession of thirty or so people walking slowly and in single file across the useless land at the side of the road near where I was parked.

The procession was mainly composed of men. All were wrapped from head to toe in their finest clothes, voluminous robes that enveloped them despite the relentless heat. Like many of the men in the area, the leader of the procession was very tall and thin. He moved purposefully but slowly, shoulders back and head held high, despite the small, swathed bundle he had in his slightly stretched-out arms. As the column drew nearer I could see tears running down this man's cheeks even though he did not glance in my direction.

Realisation swept over me; I understood that this was a funeral procession. The leader was carrying the body of his young son in his arms and members of the closely knit village were strung out behind him as all proceeded to a shallow grave prepared for the child under a baobab tree. I watched them bury the child, pray and return to their huts again in that same desperately sad and respectful single file.

I went over to the group and learnt more details of this sad event. A five-year-old boy had died that morning after four days of almost non-stop convulsions. He had contracted 'the Pauldism', that is, malaria, which had spread to involve his brain and led to his death. A wandering bush nurse had been consulted three days earlier. He examined the child, who by this stage had bitten his tongue in half, and told the alarmed but hardly surprised community that the child had malaria in the brain and would soon die. Neither he nor anybody could do anything for the child, he assured them as he departed.

During the height of the malaria season in countries such as Senegal, it is not uncommon to have six or more children die from malaria every day in the local hospital. Every year millions succumb to this terrible disease that so sorely tests human defence mechanisms.

Malaria is not caused by viruses or bacteria, nor even by fungi, but by a fourth and major class of microbial enemy—parasites.

Strictly speaking, a parasite is anything that depends on others in one way or another for its ability to survive without contributing to the well-being or the survival of the organism on which it depends.

In biological terms, a virus could be considered a parasite. However, when clinical scientists talk of parasites they exclude viruses by convention, restricting their discussion to those usually large and complicated organisms that produce long-standing infections of humans and other animals, particularly in the developing world (unfortunately a major misnomer if ever there was one). Diseases such as malaria and others with exotic names such as trypanosomiasis, leishmaniasis and filariasis are responsible, quite literally, for most of the human sickness and death in this world. While progress is being made in our ability to handle a number of these diseases, others are more prevalent and more serious than ever. This is particularly true of malaria.

The mosquito that spreads malaria is becoming increasingly resistant to insecticides, the parasite is becoming increasingly resistant to the drugs we use to treat the infection, and governments are becoming increasingly resistant to spending the huge amounts of money needed to control the problem. At least 200 million people are infected with malaria as you read these words. In Africa alone, someone dies of malaria every thirty seconds. That is nearly 3000 people each day, more than a million per year. Malaria is not just a problem for the Third World, however. In the United States about 4000 cases will be treated each year and this number is increasing. International travel exposes many to the parasitic problems of the Third World.

Parasites can be divided into two major groups, the protozoans and the helminths. The protozoan family is made up of many different types of organism, and those that cause malaria belong to this group. 'Helminth' is the technical word for worms; three major forms of worm feast on, or more accurately in, humans. Some are roundworms, including the *ascaris* that are common parasites. Some worms are flat, like fish, and these flatworms, or tapeworms as they are often called, cause us and our dogs a lot of trouble. *Taenia saginata* is a little worm that we often pick up after a delicious steak tartare. Infestation occurs in all countries where raw or undercooked beef is eaten but it is particularly prevalent in Mexico and South America. The third type of worm is the fluke. This type produces the disease schistosomiasis (sometimes called bilharzia) in 200 million inhabitants of seventy-one countries around the world. The smallest of the worms that infect humans may be only two millimetres long, while the largest may be ten metres (thirty-two feet) long.

Most protozoans and helminths have an 'intermediate' life cycle; that is, they live some part of their lives outside of the humans or animals that are their favored and ultimate hosts. Some parasites live in soil or water or other animals, preparing for their entry into the human body. The parasites that cause malaria, for example, mature in the salivary glands of a particular family of mosquitos (anopheles). Mosquitos are thus the hosts for the intermediate life cycle for these parasites. When a mosquito bites you it is of course intent on feeding on your blood, which it must draw into its stomach by means of the needle-shaped proboscis it sticks into your skin. As nothing would be more frustrating for a hungry mosquito than to be enjoying dinner and then to have the blood clot in the aspirating needle, it injects saliva containing a substance which stops blood clotting into the blood vessels before it begins its feast. With the saliva, in the case of infected mosquitos, come the parasites which have cleverly adapted themselves so that they may enter humans this way. Once malaria parasites find themselves in the bloodstream they race off to the liver, where they will dive into the cells they find there. The parasites multiply readily until the poor liver cell, acting as an unwilling host, literally bursts with the load of parasites now crowded inside. One parasite in one cell may produce 40 000 replicas of itself. The parasites released after the cell bursts now seek a new abode.

Over millions of years they have decided that the inside of the human red blood cell (erythrocyte) is most congenial. The parasites attach themselves to the membrane of the red cell and burrow inside. As survival of these species is all-important, another round of multiplication occurs inside the red cells. Forty-eight or seventy-two hours after the invasion (the time interval varies with the different members of the *plasmodium* family) the red cells burst and thousands of parasites seek new red cells to invade.

Now one of the most remarkable survival mechanisms in all Nature takes place: the parasites know that their activities may kill their host, so they must escape into another body before it is too late. Some of them multiply in red cells, but do not rupture them. They wait for the mosquito to return for a second feed.

When these infected cells are sucked back into the belly of the mosquito, the parasites burst from the red cell, develop into mature infecting organisms and migrate into the salivary gland of the intermediate host, ready to start the next heady spin through poor vulnerable humans.

Many humans die of malaria as the organisms produce a severe anemia, destroying too many red cells, and invade the brain or so damage the immune system that other organisms kill the weakened victim. However, most people who have been infected with malaria develop an uneasy truce with the enemy. It does not kill them, they do not kill it and a chronic state of ill health is established. This common chronic form of infection has a disastrous social and economic impact in developing countries.

Malaria is the most serious of all the world's infectious diseases, although the hepatitis B and AIDS viruses are closing in on the title. For generations, efforts have been made to eradicate the anopheles mosquito with insecticides. One day, in what was then Upper Volta, I was invited to take a helicopter ride and see how the aerial spraying of river banks was actually achieved. It was quite a thrill to fly across the riverside bushes at low altitude, as the pilot skilfully bombed the mosquitos. Suddenly, as he turned sharply, we nearly ran into another helicopter doing exactly the same thing. Ours was a helicopter on lease to the Government with money supplied by the World Health Organisation. The helicopter with which we nearly collided was being funded by the French Government to do exactly the same sort of work. Neither agency knew the other was even in the area, and of course there are no air traffic controllers out there.

The anopheles mosquitos were to cause one more attempt at wiping us out that day. Later in the morning, in our pursuit of the mosquito breeding beds, we must have strayed across the border into Guinea for to our horror when we looked down at the ground we saw two armed soldiers firing at us with their rifles. They missed (hard to imagine how, they obviously were not well trained) and I decided I'd seen enough—but to this day, the men who do that type of work have my fullest admiration.

From the harsh Sahara Desert in the north of Africa to the Kalahari Desert in the southern regions, the parasite *trypano-some bruceii* causes one of the most lethal of all diseases—sleeping sickness. In South America a first cousin, *trypanosome cruzi*, infects many millions, causing severe heart and gastro-intestinal damage. You may have heard of this disease under its other name—Chagas' disease. No eponym in medicine is more richly deserved, for Carlos Chagas spent his life unravelling the life cycle of the parasite responsible for this most serious disease.

The parasite that causes sleeping sickness in Africa is transmitted to humans by several species of tsetse fly. Some forms of the parasite live only in animals and are not directly harmful to humans, though they certainly harm them indirectly. It is regarded as impossible to raise animals for food in more than ten million square kilometres of Africa, simply because of the presence of tsetse files in the area.

Infected humans develop definite characteristics. The face assumes a vacant expression, the eyelids continually droop as if burdened with tiredness and the lower lips hang loosely. Arousing patients and getting their attention becomes progressively more difficult. Patients may eat the food placed in front of them but will not ask for it. They do not initiate any conversation and they become more withdrawn until coma and convulsions signal that they are entering into the final phases of the illness.

The fly in question picks up the parasites from various animals such as bushbucks. The parasites then remain expectantly within the fly until a human is bitten. Once transferred under the top layer of the human skin, the parasites, which are strand-like with a moving tail, burrow along under the skin until they burst into the circulation and then head for the heart or, particularly, the brain. It is the destruction of the brain that leads to the 'sleeping sickness'.

Untreated, the disease is always fatal. Personal protection for travellers in areas where sleeping sickness is a problem cannot be guaranteed. However, insect repellents and protective clothing are generally effective, and only 5 per cent of the flies in any endemic area are infected with the parasite.

From Chile and Argentina as far north as Mexico, the American form of this disease (Chagas' disease) affects more than twelve million South Americans and is the leading cause of heart disease. Twenty-five per cent of the deaths that occur in people aged between 25 and 44 years are attributed to trypanosomiasis. In South America the disease is not transmitted by flies but by little bugs known locally, for good reasons, as assassin bugs. Sometimes they are called 'kissing' bugs. These delightful specimens are all over South America. They prefer to live in animal burrows but will take up residence in cracks and thatches of poorly built country shanties. The bugs come out at night for a blood feed, crawling across the body to find not skin but a delicate mucous membrane to bite. They usually find this on a victim's lip where the tough skin gives way to the delicate membranes that pass on into the mouth; here they 'kiss' their victims. The bug often bites the corner of the eye if that is reached first.

The bugs do not inject the parasites into the body as the fly does. Eight to ten days before the blood feast, the bugs will have ingested the parasites that have matured in their stomachs to reach their most infectious form. As the tiny bug bites its victims and sucks in some blood it reflexly empties its intestines and drops its fecal material laden with parasites into the wound made by the bite.

There is no satisfactory form of treatment for the American form of the disease.

The debilitating disease known as leishmaniasis or kala-azar is found in parts of Europe, Asia, Africa and South and Central America. The leishmania parasites usually live in dogs and rodents and are transmitted to humans by blood-letting sandflies. About 10 per cent of the dogs around the Mediterranean are infected with organisms, though 90 per cent of the wild gerbils in the southern USSR are infected. Female sandflies suck the parasites into their bellies when feeding on animals and the parasite matures inside its intermediate host. When the sandfly bites a human, the mature parasites are injected into the victim. More than twelve million people are infected with this parasite.

After incubation of three months, a fever, swollen lymph glands, a rapid pulse rate, diarrhoea and cough may develop. The bone marrow is infected and as a result the blood cells usually made here become depleted and anemia and infections follow. Death occurs within three to thirty months in 90 per cent of victims. If caught in time, however, this disease can be adequately treated.

Schistosomiasis (bilharzia) is the most serious human worm infestation. More than 200 million individuals living between the Tropics of Capricorn and Cancer are infected. More than 500 000 people who now live in the USA picked up this disease before taking up residence in that country. The parasites that cause the disease are worms called flukes, belonging to the family Schistosomitidae. These worms like to live in the veins that drain blood from the intestine to the liver. There they lay their eggs, as well as in the blood vessels of the bladder, colon, liver, lungs and brain. Terrible damage to the host results.

The adult worms are about one to two centimetres in length and they grow in the liver area. The male worms have a central trough running the full length of their body and the female worm lies all day and night within this groove, simultaneously and continuously eating and copulating. The delicate scientific phrase for such activity is '*in copulo*'.

The worms that cause this disease may live for almost thirty years and can lay as many as 3000 eggs per day. The male worm carries the fertilised female upstream against the flow of blood, like a salmon fighting its way upstream to mate. In this way the female is able to deposit her eggs in many different places. Some will survive and secrete a chemical which allows them to break down blood vessels and tissues until they find themselves in the intestinal tract or bladder of their victim. Some eggs must, for the sake of survival of the worm species, reach the bladder or colon so that they can leave the body in urine and feces. (As we have seen before, parasites must be certain they can get into a new body if they kill the first host.)

The worms deposited with urine and feces in water or soil wait there for their next victim. To survive, they must find and penetrate a specific snail within eight hours of leaving the body. In the snail they multiply and then come out of the snail back to where they can latch on to and then burrow under any human skin that walks by. No wonder there is so much of this disease in Third World countries where rice crops are fertilised with human feces. The disease is very difficult to control, as it requires massive changes in habits. Fortunately, since the first edition of this book was written a very useful drug, Praziquantel, has been developed which cures about 80 per cent of patients adequately treated.

Tapeworms are ribbon-shaped, segmented hermaphrodites. They inhabit the intestinal tract of many vertebrates and unlike many other worms they have no digestive system, so they absorb nutrients along the entire length of their body. On the head of such worms, one finds various numbers of sucking cups and hooklets, depending on which member of the family one is observing. These cups and hooks allow the worm to attach itself firmly to the lining of the intestinal tract. The top part of the worm copulates with the bottom part. The worm can be found in Africa, Chile, along the Pacific coast of America and in northern Florida.

The most dramatic tapeworm infection is diphyllobothriasis, common in Scandinavian and Baltic countries, Russia and Japan. The worm is ingested by fish, which pick it up from raw sewage dumped into the sea. If this fish is eaten raw (as it often is) the worm living inside the fish has an ideal opportunity to enter a new host. The worm can grow to be ten metres (thirty-two feet) in length and live for twenty years. Once diagnosed, the infection can be cured. Perhaps the most amazing thing about this infection is that often the human host suffers only minor symptoms of abdominal discomfort and anemia. Occasionally, the worms spontaneously decide to leave the human host. The amazed victim will be psychologically if not physically damaged for some time.

Twenty-five per cent of the world's population, including four million Americans, are infected with a roundworm called ascaris. The adults grow to forty centimetres (fifteen inches) in length. The female releases millions of eggs into the fecal stream in the six to eighteen months of her life, at a rate of about 200 000 eggs per day per worm. Once discharged from the body, the eggs may live in soil for almost six years and are taken into their next victim when contaminated food or soil is ingested. In dry windy climates, eggs can become airborne and inadvertently swallowed. The worms may damage the lungs and the intestinal tract and, although most patients have fewer than fifty worms in their body at any one time, as many as 2000 are not uncommon. Treatment is satisfactory but only education and first-class personal hygiene with adequate toilet facilities will cut down on the attack rate of this trouble-some parasite.

Well, with that catalogue of potential horrors behind us, it is time to look at the defensive army we have generated after millions of years of effort which enables us to fight off the majority of these would-be invaders and to survive in this dangerous world.

2

The organisation of defence

J UST as our modern arsenals are ever changing as the weaponry of a potential enemy becomes more sophisticated, so our immune system has adapted itself many times to counter survival moves made by the microbial world. When an organism reproduces it has the chance to rearrange its genes, i.e. its blueprints for life. Sometimes the products produced by the rearranged genetic template will improve the survival chances of the organism. Some rearrangements, however, may produce no benefit at all and some could be positively harmful. The process is a random one; a bit like throwing paint at the wall and hoping to produce a Rembrandt. Obviously, survival advantages will ensure that the improved model will prosper.

Because of the ability of genes to rearrange themselves, no living species (in contradistinction to an individual specimen of a species) is locked into a poor design for survival. Throughout most of time, biological enemies have invested much of their natural energies in efforts to outsmart each other and therefore survive.

Change in the world of Nature can be rapid: in only a few years, many bacteria have become resistant to certain anti-biotics. But more often change is very slow by human standards. When we talk of the body's defences, we mean a system that evolved among developing species over hundreds of millions of years. It was already advanced when humans began their battles with parasites and other enemies some forty to fifty thousand years ago. It is humbling to think that if the history of our planet was condensed into twenty-four hours, and in the last second before the end of that day one was to flash a light beam, that momentary brightness would encompass our time on the planet we now feel we rule.

If we could go back to that primitive time when earthworms first burrowed through the soil and primitive jellyfish lapped at an evolving shoreline, we would find that these simple creatures had already begun the painstaking experiments that would lead to the assembly of the necessary apparatus for defence. From such humble beginnings developed our modern immune system which, as we will see, is complex. This complexity has been constructed by the constant addition of logical but subtle refinements to the system. The development is analogous to the way that the complexity of a Mahler symphony can be seen to have developed stepwise and logically from the simplest harmonies of the Renaissance madrigal.

The system that we are about to analyse is extraordinarily powerful. Just a few tiny cells from the immune system of a mouse, when injected into an animal of a slightly different strain that has been deliberately made an immunological cripple, can destroy that animal by the fury of the attack that will be launched in just a few days.

Power of this kind brings problems as well as benefits, and much of the necessary complexity of the immune system is generated by the need to *control* these forces within our own bodies. Of all the control mechanisms we have inherited from millennia of experiments, there is one with which our defence system has been most preoccupied. This is a mechanism which should prevent us from making the most awful of immunological mistakes—the attacking of self.

When you are the ever-vigilant protector of the sacrosanct environment of a body, anything foreign that should dare to invade that environment must be rapidly detected and removed. However, finding certain invaders and recognising them as foreign can be very difficult. A major reason for this difficulty is that many invaders look very much like us, not us in the totality of our human form of course, but in terms of some specific structures that may contribute to the construction of cells. It can be as difficult for our immune system to detect foreignness as it would be for a Caucasian to pick out a particular Chinese interloper at a crowded ceremony in Beijing's main square.

Some of the proteins produced by micro-organisms are identical or nearly identical to a number of our own proteins. The latter of course we have learnt to recognise as 'us', structures not to be attacked under any circumstances. This 'molecular mimicry', as it is called, may give organisms a survival advantage and certainly tests the discriminatory power of our immune system. When we fail to distinguish foreignness from self, we may not attack an enemy when we should or we may become confused and actually attack our own tissues and produce an autoimmune disease. The results of such a mistake are frequently dramatic, but the real miracle is the rarity with which our sophisticated and complicated immune system makes such a mistake.

We will examine our immunological arsenal and its uses from the evolutionary point of view, starting with the most primitive system and adding layer upon layer for an overview of the entire system.

Perhaps we can best approach the complexities of our immune system with an admittedly simplified analogy. Let's imagine that we are examining a particular security system that has been designed for an ultra-important, indeed ultra-secret, industrial complex. The security system is devised to keep out intruders and to detect rapidly any that do happen to make it inside. The security problem is made more complex by the fact that, during the day, the plant employs two thousand men and women who work at a myriad of different tasks scattered over a very large area. Legitimate members of the plant's family of workers must be readily identifiable, and of course provoke no response from the security forces.

A relatively primitive, non-specific deterrent in the form of a high fence topped with barbed wire surrounds the building, which has only a limited number of entrances. It's certainly not easy to get through this first barrier, but it's not impossible. When the plant is not working, a second, still rather primitive, system is used for defence. Guard dogs patrol around the building and they have been trained to attack anyone they find inside the premises. With the exception of their trainers, they cannot distinguish between employees and intruders. This is a relatively efficient system but the dogs can't be everywhere at once and therefore a more sophisticated back-up system is required, which will be more severely tested during the day when the place is teeming with legitimate workers.

Security personnel patrol the premises randomly but frequently, picking up individuals who are taken to specifically equipped locations for a security check. Now the particular security personnel we are discussing are not inherently suspicious; they just bring in anyone and everyone for a check. It's a bit like the police carrying out a random blood check for drinking drivers.

At the security checkpoint the protection experts are gathered. Between them, they have a number of different mechanisms useful for checking the legitimacy or otherwise of individuals brought for inspection. If Jack Smith, who knows he is in for a busy day and wants to get his security clearance out of the way, pops his head in the door and asks to be screened, he will be out of luck; security heavies are only interested in their random check system.

On the other hand, if Jack Smith is presented by the patrolling security personnel to the identification team they will spring into action. They will take a good look at Jack, who is at this stage held tightly by the security personnel, who are taking no chances. In the security station are soldiers who are quite willing to dispose of Jack if given the OK, but his fate is decided by a supervisor, a sort of General, who recognises him and gives the all-clear. Jack is released and goes back to work, for of course the security forces are necessarily 'tolerant' of their own people; productivity within the complex wouldn't survive for long if they were not.

If an individual brought in for an identity check is recognised as an intruder, he is indeed in a lot of trouble. Now, the supervisor actually doing the identification screening is not going to get his hands dirty, for he has specialised troops ready to eliminate this enemy. How harsh will the punishment be? Well, there are only two alternatives—death, and a not very pleasant death at that, or summary expulsion from the plant. If the intruder protests his innocence and says he was just wandering around and didn't mean any harm, and the security personnel who brought him in confirm this fact, specialised 'eliminators' specifically trained to handle this particular fellow will grab hold of him and call in some of the not-so-intelligent bouncers they employ. Then together they will haul this fellow to the front door and hurl him out into the street. On the way, he will have been 'taught a lesson' by the bouncers and he will be very much battered and bruised when he reaches the outside world.

Back at the security station, the Generals will have called in and despatched many highly trained soldiers that can recognise this particular type of intruder. They are told to race around the entire factory to see if they can find look-alike accomplices.

Had the security personnel presented the intruder to the Generals and described destructive behaviour or some other obvious attempt to cause harm to the plant, then it's the death penalty that would be handed down, I'm afraid. Quite destructive soldiers, kept for this purpose, would seize upon the hapless violater and kill him with a combination of chemicals and repeated stabbings—the security business is not a pretty one.

Execution, clean and simple, in a security station designed for the purpose is the ideal. But battles against significant forces which have already become entrenched in this or that area of the plant are far more damaging. The spotters who find the intruders can signal to the chiefs to come running, with their soldiers, to the zone that's under attack. So sophisticated is the security system in this plant, that the spotters can activate a mechanism that will light up the most direct pathway from the security office to the area where the battle must be fought. The troops are guided in the way that a sub-way map in London may show you, after you push an appropriate button, the most direct way to move from Holborn to Kensington Gardens.

Now, as you can imagine, the battle will be brief or protracted, violent or otherwise, depending on the speed with which the in-truder is recognised (once established in a secure spot he may be much harder to dislodge), the weaponry he has for resistance and the forces the plant can effectively marshal. One thing is certain: in this highly sophisticated plant bristling with valuable and sensitive equipment, unnecessary force is to be avoided. No use shooting the intruder in the computer room and at the same time permanently damaging the computer. Some innocent bystander damage may have to be tolerated, but one wishes at all times to keep this to a minimum.

As we all know, commandos can get carried away with the glory of the battle and launch a missile when a hand grenade would be perfectly satisfactory. Therefore, when our inspectors alert the response force they also pass the same information to the plant's management team, who ultimately have control over matters from that point forward. They must determine the nature and the intensity of the response to be launched for it is their responsibility to ensure appropriateness—enough force to do the job but not more than enough, for excesses may damage the plant unnecessarily.

These management types have also been specifically trained in the business of recognising who is family and who is not, and can thus check the decision making of the team that has sounded the alarm. Via radio communications these super-managers can control with ultimate authority both the inspectors and the soldiers. In this way, security is maintained and the damage to the plant minimised.

An attack on such an establishment always forms a learning process and good management demands that security be strength-ened in an area where an attack or infringement was even partially successful. If on two occasions intruders have had some success entering a plant via its large air-conditioning ducts, the team that looks after this area must be expanded and equipped for a faster, more powerful response should this previously vulnerable area ever be approached again.

The specialised nature of the work of each of these teams requires personnel who are highly trained. It is not surprising that establish-ments are available where these skills can be gained and perfected so that on graduation the successful candidates are ready for a particular role in the chain or net-work of security measures that protect the plant.

This fanciful sketch, as you will no doubt have guessed, incorporates the major design features of our immune system. The development of the biological system that works on the above principles can now be described.

Tens of millions of years ago, as Nature was designing its first defensive mechanisms, cells developed which were capable of removing large pieces of foreign material that entered the body. The one type of cell responded to all challenges and there were no control mechanisms. For example, a jellyfish could reject a thorn that pierced its flesh in a non-specific fashion. However, the increasing complexity of potential challenges called for a far more sophisticate defensive system. To the cells that supplied this immature protection (the guard dogs in our industrial complex) were slowly added cells that could recognise both foreignness and self and react differently to each.

Throughout this book, we will use the term immunologists constantly use to describe structures that engage our immune system, i.e. 'antigens'. The word 'engage' is chosen to emphasise that sometimes antigens are recognised but do not provoke an immunological attack. A substance that provokes an attack is an 'immunogen'; most antigens, as we will see, are in fact immunogens. Most of the time, when we refer to antigens, we will be discussing foreign substances worthy of attack and rejection by our immune system. We might therefore call a virus an antigen and so it is but, in reality, even though it's so tiny we cannot see it even with an ordinary light microscope, to our immune system it's a monster and one that must be broken down into bite-size pieces if our immune system is to attack. Such degradation products that become targets for our immunological soldiers are known as antigenic determinants.

As primitive species became less primitive, cells that could recognise and attack antigens were added to their defensive repertoire. In further developmental steps, control mechanisms evolved. It took many eons to refine the usually super-efficient system with which we are blessed.

We can examine this evolutionary process in some detail by looking at the way in which a tiny human fetus, starting with just a few cells, builds up the complexity of its immune system. Starting after just a few weeks of intra-uterine life, the fetus recapitulates most of the evolutionary steps that have gone before, so that each of us during this developmental phase becomes a sort of biological history book.

The sole heart and brain of our sophisticated immune system is the thymus gland. Not the most famous gland in the body, you may be thinking, but certainly as interesting as any and arguably the most important. The thymus gland, which lies right on top of the heart, intimately embracing the great vessels that bring blood into and out of the 'pump of life', can be thought of as a finishing school. The graduands are known as T lymphocytes (T for thymus), although for convenience sake they are often simply referred to as T cells. Lymphocytes are part of the family of white blood cells that circulate in our bloodstream.

The thymus has developed and is ready for its first pupils by the time the tiny human fetus is ten weeks old. Each and every thymus gland develops with the genetic wisdom needed to program the major elements of our immune system displayed in the cells of its biological library. All this wisdom is available to neophyte cells which will learn vital skills during their sojourn in the gland.

In order to attract cells into the thymus gland where they can be educated, the gland secretes chemicals that are irresistibly attractive to certain cells, most of which come from the liver of the fetus. The liver has little to do during fetal life compared with the hugely important role it plays after birth, but it is extremely important in generating pluripotential cells. (See Figure 1, p. 8.) After fetal life, the pupils destined to be educated in the thymus gland come from the bone marrow rather than the liver.

Through the earliest weeks of life primitive 'stem' cells, as they are called, leave the liver and spread through the body via the blood vessels. As explained earlier, each of these cells has locked up in its nucleus all the genetic information available to the body as a whole, and the trick that will turn our uneducated 'primitive' stem cells into useful members of the body's machinery involves activating specific genetic programs within a particular cell.

Responding to the thymus, some fetal liver cells begin to fill the empty spaces within the gland. They move, predictably, further and further into the depths of the gland as they successfully master this step then that. Each thymus gland educates more than five hundred billion individual T cells and each cell must receive special attention. By far the most important lesson to be learnt by would-be T cells is how to recognise antigens. To discuss this matter further, we must introduce an immunological dilemma of great significance.

There are more than one million foreign antigens that we must learn to recognise if we are to be prepared for all conceivable challenges from the environment. The recognition of antigens is the responsibility of individual T cells. In the thymus, the appropriate genes in a student cell are activated and the cell constructs an antenna-like structure, which it will mount on its surface so that it actually projects into the environment surrounding the cell. This antenna is known as the T cell receptor (TCR). Unlike a radio antenna, however, which can recognise many signals, the TCR can recognise only one: 'its special signal'. The TCR is composed of two chains, called alpha and beta. While the parts of the chain nearest the surface of the cell are identical on all T cells in one person's body, the portions furthest away from the cell will take on a three-dimensional configuration that in fact creates a highly complicated lock. Into this lock, only one key will fit perfectly. Any T cell has the capacity to recognise one and only one antigenic determinant. If you are a T cell programmed to recognise a bit of the measles virus, you will patrol the body waiting for that big moment when, perhaps at a birthday party, your young owner is coughed on by someone who has measles virus particles in their saliva. Then and only then will you, the cell, have found the purpose of life. (Figure 4.)

Now Nature could have constructed a huge biological checklist in the thymus and programmed consecutive stem cells to recognise the next antigen on the list. Five hundred cells might be programmed to recognise fish haemoglobin, which seldom attacks us, while fifty thousand might be programmed to recognise a particular influenza virus. We would need many more genes than we have available to us to program T cells in this way. Nature in fact sees to it that, through a set of genetic instructions, all the permutations and combinations possible within the variable region of the TCR are created. The arms of the receptor are bent every which way to create randomly the millions of 'locks' needed. However, and here is the dilemma, such a process doesn't limit the recognition units created to ones that will only recognise foreign substances. We literally learn to recognise everything and our own tissues are part of everything. In programming in the capacity to recognise a million or more foreign substances we generate T cells that can recognise all of our own structures, i.e. self.

We talk about tissues containing 'self' antigens and this can be a little confusing, because 99 per cent of the time when we talk of antigens we are talking of something foreign to our body. But of course you only have to see what happens when you transplant a kidney from one person into another to see how antigenic, indeed immunogenic, are our own tissues.

How can we control the potentially dangerous situation associated with the generation of T cells capable of attacking us? In the industrial complex analogy used earlier, we had personnel who could recognise employees and not attack. How is this situation handled biologically?

We have known for many years that the thymus gland is a harsh environment, a tough school indeed because many of the cells that enter never leave. They are killed during the educational process. Many of the cells that actually die are those that have, through bad luck in their genetic rearrangement, ended up with receptors for certain 'self' antigens.

Figure 4. The production of **T** CELLS in the thymus gland

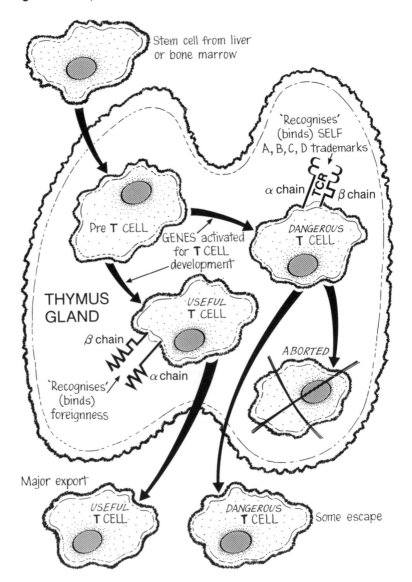

Such a murderous system would provide the ideal solution of course. Before they even left the thymus where they could cause trouble, T cells recognising self would be aborted. A family of cells capable of recognising the one antigenic determinant is called, in immunology, a clone. Hence the process we are talking about is referred to as clonal abortion. We now know that immature T cells, still progressing through the thymus gland, that experience a key being inserted into their lock may die rather than mature. Theoretically, inside a young fetus, tucked away safely inside mother's uterus, all that could possibly be presented to T cells is self.

OK, I can hear you say, T cells that can recognise a part of my kidney or heart or liver might be killed in the thymus if they recognised these tissues, but how will this happen—there are no kidney, heart or liver antigens in the thymus, are there? No, there aren't, and thus clonal abortion does not provide the complete answer to the problem; but it is important nonetheless.

Every cell in our body displays a series of 'biological trademarks', and any given individual's set of trademarks is almost unique. These trademarks are powerful antigens and, as we will discuss in detail in the chapter on transplantation, are the molecules that so annoy the immune system of an organ recipient. To be accurate, these markers are not absolutely unique to one individual. Nature's permutations and combinations with these markers are finite. Thus we can calculate that something like two people in every 400 000 will be identical. This is very important when it comes to tissue transplantation.

Now, the set of proteins on almost all the cells of our body were not put there to make transplantation of organs difficult, although they do. They were designed to help introduce antigens to T cells. They are antigen-presenting molecules, 'take a look at this' molecules, primarily involved as we will see in letting T cells know that a given cell is infected with a virus. The receptors on T cells only recognise antigens presented by these extraordinary proteins. Back we go to the excitement in the thymus gland.

There are six to eight of these major trademarks on our cells and we generate T cells in the thymus that could recognise and subsequently attack them. In the middle of the thymus, however, conveniently situated so that immature T cells passing from junior into high school must encounter them, are cells which vividly display these self antigens on their surface. Most of the cells that do recognise (bind to) these structures are killed by mechanisms that are still somewhat unclear. (Look at Figure 4 again.)

This process rids us of a set of very dangerous cells but others capable of recognising unique proteins in specific tissues will make it and graduate from the thymus, and must therefore be controlled if we are to avoid the development of autoimmune disease processes. We handle these characters in two ways. During early fetal life, as the newly graduated cells whizz around the body looking for trouble, those cells that actually believe they have found it—that is, that bind antigen—are not killed but rather are 'shocked' in a biological sense into a state of non-reactivity. This phenomenon may well explain the observation that the rubella (German measles) virus, for example, infecting a seven-month-old fetus will provoke an immune response and be destroyed, while the same virus entering a three-month-old fetus will not be attacked then or later. T cells that can recognise this virus are stunned; clonal anergy (lack of energy) occurs. Nature presumably hopes that in the critical phase when clonal anergy can easily be induced, T cells are only encountering self.

The failure to completely eliminate self reactive cells (i.e. cells reacting to what we have called 'self') is clearly one of the few mistakes made by the great immunologist in the sky, and it may well be that over the next few million years with the help of Mother Nature such defects might be corrected. Our descendants in the far distant future may talk about our primitive immune system in their textbooks. Because we have cells circulating in our body that can recognise specific tissues in exactly the same way that other cells can recognise foreignness, humans become potential victims of autoimmunity, i.e. the turning of the immune system against self. This occurs relatively frequently. Thus it is clear that some T cells, capable of recognising self, either escape abortion and being shocked into non-reactivity or recover from the effects of the stun gun to become potentially dangerous. If such self reactive T cells do what comes naturally, we may end up with diseases such as rheumatoid arthritis, pernicious anemia, diabetes, thyroid disease and a host of other ills.

Having these potentially autoreactive time bombs inside us means that such cells must be selectively controlled. This is the third and perhaps the most important fail–safe mechanism we bring to bear in an attempt to prevent immunological reactions to self. A cell that is present in our tissues or circulating in our bloodstream that would like to attack the lung, for example, must be told not to do so; in order to set this up the thymus produces a family of unique T cells that have the job of keeping autoreactive cells under control throughout our lifetime. (Figure 5.) They in fact do other things associated with ensuring that our immunological soldiers behave appropriately, and we will return to discuss these cells many times in this book.

To summarise this story to date, we can see that Nature has supplied us with a gland that educates cells from the fetal liver and,

Figure 5. These **T** CELLS escaped death in the thymus; they can recognise SELF but are prevented from attacking by various 'fail – safe' mechanisms

KIDNEY – recognising T CELL

HEART – recognising T CELL

LIVER – recognising T CELL

KIDNEY CELL

HEART MUSCLE CELL

LIVER CELL

later, the bone marrow to recognise specific molecules. Such cells (T cells) have receptors for antigen, which are composed of two arms that project out into space from the surface of the cell with the 'hands' of the arms frozen into a particular three-dimensional space, into which one antigenic determinant will have a best fit. Thousands of identical receptors pepper the surface of any given T cell. The generation of sufficient diversity to allow us to recognise more than a million determinants involves the creation of every possible 'lock', including some that can recognise our own tissues. Cells with this capacity are particularly dangerous and so are either killed in the thymus or rendered tolerant as they circulate in the body in early fetal life, or are kept under control throughout life by regulatory cells (the officials in our industrial plant that stop soldiers from attacking employees).

At the end of the 1960s, when we first went to the moon, our knowledge of antigen recognition mechanisms was primitive and scientists working for NASA wondered what might happen if the astronauts met up with a 'moonococcus', the recognition of which was not programmed into the TCR repertoire. It was guessed that any such bug would declare its presence in the astronauts within the first three weeks after they returned! The poor fellows were thus isolated for three weeks on returning to Earth and we now know that they did not encounter moonococci or even little green men!

Earlier, we likened the thymus gland to a school but university might have been more accurate, for a number of different courses are available that will determine lifetime careers. Many T cells live for more than sixty years so we must hope that they enjoy their designated biological roles. The thymus gland actually graduates four functionally and physically distinct T cell types, and it is to these that we must turn our attention.

If you have seen any science fiction movies of late, you will have noticed that as the intrepid pilot of a spaceship approaches a station rotating slowly in all that nothingness, the complex feature of the station's exterior becomes increasingly clear. The surface is highly featured with antennae for receiving and sending signals, and entrances to allow appropriate individuals and supplies to enter and leave are quite prominent. While many a space station out there will have numerous features in common, the design requirements for unique functions will give different stations some unique physical characteristics. T cells can be likened to this arrangement. The different functions played by the four T cell types are associated with surface features that are discriminatory. (Figure 6.)

If you found yourself in the midst of a few million T cells (a 'cluster' of T cells) and you had the appropriate microscopic vision, you could identify the surface features which differentiate one functional type from another. Such individual structures are thus referred to as 'cluster of differentiation' antigens; a term that is usually abbreviated to 'CD'. As we have identified more and more distinguishing antigens, each has been given a number. Currently, we have more than 60 such features, designated CD1–CD60 and more are being discovered at a steady pace. Thus we can describe the function of the four T cell types and work out a convenient way of referring to them in the biological dramas that are to be described later.

Figure 6. As **T** CELLS mature in the thymus they differentiate and take on specific functions

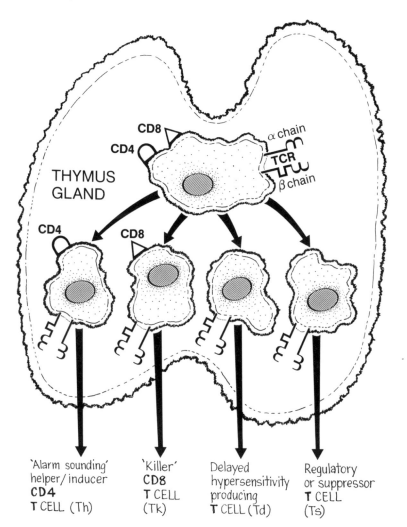

As is true at any university, all the pupils in the thymus develop a set of basic skills before they begin to specialise. Advanced training provides us with a major T cell subset responsible for sounding the alarm by recognising foreignness and initiating the chain reaction designed to eliminate any invader. These cells help induce an immune response by helping other cells prepare to attack. For these reasons, the cells are often referred to as 'inducer' or 'helper' T cells. I prefer the former name as it highlights the absolutely pivotal role that these cells play in initiating the response to individual antigens.

These cells display vividly on their outer membranes the CD antigen given the number 4. Thus our alarm-sounding cells are often referred to as CD4 lymphocytes. Even that is a little cumbersome so it is acceptable to compromise, as we shall, and call these lymphocytes T4 cells. We will examine how T4 cells activate the immune response shortly.

Two of the T cell types produced by the thymus are fighters. One set is referred to colorfully and accurately as 'killer T cells'. These cells have on their surface the CD8 antigen and are often referred to as 'T8 cells'. They are equipped with the weapons necessary to kill our own cells unlucky enough to be harbouring an organism, for example a virus. Organisms which actually reside inside our cells are naturally enough referred to as intracellular pathogens. Many foreign antigens do not get into our cells and, as we will see, are handled differently. We will discuss cancer in detail in its own chapter but T8 cells can also kill many types of tumour cells. To do their killing, T8 cells secrete toxins and actually develop projections that emerge from their surfaces to 'spear' the cells that must be killed. Remember the chemicals and stabbing in our plant security analogy?

The third member of the T cell family attacks antigens in our tissues in a different manner. Once activated, these cells hover around their target and summon partners to help them attack. They are designed to work in concert with specialised cells known as macrophages (*macro* meaning big, *phages* meaning swallow). The T cells we are discussing take some time to get their attack ready. They secrete the chemicals which attract the macrophages and gradually the troop's strength intensifies and the battle is launched. In humans, this can require forty-eight hours of preparation.

Once into the battle, the antigen is attacked by chemicals released by these T cells and the macrophages, and the invader is actually swallowed by the macrophages. Once inside these giant cells, the engulfed material is destroyed by enzymes (chemicals with the ability to break down protein). The reactions we are describing are referred to as 'delayed-type hypersensitivity' while the T cell involved is given the abbreviation 'Td', for no single differentiation (CD) antigen can be used to describe these cells. (Take another look at Figure 6.)

Macrophages are formed in the bone marrow, the space within certain bones that acts as a factory for producing both red and white blood cells. Red cells are red because they have a pigment inside them called hemoglobin, which is a red color; white cells are not really white, but colorless. Macrophages start life by circulating in the bloodstream, having been released from the bone marrow in a somewhat immature form, at which stage they are called mono- cytes. Once they are attracted into the tissues to do battle with an invader, they rapidly mature and are called macrophages.

The fourth family of T cells are immunoregulatory cells, the Generals in charge of the intensity and duration of the battle waged by the attacking cells. These T cells have two major functions. The first is to determine the appropriateness of the vigor of a particular immunological attack. If you have viruses infecting cells lining your throat, then in the battle to save you from these invaders you are going to suffer—your throat may get very sore indeed. If a hand grenade will do the job we don't need to use plastic explosives and we certainly want the battle called off as soon as the enemy is accounted for.

Much of the time, these immunoregulatory T cells are moderating or suppressing the soldiers doing the destroying in an immunological response. They are often referred to as 'suppressor' T cells, or 'Ts' cells. Sometimes, however, they must increase the intensity of the fighting and are thus better referred to as immunoregulatory T cells, and this is how we shall refer to them in the pages to come.

The second major function of these cells is the containment of the natural urges possessed by those T8 killer cells (sometimes referred to as cytotoxic T cells) that have receptors which enable them to recognise self and that have escaped clonal abortion. They must of course be kept in check throughout life. Immunoregulatory T cells must be ever-vigilant and prevent such cells doing any damage to our own tissues. Immunoregulatory T cells can be identified by a group of different antigens on their surface but as the numbering involved is somewhat complex, we won't use a CD terminology for these cells.

Thus we have seen that the thymus gland is, from the time we are ten weeks old, producing T cells that can recognise 'foreignness' when it binds, key in lock fashion, to their surface receptors. Some cells are charged with the responsibility for sounding the alarm and giving the permissive signal to others which can kill cells infected by an organism or certain cancerous cells or which can produce delayed- type hyper-sensitivity with the help of friends called macrophages.

Dr Paul Ehrlich in 1896, when he was astounding the world with his theories about immunology.

Finally, there are the Generals who keep our immunological arsenal in order. The immune system is powerful, multi-faceted, finely poised between perfection and perfidy. The regulatory cells may have the most difficult job of all.

All this is relatively recent knowledge; twenty years ago, the picture was far less clear. Thirty-five years ago, if you had tried to suggest that a T lymphocyte graduated from the thymus with the capacity to recognise one particular invading antigen, you would have been held up to ridicule. That is what happened to the great scientist Paul Ehrlich in 1896 when he drew a picture of a cell that looked remarkably like a T lymphocyte and claimed that this cell, for example, might have the capacity to respond to diphtheria and nothing else.

Paul Ehrlich was seventy years ahead of his time. Even twenty-five years ago, scientists considered lymphocytes to be like soft rubber balls. They claimed that when an antigen (say, a specific type of bacteria) bounced on the wall of one of these immune cells, the indentation so made would remain and the mould obtained from these physical changes could act as a template for the production of specific chemicals that would attack the antigen. Alternatively, it was suggested that antigen could be taken into all lymphocytes and held in place while the cell's machinery produced a complementary molecule. This 'template theory' held sway for a long time in immunobiology and it is, of course, now interesting to read that Ehrlich ridiculed it before the turn of the century.

Now, with one more piece of information we are ready to try to put all of the above together by examining, in step-wise fashion, the happenings featured during the response to a real invasion.

Much, indeed most, of the signalling done by the cells of the immune system as they talk to each other—giving permission, suspending the operation, calling for help from this cell or that, etc.— is achieved by chemical messages released by the cells in question. Such chemicals belong to the general family of soluble messengers known as cytokines (*cyto* refers to cell); and, logically, the ones emerging from lymphocytes, that family of white blood cells to which T cells belong, are called lymphokines. A number of individual chemicals produced by the cells of the immune system are referred to as interleukins (they deliver messages between white blood cells or *leuco*cytes) and, as they are identified, they are also given a number: IL1, IL2, etc. Okay, let's take a common enough scenario and see if we can fit together pieces of the immunological jigsaw puzzle, thus creating a grand, logical and indeed fascinating pattern.

'What do you get when you kiss a boy? You get enough germs to catch pneumonia, after you do he'll never phone you . . .' So run the words of Mr Baccarach's cynical song. Well, Jenny may have received a few million influenza A viruses from Jack as he kissed her goodnight, or she may have inhaled them from the air after he sneezed at the dinner table (both are possible), but get a dose of such viruses she most certainly did. All viruses prefer to live in specific host cells and the influenza virus is very partial to the cells lining our throat. To get inside, they actually have on their surface a binding protein that helps them find their resting place.

Now, had Jack been only moderately infectious and relatively few viruses been transferred, Jenny's T cells might never have been called upon to eradicate the few flu viruses involved. Cells providing her immune system with a first line of defence might have crippled the invader. Primitive T-like cells called natural killer cells kill indiscriminately; they are equivalent to the guard dogs in our industrial plant and they are often helped by phagocytic cells such as macrophages. If *many* viruses made it safely into the cells lining Jenny's throat, however, the big guns we have discussed above would be called into action. Now, to follow this action, I want you to imagine that you could be made tiny enough to enter Jenny's tissues and watch the drama at first hand. A fascinating movie was made some years ago using this concept and the intrepid adventurers certainly had a rough time swimming in the body's turbulent bloodstream, as I recall.

Among the cells that combine to form the lining of Jenny's throat are specialised cells known as antigen-presenting cells or APCs.

Figure 7. Steps involved in attacking the influenza virus

(i) **ANTIGEN**-presenting cell displays **VIRUS** fragments for **T** CELL perusal

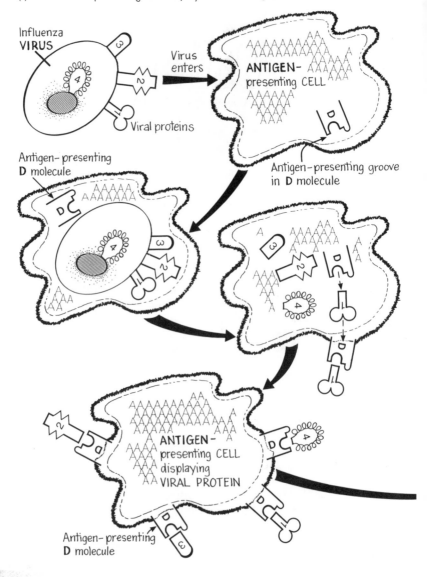

Anything that enters the tissues, be it self or foreignness, is seized and dragged inside this type of cell. Thus, if we were there to watch, we would notice what would appear to be a huge antigen-presenting cell (many are macrophages) seizing a large influenza A virus particle and swallowing it. If we could somehow sneak inside the APC with the virus, we would be able to observe the enemy being systematically chopped up into little pieces.

T cells cannot recognise a whole influenza virus; rather it must be presented in 'bite-size' pieces. Viruses are composed of proteins and proteins are made up of building blocks called amino acids. Small segments of protein, i.e. subunits made up of a few amino acids, are called peptides. What we are observing in the factory inside the APC is the breaking down of the influenza A virus into peptide fragments. T cells *can* recognise peptides. (Figure 7i.)

Now, you can probably guess that those fragments of viruses prepared in the interior of the APC are destined to be raced up to the surface again, to be presented to the body's T cells in order to see if any are interested—i.e. recognise foreignness. Even before the peptides are taken to the surface, the APCs are making arrangements for the T cell inspection.

Our APCs secrete chemicals while they are readying the peptide fragments and Jenny knows all about one of them. The young lady is feeling poorly. She has developed a fever and has already decided to stay in bed for the morning. Her throat is not sore but she has that flu-like feeling. Her muscles are aching, she is shivering and she has a headache.

The influenza virus is not responsible for her symptoms. The

ANTIGEN (PEPTIDE) in groove

T CELL receptor

T4 CELL capable of recognising a PEPTIDE from influenza VIRUS

Binds ANTIGEN-presenting D molecule as well as PEPTIDE

APCs working on the virus have secreted a substance known as interleukin 1, which has many functions, one of which is to produce a fever. IL1 is capable of activating mechanisms in the brain that control our body's temperature, and thus the thermostat is turned up. Why? Because many of the cells of the immune system work better when our body temperature rises.

Other chemicals released by APCs in the throat quickly work to alter 'the traffic lights' in the nearby blood vessels. Changes induced in the blood vessel wall cause receptors to reach out from the wall into the flow of blood. These particular structures will recognise any T cells passing through in the bloodstream and binding actually occurs. T cells bound in this fashion squeeze through tiny pores in the walls of the blood vessels and are then directed towards the area where the APCs are preparing the suspects for inspection.

The alerting of the T cells in the bloodstream has caused them to display on their surface other structures that allow them to bump into signposts that appear in the tissues around the APC. In this way, if we were standing in the throat tissue beside the antigen-presenting cells, we would watch, no doubt with some trepidation (see the pictures in the middle of the book), as numerous T cells arrive to find out what's causing all this excitement. The T cells coming into Jenny's throat, of course, are in no way selected for their capacity to recognise influenza A virus. *All* passing T cells are summoned to the scene.

We have now reached the stage where Jenny is curled up in bed with her fever, and it's time to show the T cells the peptides prepared from the virus. But, to understand the next step, we need to pause and explain a facet of the immune response that is very complicated. Indeed, let me assure you that if you grasp the concept that we are about to discuss, everything else in immunology will seem easy.

We must return to those biological trademarks on our cells that we discussed earlier. So far, we have seen that many T cells that can recognise these structures that identify 'me' as 'me' are destroyed in the thymus (clonal abortion). We know that the elimination process is not perfect. We have also observed that the display of these characters on foreign tissue (for example, someone else's heart) leads us to mount a vicious attack against them—they are indeed the 'red rag to the bull' of immunology (what a pity that we now know that bulls are color blind, it does destroy the impact of the old saying does it not?). Their major function, however, is the facilitation of immunological reactions.

Earlier, we saw that there are six to eight of these trademark proteins on the surface of all of our cells. They are products, the blueprints for which (genes) can be found on the two chromosomes that are designated as pair number six. As described earlier, chromosomes do hang out in pairs, with one of the chromosomes being inherited from mother and one from father. The genes that we are discussing occupy a space (locus) on chromosome six from mum and dad called A, B, C, and D. On every cell in your body— except your red blood cells, which have their own biological trademarks, the well-known A, B, O system—you can find proteins coded for by the genes at sites A, B and C, i.e. three proteins courtesy of mum and three courtesy of dad. Only on antigen-presenting cells do we find, along with the A, B and C proteins expressed on the surface of the cell, those coded for at site D on chromosome pair number six. For completeness' sake I should point out that the D-locus has recently been found to have up to four subdivisions on each chromosome, so that in reality we have fourteen possible major A, B, C and D coded molecules on the surface of our cells. In this book, however, we will continue to group all the relevant genes within the D area of chromosome six to prevent unnecessary confusion as we explore major principles.

To understand the relevance of all these genetic programs, let's go back to the drama unfolding in Jenny's throat. Our vigilant APCs, having set up the review processes, turn on their D-locus genes and produce the D-proteins, which are fascinating molecules that actually have a groove running along them which looks like the cargo hold of one of NASA's space shuttles. The groove is open along its length but closed at either end. Into the 'hold' is inserted a peptide derived from the influenza virus. D-locus proteins bearing a particular peptide fragment move back to the surface of the APCs, there to arrive like a diver surfacing from the sea. D-proteins, clutching the suspect, are displayed on the surface of an antigen-presenting cell for any passing T cell to have a look at.

Now, the receptors for antigen on T cells that we described earlier (TCR) are actually receptor complexes made up on the alpha and beta chains of the TCR and an adjacent but integrated complex three-dimensional structure into which can fit antigen-presenting molecules. For the peptide to slip into the TCR comfortably, the antigen-presenting molecule must also bind to the T cell. Only when a T cell binds both peptide and an antigen-presenting molecule will the T cell be activated. Recognising antigenic determinants (peptides) on their own is not sufficient. (Look at Figure 7 again.)

T4 cells, the ones responsible for sounding the alarm or inducing the immune response, *can only recognise a peptide-D complex*. All the T4 cells called in to look at the suspect peptides can recognise the antigen-presenting molecule D but very few will recognise the peptide. Hence there is some delay in firing off a response but once recognition does occur all immunological hell breaks loose.

Jenny's kiss has led to influenza A virus entering the cells lining

Figure 7. Steps involved in attacking the influenza virus CONTINUED

(ii) Killing **INFLUENZA VIRUS** by killing influenza-infected cells

T4 CELL
releases chemicals
(e.g. IL2) to allow
CD8 to respond

Influenza PEPTIDE-
recognising **CD8**
'killer' **T** CELL

A, B or C antigen-presenting
molecule

Influenza virus PEPTIDE in
antigen-presenting groove

AIRWAYS CELL
infected with
influenza virus

MACROPHAGE

Influenza PEPTIDE-
recognising **T** CELL
capable of producing
DELAYED HYPERSENSITIVITY

Chemicals
call in
MACROPHAGES
to help

her throat and airways. Left to their own devices, all the viruses wish to do is to multiply in their safe haven and send new copies out of the cell to invade other cells and continue the cycle. Unfortunately, we don't have a mechanism for ridding ourselves of a virus once it's inside a cell except by killing the invaded cell and therefore the viruses housed within.

Inside the cells of Jenny's throat parasitised by the influenza virus, the virus reproduces but again samples of the virus are digested into peptides by the cell and these are displayed on the surface of infected cells in the groove of A, B and C locus products. Inside the infected cell, it is the attempt by a virus or other micro-organism to reproduce that leads to its presentation on the surface of the cell complexed to A, B and C proteins. Nature doesn't want to kill a normal cell if something harmless enters. For the same reason, killer T cells (T8 cells), which can destroy a virus-infected cell, only recognise peptides complexed to A, B and C proteins. The TCR of T8 cells is so constructed that both the peptide in the groove of an A, B or C presenting protein and that protein itself must bind to the cell to signal it to commence the killing.

You may now be confused by our use of the term antigen-presenting cell when the description above suggests that all cells can present antigen, at least to T8 cells, because all cells can express A, B and C proteins on their surface. Well, that's true but in fact we restrict the term antigen-presenting cell to those cells that can present antigen to the T4 cell, as it's that step that starts the immunological bandwagon rolling. You may remember that we have already discussed the fact that any T8 cell must receive permission from a T4 cell before it can attack.

Back once more to Jenny's throat. (Figure 7ii.) As a result of the antigen-presenting cell's industriousness, T4 and T8 cells have arrived at the area under attack. The T4 cells, capable of recognising the viral peptides attached to D-proteins, do so and secrete a bevy of chemicals, including one interleukin 2 (IL2) which attaches to a receptor for itself, which is displayed on the surface of T8 cells once they recognise the antigen they wish to attack.

To this point, the virus is having an easy time of it, but with permission being given to the T8 cells to attack, they do; and of course Jenny's in for a few days when her throat will be sore as virus-infected cells are destroyed and replaced with new, healthy ones. As the T8 cells attack, they release many different chemicals including one called interferon, which actually interferes with the ability of viruses to multiply. Like so many of the chemicals involved in the immune response, however, interferon has many other functions, some of which we will refer to later.

In many situations, the T cells capable of calling in macrophages to create the delayed-type hypersensitivity reaction described earlier will also be involved in the immune response after these T cells see antigenic peptides that they can recognise, presented of course by the correct antigen-presenting proteins. Finally, we must acknowledge that monitoring the appropriateness of all this activity are the immunoregulatory T cells that can secrete their own chemicals or interleukins, such as IL10, which can interfere with the T4 cell's ability to activate other cells and many other immunological mechanisms.

Now, perhaps, if you re-read our fanciful analogy about the security mechanisms put into action in an industrial complex, everything will click into place.

When any of the T cells that we have described see 'their' antigen for the first time the reaction that follows is called, reasonably enough, a 'primary immune response'. This is somewhat slow as time is needed for specific T cells to meet their antigen and sound the alarm. Quite a few days could pass between the infection and an effective reaction. The second time that we encounter such an antigen, however, we are much better prepared. First encounters not only lead to an attack on the invader, they also cause a geometric expansion of the cells which have the capacity to recognise the invader during our lifetime. (We will probably meet relatively few of the million or more things that we can recognise.) This state of heightened preparedness is called immunological memory and is the basis on which all vaccines work; if you get a dose of an invading antigen in a harmless form, you are really prepared for when it enters your body in a dangerous form.

At this point, we must introduce a concept that is without doubt as important as any in biology. We humans, and indeed the members of all species, are set to self-destruct. Nature (natural processes) cares for the *species* with all the devotion and tenderness of a first-class mother but appears to care absolutely nothing for the individual member of the species. It's the genes we pass on to our offspring that are all-important to Mother Nature. For over time there is no doubt that the genetic experimentation that leads to survival advantages associated with specific genes will ensure that the carrier of those genes is in fact able to pass them on, and thus ever so slowly improve on older models. As we will discuss again later, it's not too biologically fanciful to suggest that Nature actually plans our departure from this earth.

Our thymus gland, for example, works flat out for the first few years of life and then rapidly shuts down production. It leaves us with a lifetime's worth of T cells. After they go, so do we.

By the age of sixty to sixty-five in most people, the number and functional integrity of the T cells in our bodies has diminished. As a result those cancer cells that we destroy with ease at twenty-one become a far more significant problem. Infections become very much more of a problem with older people because of T cell ageing. This means, of course, that we must look after the T cells we possess; they are precious. As you will see when we discuss AIDS, their destruction in adult life leaves us in a hopeless situation. The elusive 'elixir of youth' will need to be capable of rejuvenating T cells.

We have a T cell system composed of regulatory, alarm-sounding and destructive cells that must work perfectly and in harmony on a daily basis to keep us alive. The system itself is a very old one; in a primitive, early and tentative phase of development it can be found in an earthworm. Our sophisticated system is a result of much experimentation over millions of years. The capacity of lymphocytes to recognise, 'learn' by experience, retain memory function and have the self-discipline to act differently and yet appropriately in varying situations makes such cells truly wondrous creations of Nature.

T lymphocytes have a home, or more accurately homes, within the body, although for most of their life they travel constantly alongside the blood vessels and in smaller 'roads' that carry along the cells of the immune system.

When nine-year-old Christine fell from her bike onto a thorny bush, she sustained minor abrasions to her hands and major bruises to her ego as her accident had resulted from her inability to keep up with her eleven-year-old brother. Her mother washed her hands, placed a kiss and a bandaid over the small cut on her hand, and life went on. Into that minor wound, however, had entered some bacteria picked up from the thorns and the next day they were making their presence felt. The wound itself was red and a little tender but something was even more noticeable. Christine had a very visible red streak running all the way from her cut hand along her forearm to the crook in her elbow.

In various strategic sites in our body, immune stations have been established called lymph nodes (often but inaccurately described as lymph glands). Running through our tissues, usually in close proximity to our blood vessels, are specialised 'lymph vessels' that have a fluid circulating in them that is not blood but rather lymph. Lymph vessels and lymph itself supply a highway and a transport medium respectively for T cells, and can also pick up an invading antigen that has pierced the skin and transport it in the strong current of lymph to the nearest lymph node. Here, the invader is unceremoniously dumped into the middle of the immune army, for it is in the lymph nodes that the major cells of the immune system reside. Under our arms, in our groin, in the crook of our elbow, at the back of our throat (tonsils and adenoids), in our neck and in our belly (the spleen) are collections of immunological cells grouped together in such a way that they can evaluate anything flowing into the nodes in lymph.

In this way, Nature facilitates the recognition of an invading antigen by those very few specific cells that have the necessary recognition capacity.

Sometimes the invading organisms being unwillingly swept along in the lymph vessels secrete toxins that irritate them, and sometimes immune cells start to fight an invader even while it is still present in the lymph vessels. In such cases the vessels become inflamed and therefore red and visible. This is called lymphangitis ('itis' always means inflammation). That is why Christine had a red line running up her arm. Once Christine's invaders reached her lymph nodes she recovered quickly, for numerous cells were despatched to kill the organisms present in her lymph vessels, and anywhere else for that matter.

Lymph nodes, then, are the sites at which Nature prefers to carry out immunological battles; on home ground, so to speak. When a significant fight is underway, these lymph nodes swell. How often do we hear people referring to a child's swollen neck 'glands' that so often accompany a sore throat?

The nodes themselves are wonders of organisational planning, with T cells living in one section of the gland while B cells, which we have yet to discuss, live in an anatomically distinct compartment. T cells circulating in the blood may leave blood vessels as the vessels pass through a lymph node, only to leave the node again in lymphatic vessels that may return them back into the bloodstream in the chest, where the largest lymphatic vessel of all—the thoracic duct—empties its contents into one of the major veins in the body.

As the lymph vessels in the chest are very big, and large volumes of lymph containing precious T cells race through these areas, you might understand the concern associated with the following story. A few years ago, I was called to see a fifteen-year-old boy who had been admitted for surgery to correct a congenital defect in his aorta, the major blood vessel taking blood from the heart. In carrying out the repair, which had been entirely successful, the surgeon had inadvertently nicked the thoracic duct with his scalpel blade. Consequently this vessel was leaking lymph containing many T cells into the patient's chest. So much fluid was accumulating at the base of the lungs that a drain had to be inserted to allow the fluid to escape from the chest cavity and not impair the function of the lungs. But what about all those T cells running away to be lost forever? Billions of vital cells could be lost in a day and a week or more could elapse before those thoracic duct tears healed and the leak stopped.

So important are T cells that we hastily arranged to collect all the draining lymph, race it to my laboratory where we washed the temporarily homeless cells, making sure they remained both viable and sterile, and then infused them back into their original owner. More than 200 billion T cells were replaced over a week in this fashion.

One further piece of T cell biology needs explanation. We are not all born equal when it comes to the T cell system. Within the human family there is a range or spectrum of performance, which means that the ideal of which I have been talking is not always accomplished in a given individual. The consequences of having a second-class T cell system are enormous, as we shall see. While environmental factors can influence the variation, basically it is a genetic matter; we inherit a better or worse T cell system as a result of our parents' combining their genetic information.

Recent evidence suggests that some of us are much better at presenting certain antigens to T cells than are others, and that such variations may well determine whether we can effectively handle a certain infection. How often have we observed in everyday life that two people living together cross-infect each other with a virus but one may suffer much more than the other?

The B cell system

During our detailed examination of the T cell system, you may have been wondering where 'antibodies' come into the story of immunology. Because the term is commonly used, you are almost certain to have heard of these proteins. Antibodies enter our discussion at this point, and not earlier, as we are approaching the complexity of immunology in an evolutionary sense. The T cell, in a primitive stage of its evolution, was functioning for 200 million years before antibodies made their first appearance. Why was there a need to expand our immunological repertoire?

The development and function of the T cell system is impressive but T cells do have a few limitations. T cells are designed to attack an antigen held by an antigen-presenting cell. Some antigens in the bloodstream or tissues need to be disarmed or destroyed before the events described above allow T cells to have a crack at them. It would be an advantage if viruses could be rendered harmless before they entered our cells. T cells can be called into the area below our delicate mucous membranes, those smooth walls that line our mouth, intestinal tract, vagina and bladder, but it would be an advantage to have a protective mechanism operating on top of the membranes that was capable of preventing antigens from getting inside at all.

The greatest evolutionary pressure requiring the development of antibodies, however, was supplied by the need to handle evermore sophisticated and dangerous bacteria. These organisms are large compared with a virus and can multiply very quickly. A different weapon system was required.

Over thousands of years of recorded medical history, many doctors have pondered on the mechanisms responsible for immunity. The ancients knew that once a patient had recovered from a specific infectious disease he would usually not have it again, even if he nursed someone who was acutely ill with the disease. Towards the end of the nineteenth century, scientists discovered that serum contained a protective element. (Serum is blood minus the cells that circulate in it.) This protective substance in serum could be detected only after someone had successfully won a battle with a specific micro-organism.

With the discovery of bacteria and the development of the means of growing the organisms in a test tube, experiments could be performed in which such bacteria could be exposed to serum from an individual thought to be immune to that organism. The serum and the organism could be mixed together and the results observed. The ability of something in the serum to damage micro-organisms led to the discovery of 'antibodies'.

The system was called, and still is called, for nostalgic reasons, the 'humoral immune system'. Why? Because those early scientists knew that what, for them, were necessarily invisible factors or chemicals in serum must be responsible for the antibacterial effects they observed. At the time in question, such mysterious, elusive factors were collectively referred to as the 'humors'.

Early experiments revealed that whatever collection of 'humors' was responsible for the magic disappeared if you heated serum to 56°C. Pioneering experiments followed that revealed that the 'humors' in question were in fact composed of antibodies and chemicals belonging to a family of substances that together supply us with what is referred to as the complement system, which helps antibodies eliminate antigens and which will be discussed later. Today, we frequently refer to antibodies using more chemically orientated terminology, i.e. gammaglobulins or immunoglobulins. A globulin is not, as one student told me, something that runs around the bottom of an Irish garden. A globulin is a specialised form of protein which in this case has some carbohydrate attached.

Immunoglobulins are fascinating molecules without which we cannot live. They have an anatomy that provides them with antigen-binding properties that are similar to but more advanced that those displayed by the T cell receptor. One end of an immunoglobulin molecule (the variable region) has developed a binding site, the

Figure 8. Anatomy of an antibody

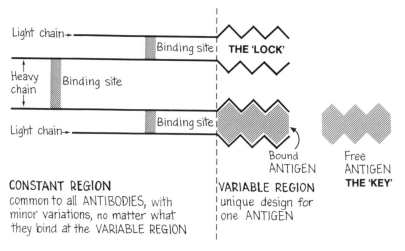

The **ANTIBODY MOLECULE** is the product of PLASMA CELLS

Light chain→

Binding site   THE 'LOCK'

Heavy chain

Binding site

Light chain→

Binding site

Bound ANTIGEN   Free ANTIGEN   **THE 'KEY'**

CONSTANT REGION
common to all ANTIBODIES, with minor variations, no matter what they bind at the VARIABLE REGION

VARIABLE REGION
unique design for one ANTIGEN

three-dimensional characteristics of which make it a lock into which one, and only one, very complicated key can have a best fit. Antibodies are composed of two long chains of amino acids and, at the antigen-binding end, two short chains of amino acids; and all four chains are joined to each other by what are known as di-sulphide bridges. Because the long chains are in chemical terms heavier than the smaller chains, we refer to heavy and light rather than long and short chains when describing the anatomy of the immunoglobulin molecules.

The arrangement of the four chains is designed to give us a binding molecule that can hold on to antigens with two hands, rather than one as is the case for the T cell receptor. Imagine your arms fully extended above your head with the fingers of both hands cupped in an identical fashion, and you'll get the idea. (Figure 8.)

Where do antibodies come from and how do they fit into the great immunological scheme of things? As is true of all the body's chemicals, antibodies are the products of specialised cells, in this case however not 'T' cells but rather 'B' cells. The story of how they came to be called B lymphocytes is interesting and instructive.

All birds have a lymph gland–like structure just a little way from their anus or cloaca, known as the 'bursa of Fabricius'. After I had been teaching students about this bursa for many years I decided to find out more about the man Fabricius. He was a leading professor at the University of Padua at the end of the fifteenth century. He was a scientist, lecturer, physician and anatomist who was the first to describe the fact that veins have valves that stop blood flowing in the wrong direction. What this famous man was doing dissecting the backside of birds in 1492 is not easily discovered, but he found the bursa and immortality was his. All birds have a bursa, but what does it do?

As so often happens in science, a series of experiments and chance observations occurring simultaneously in many laboratories supplied us with the answer to this question. At the end of the 1960s the United States Department of Agriculture was performing experiments to see if chickens could be made to grow faster and hence become more meaty in less than the normal amount of time. Some scientists had the idea of injecting testosterone (male sex hormones) into the embryonic chick before it was hatched to see if this would result in a meatier bird. I guess all the scientists were hoping that the treated chicken embryos would burst forth from their shells beating impressively muscular breasts. The experiments failed; indeed, the little chickens that did come somewhat reluctantly from their eggshells died of overwhelming bacterial infection within a few days of birth. Examination of these animals showed that they had failed to develop the famous but puzzling bursa of Fabricius. It soon became clear from this and other more direct observations that the bursa was the site in birds for the development of those lymphocytes that make antibodies. Birds without a bursa were bereft of bacteria-fighting ability.

With the discovery of the bursa in birds, the hunt was on for an equivalent structure in humans. It seemed reasonably certain that no organ of great significance existed in the same anatomical location in humans, and scientists speculated about the possibility that tonsils or the lymph nodes found in the intestinal tract might provide a bursal equivalent. These did not, however, but the bone marrow of humans did. Thus, we have the fortunate linguistic coincidence of being able to refer to B cells where the 'B' stands for bursa in birds but bone marrow in humans.

In the human fetus, stem cells from the liver migrate into the bone marrow in a similar fashion to their movement into the thymus. After birth the bone marrow makes its own stem cells and 'educates' them on the spot.

As is true of all cells, the stem cells that wish to become B cells carry with them all of the body's genetic programs. Some of these programs are devoted to the production of anti-bodies. In the bone marrow, these programs are activated. We need to pour out of the bone marrow B cells that give us the capacity to make antibodies to a million or more different antigens. As is true for T cells, any individual B cell is only interested in one of these antigens.

To generate the required diversity, there is a huge number of variable genes activated within the budding B cell that result in many different antibody binding sites being formed. Random experiments in the cell's production line lead to the generation of further unique binding sites. As a result of all this frantic genetic activity, we produce from early fetal life B cells that are distinguished by the presence on their surface of antibody molecules, which have one end partially buried in the cell's membrane and the antigen-binding portion projecting out into space. Five hundred thousand of these identical receptor molecules may pepper the surface of an individual B cell. It is a system identical in principle to that we have already described for the T cell.

Turned loose from the bone marrow, B cells are less inclined than T cells to patrol around the body looking for trouble. They home in to the lymph nodes where they have their own anatomical compartment in which to live. This is called the lymphocytic follicle. B cells wait there for an antigen that enters the node.

When an antigen is recognised by its B cell, it is of course trapped in the cell's receptor; but B cells are also under the control of the T cell masters of the immunological universe. They can't start the attack process any more than a T8 killer cell can before receiving permission from an inducer T4 cell. To facilitate matters, therefore, B cells are themselves antigen-presenting cells. They swallow some of the antigen, break it up into peptide fragments, and display these on their surface in the groove of a D-locus protein as described earlier for other antigen-presenting cells. T4 cells passing by and recognising the peptide-D combination 'realise' that the B cell has trapped foreignness. They not only give permission for the B cell to move to stage 2, but also secrete chemicals which drive the process forward and control subsequent events. Interleukins 2, 4, 6 and 10, released by T4 cells, play the major roles.

Given permission, B cells start to multiply and mature and the end product is a cell which should be called just that, a mature B cell, but isn't; such cells were given the name 'plasma cells' before their lineage was recognised, and it stuck.

Plasma cells are factories that produce and secrete two thousand molecules per second of the receptor immunoglobulin that the B cells use to trap antigen in the first place. The idea here is to flood the body with these molecules, which can attack what they recognise without further permission being required from any cell. Into every nook and cranny of the body they must go seeking antigens that may have been lucky enough not to be trapped in a lymph node. In the security arrangements for our mythical industrial complex, you may remember that we discussed the despatch of troops to look for specific intruders. Those troops were the equivalent of these antibodies.

The plasma cells make their antibodies in the middle of the lymphocytic follicles in the lymph node, with the area being referred to as a germinal centre. These cells, unlike the majority of T cells, have a relatively short lifespan and thus our bone marrow must replenish the supply constantly throughout life. When B cells divide to produce plasma cells, some of the progeny hold back to supply us with memory cells capable of responding quickly the second time we meet antigens. They respond more quickly as their need for T cell help is lessened and there are a lot more of them capable of recognising a given antigen the second time around. As you have probably guessed we do have B cells capable of recognising our own tissues, but no serious problems develop unless T cells give them permission to manufacture the antibodies which could harm us. As we will see later, it is unfortunate that occasionally such permission is given.

Humans make five different types of immunoglobulin. These various types are referred to as classes and they evolve one by one. With each new model that appears, we add something to our infection-fighting repertoire.

The first antibody to come off the assembly line from inside a plasma cell is called immunoglobulin M or IgM, Nature's first effort at making an antibody. It is not very efficient: it does not last long and it is a biological coward. Five of these antibodies cluster in a pack to watch out for the enemy. This makes the group so big that IgM cannot get into the tissues and it simply floats around in the bloodstream. It is therefore limited in its ability to help us fight organisms.

Some primitive species still alive on earth today (some sharks, for example) can only make IgM. However, humans cannot survive in their world if they can make only this one primitive form of antibody. Occasionally doctors must care for children who are born with their immune capacity limited in this way and who will die if they are not given infusions containing the more important classes of antibody.

When the family doctor gives a six-week-old baby the first shot of vaccine against diphtheria, pertussis and tetanus, it stimulates the baby's B cells that can recognise these organisms. Soon IgM antibodies to these agents will appear in the bloodstream, but the baby must go on from there to develop a more sophisticated defence.

The next antibody model to appear after we are challenged by an antigen is called IgD. We know very little about it, as it seems to be secreted only in tiny amounts before plasma cells secrete the next model. It may be important in helping B cells interact with T cells.

The third model off the line is usually IgE. (By the way, a T cell tells the plasma cell 'factory' when to switch production to a new model.) IgE is a fascinating immunoglobulin, the subject of a later chapter of its own, for it is the antibody which, if produced in excess, is responsible for the development of certain 'allergies'.

Most of the cells that rush to a tissue's defence when it is attacked by an antigen are delivered to the site of the invasion via the bloodstream. As they approach the area under attack the blood vessels dilate, stretching the pores in their wall to a size that is sufficient for the antigen-seeking cells to leave the blood vessels and move into the tissues. (Unless the blood vessels dilate, the cells will remain trapped within them.) IgE is specifically designed to release histamine-like agents from specific cells to achieve this purpose. For this reason, IgE is often referred to as the immunological gatekeeper as these chemicals relax the muscles in the walls of the vessels.

After the production of IgE, T cells switch production to IgG, the major antibody we humans produce. So important has this molecule been to our defence mechanisms that over the eons it has undergone a number of changes; we can now recognise four subtypes of IgG.

The minor variations in the molecules we produce are very important. They are called, logically enough, IgG1, IgG2, IgG3, IgG4.

Number one protects our tissues from most bacteria, except those that wrap themselves in a coat of sugar. Organisms that can do this include the meningococcus that causes meningitis, the gonococcus causing the sexually transmitted disease gonorrhea, and the pneumococcus responsible for so many problems in the lungs, upper respiratory tract and ears of young and old.

As a response to this defensive use of sugar by bacteria Nature developed IgG2, specifically capable of attacking and destroying these organisms. An inherited lack of the ability to make this particular form of antibody caused the disasters described in Chapter 1 when the young mother lost three children to sugar- or polysaccharide-encapsulated bacteria.

IgG3 neutralises certain viruses that race through the bloodstream before diving to safety inside a cell. Once inside a cell, they are immune to the effects of antibodies which are unable to penetrate the cell attacked by the virus.

IgG4 is a little like IgE, being able to manipulate the chemical-containing cells that open blood vessels. It may play an important role in protecting the lower part of our airways.

The fifth and final major class of immunoglobulin to be produced after attack by something foreign is IgA, an antibody that works on our mucous membranes and forms a protective barrier for our 'inner skin'—the delicate membranes that coat our nostrils, mouth, intestinal tract, bladder and vagina.

With the expansion of our antibody repertoire, the body has gained great flexibility in its ability to defend itself.

An antibody is very much like the laser beam in an expensive compact disc player. It can clearly tell the difference between Beethoven's Fifth Symphony and a piece by the Rolling Stones, but just as the music detected by the laser beam must be amplified if we are to hear how accurately it has tracked the music, antibody detection of an invader must result in amplification of the message so that an all-out attack can be launched.

Just as T cells use macrophages, antibodies have comrades-in-arms that they can call upon. One such comrade is the complement system. This is a fascinating series of eleven chemicals always present in the bloodstream. These can create a chain reaction, each one becoming activated and then activating the next member of the chain. IgM and IgG antibodies, when they bind antigen, can activate the first member of the complement cascade. The activation of these normally inactive chemicals in our bloodstream leads to the amplification of the response that leads to the destruction of the bacteria.

Each activated complement component does something to help eliminate the enemy. Some chemicals dilate blood vessels, others can destroy the membranes of bacterial cells. Most importantly, some of these chemicals attract into the battle a cell we must now discuss. This is known as a granulocyte or polymorphonuclear cell, one that has many shapes and more than one lobe to its nucleus. These cells are extremely important, being our best eaters and destroyers of bacteria. For simplicity's sake they are often referred to as 'polys' and we will take advantage of this terminology.

The cells love nothing better than a sandwich of bacteria 'buttered' with antibodies and complement. This cell does the killing in the B cell system. Obviously, it is not much use having the ability to make antibodies if our complement system or our polys are deficient. Clinical immunologists deal with patients who can make antibodies but have problems in these areas, though fortunately such mishaps are rare.

IgA is the 'quiet' member of the family of antibodies. It simply binds antigen and immobilises it so that the complex of IgA and enemy can be moved out of the body as we shed mucus, the viscous fluid that lines our mucous membranes. IgA is manufactured in the specialised lymph nodes that are situated deep in the tissues below our mucous membranes. When plasma cells secrete IgA, two antibody molecules join together at their non-antigen-binding ends. A specialised transport protein attaches to the fused chains and transports IgA to the surface, where electrical forces orientate it on the mucous membranes so that the antigen-binding arms project into the space lined by such membranes. We don't want to use complement or call in 'polys' on these delicate surfaces; for the innocent bystander suffering would be considerable. Thus IgA binds antigenic fragments and the complex of mucus, IgA and antigen is silently shed.

Nature realised that humans must make IgM before making IgG, and must make IgG before making IgA. Because of this time delay, special arrangements must be made to help newborn babies who might become infected with bacteria: at that stage of life humans are so fragile and so many systems are incomplete that bacteria could overcome us if we were not rapidly defended.

Newborn infants are therefore adequately supplied with both IgG and IgA. From the eighteenth week of fetal life, IgG circulating in the mother's serum is allowed to cross the placenta into the baby's bloodstream. This is brilliant, for a baby is likely to be born into the microbial environment to which the mother's immune system has been reacting during the months before delivery. The mother's immune system will therefore be topped up with antibodies against potentially dangerous organisms likely to be encountered by the baby after birth.

The mother can, therefore, passively protect her infant by donating her immunological experience in this fashion. Via this mechanism, babies are born with adult levels of IgG. The amount of antibody they receive will last them approximately three months, usually a satisfactory arrangement, for after the second month of life babies are capable of making their own IgG efficiently.

This system works better when Nature is left to run it. In many Third World countries, for example, women will take a few hours away from their work to deliver their babies, squatting down and allowing the baby to fall to the ground. After the mother bites the umbilical cord, life can proceed for both. In this situation it is certainly likely that any organisms a baby might encounter will have recently been 'seen' by the mother's immune system.

Modern health care systems have interfered with this in a significant way. When a baby is born in a modern hospital it is likely to encounter organisms that reside in such places and are not present in the general community (nosocomial infections). Consequently, we occasionally face problems because a baby will become infected with a hospital organism. Mother's IgG will not be capable of reacting with this unusual agent.

If a baby is born prematurely, it will receive less of mother's IgG than is desirable and this can increase the risk of infection for such frail infants. Fortunately we now have the ability to 'top up' babies' IgG levels by an intravenous infusion of concentrated, commercially available IgG.

What about IgA? Babies are very likely to encounter potentially dangerous organisms that land on their mucous membranes. This is particularly true for the intestinal tract. Nature has solved the dilemma associated with the inability of babies to make IgA by ensuring that breast milk contains abundant amounts. No biological fluid has a higher concentration of IgA than colostrum, the early milk secreted by the breast in the first few days after delivery. Even after milk flow is well established, the fluid remains rich in IgA.

The same principles discussed with IgG apply with IgA. It is very likely that any organisms that will infect the intestinal tract of a baby have recently been experienced by the mother, therefore her IgA is likely to protect her baby. IgA is able to survive passage through the stomach; particularly important to children who must enter the world in less than perfectly hygienic circumstances. This, of course, is why immunologists are anxious to see breast feeding rather than formula feeding emphasised in Third World countries. From an immunological point of view, Nature seems anxious for mothers to breast feed babies for the first six months of life—after that time, the amount of IgA in breast milk starts to fall quite significantly.

In recent years, doctors have been trying to capitalise on the immunological properties of breast milk by using colostrum and even milk as medicine. Breast milk has been found to be very efficient when used as eye drops, ear drops and nose drops. Indeed, if there was enough of it, giving breast milk to infants with diarrhoeal diseases would probably be very much more commonplace. In Scandinavia, there are milk banks where sufficient human breast milk has been stored for therapeutic purposes.

Apart from IgA and other nutritional wonders, breast milk also contains a number of white blood cells. There are significant numbers of both T and B lymphocytes in breast milk, though it is unclear why this is so. It has been suggested that the presence of foreign cells in the baby's intestinal tract may speed up the maturation of the lymph nodes that line it. Occasionally a mother may breastfeed her baby without knowing that it has been born without T cells; under these circumstances the T cells in the breast milk may recognise the baby as 'foreign' and launch an attack that can be fatal. Normally, of course, the small number of T cells in breast milk would be no match for the baby's fully armed T cell system.

We will return to the significance of T cells and breast milk when we discuss AIDS.

NK cells (K cells)

There are cells circulating in the body and living in lymph nodes that look like lymphocytes, and indeed are probably ancestors of modern T cells. They do not have enough physical characteristics in common with T or B cells to be grouped in either family, but recent evidence suggests that these cells do possess a part of the T cell receptor complex; hence our feeling that they are likely to be primitive T cells. The truth is that we know more about the function of these cells than we do about their heritage. They are referred to as natural killer cells or NK cells and are not to be confused with the T lymphocytes (T8 cells) that are capable of killing virus-infected and tumour cells. NK cells do have the ability to kill tumour and virus-infected cells but not in any antigen-specific manner. They are particularly good at killing cells that have been coated with antibodies. Such cells are also referred to at times as K cells.

Thus NK cells may be particularly important in our defence against cancer. Cancer cells cannot be destroyed by antibodies. We do make antibodies that can bind to cancer cells but they are not very effective in destroying these malignant, unruly and often invasive cells. However, NK cells have the ability to kill many cells more efficiently if they are coated with antibody. Just how important these cells are in the human defence system is still not clear but they certainly seem to offer a first line of defence, and we referred to that role earlier in this chapter. Certainly NK cells seem to work more efficiently when in the presence of chemicals released by activated T cells, which in that sense may be thought of as harnessing the capacity of NK cells to help in the fight against antigens. We have talked about interleukins, which can deliver permissive signals to both T and B cells, but it is the potent chemical called interferon released by both T cells and macrophages that is of particular relevance here. As we have mentioned, the chemical has the capacity to interfere with the multiplication of viruses but its anti-cancer properties seem to involve the stimulation of NK cells, which certainly are activated by this cytokine. There seems to be a connection between the performance of NK cells and various psychological factors related to stress. That matter will be explored later in the book.

Well, there you have it. A sophisticated, integrated army that for most of us performs splendidly for seventy years or more. Clearly, we are talking about one of the glories of biology.

3

Ancient concepts of immunity: a short history of immunological thought

WHY is an historical perspective on science important? It would be enough to point out that it is as fascinating to look at the evolution of ideas as it is to look at the evolution of species, for here is the drama of missed opportunities, great mistakes and brilliant intuition. But there are other compelling reasons for historical perspectives. History reminds us to encourage intellectual leaps and not to be constantly satisfied with moving from A to B to C. Time and time again we can find an accurate hypothesis being summarily dismissed by unimaginative scientists, only to become firmly established as fact many years after mainstream science moved far away from the correct concept. History keeps us humble. When we examine how little was known about immunology a hundred years ago, we must expect that our apparently sophisticated knowledge of the immune system will seem trivial to reviewers looking at current perspectives this time next century.

In the beginning

From the earliest clustering of human beings into primitive societal units, there must have been an appreciation of the obvious fact that survivors of certain diseases, characterisable by a set of specific features, would not be visited by the same affliction a second time. Certainly, from the earliest periods of written history this fact was often noted. While there were no speculations in ancient Chinese writings on the *mechanism* which might have been involved, we do know that an awareness of immunity led to an empiric approach to immunotherapy as long ago as 5000 BC. Very likely, the first significant and dangerous immunological experiments involved attempts to protect humans from the scourge that was smallpox. As was mentioned in our prologue, it was well known to the ancients that one did not suffer a second attack of the 'pox', and it was realised that the healing scars of survivors contained some material which could protect those not yet infected. Thus, it was the Chinese who introduced a technique of inoculation of smallpox dust obtained from scars for the prevention of the lethal disease. The dust was blown through a silver tube into the left nostril of males and the right nostril of females, and protection could follow if the disease which ensued was itself not fatal. The procedure was associated with a death rate of about 4 per cent, but the natural disease frequently burst upon communities killing huge numbers of those infected. We know that in many early societies, citizens would deliberately seek physical contact with an infected, but recovering, smallpox patient.

An appreciation of immunity was obvious in Thucydides' description of the plague which swept through Athens in 430 BC. He noted that the sick and the dying found help and compassion most readily among those who had recovered from the disease: 'these knew what it was from experience and had now no fear for themselves, for the same man was never attacked twice—never at least fatally'.

While smallpox forced early societies to think about immunity, the then current concepts of disease and body function ensured that no understanding of the phenomenon was possible. For centuries, disease was seen as a punishment which destroyed health by interfering with the balance within the body of the vital fluids: blood, phlegm, yellow and black bile.

Disease as pestilence

As early as 2000 BC, the Babylonians were reporting the 'visitation of pestilence'. Disease was attributed in most early societies to the manipulation of health by demons, spirits or gods, usually as punishment for sin. So ingrained was this concept in ancient Egypt that they decided that there must be a god of disease. The ancient Greeks accused an annoyed Apollo of firing plague arrows and were convinced that the misdeeds of Oedipus Rex resulted in the Greek people suffering the plague of Thebes.

In the Old Testament, God regularly 'smote' the chosen people and their enemies with pestilence. Whether it was David annoying God by numbering the people or the Egyptians, Philistines or Assyrians attacking his people, punishment in the form of disease was at hand.

If disease was punishment, recovery must signal forgiveness. The bigger the sin the worse the disease, and recovery could only mean that a cleansing of the soul had occurred. After such an experience, one would be unlikely to sin again and was thus immune to the recurrence of the process. So strong was this sentiment in the early Christian church that no other explanation for immunity would have been considered.

If religious conviction left the masses satisfied that they understood the extraordinary reality of immunity, the convictions of the Hippocratic School of Medicine, passed on to physicians for century after century, very much restricted the framework within which early scientific minds could explore other possibilities. Body dynamics could only be viewed in terms of fluid changes. The sick vomited, had diarrhoea, sweated, passed copious amounts of urine or bled, etc. Thus, it was with such concepts that the remarkable Islamic physician, Rhazes, approached the problem of immunity in the tenth century. He acknowledged that recovery from measles and smallpox (which he quite clearly differentiated) was associated with immunity to these diseases, but he explained the phenomenon in terms of an 'excessive moisture' theory. Smallpox was associated with fever, as a result of which blood would ferment and be expelled through pustules. He and others believed that excessive fluid normally circulated in the body of the young. Smallpox was not a bad thing as this fluid must be expelled if health was to be established for adult life. Once the excessive and therefore offensive fluid was removed, the problem was solved and one became immune to smallpox.

In the eleventh century another great early thinker, Avicenna, introduced the concept of germs, which he thought of as small seeds (seminaria) with special predilection for growing in this or that bodily region. Such seeds could be passed from one person to another, thus being infectious. We know little of the reception given to Avicenna's theories in the eleventh century, but in 1546 a fascinating book significantly entitled *On Contagion* was published by the Italian physician, Fracastoro. He claimed that smallpox seeds fermented best in menstrual blood. He believed that all babies were contaminated with menstrual blood, which must be expelled from their bodies if they were to become healthy. Smallpox seeds fermented in the contaminating menstrual blood, which then escaped through the obvious pustules. Once free of this contaminating blood, you could not be troubled by smallpox seeds as they could only grow in menstrual blood. Others picked up this idea and proposed that certain germs were needed to rid the young of contaminating amniotic fluid (the fluid in which babies swim for nine months) and umbilical blood. One must admit that there was something vaguely sexist about these theories.

It is easy to understand the concentration in these early writings on children with infectious diseases, for they were so often associated with skin manifestations not seen in the older and therefore 'purified' population.

These 'depletion theories' held their currency until the time of Louis Pasteur, but there evolved a number of variations on the theme. As we have already noted, inoculation procedures to protect one from smallpox gained favour in the Europe of the early eighteenth century. After the Prince of Wales allowed his children to be inoculated in 1722, the now respectable technique was subjected to more scientific scrutiny. Many considered that inoculation would utilise all of the available but irreplaceable substances needed if a germ was to flourish. The seeds were cheated of 'those Humours in the Blood which the Invader makes a Seizure on'.

During the seventeenth and eighteenth centuries, yet another variation on this theme emerged stating that all of us are born with all the seeds (or ovula as they were described by Thomas Fuller) necessary for every disease process. Once fertilised by a specific and contagious co-factor a particular germ would flourish and cause 'its' disease, ... and when these had been impregnated and delivered of their morbid fetus there is an end of them. Upon this account no man can possibly be infected with any of the respective distempers more than once'. With this historical perspective on acquired immunity it is not surprising that, with the discovery of real germs in the form of bacteria by Hansen, Koch and others, the great Louis Pasteur tried to explain his first great observation using these well-entrenched concepts.

Pasteur had been experimenting with the bacteria that produced the deadly intestinal infection cholera in chickens. As is so often the case with scientific breakthroughs, chance played into Pasteur's talented hands. A strain of the bacteria that he was using for his experiments was left unattended in his laboratory while he went for a holiday. When he returned, he found that the languishing bacteria could no longer produce disease when injected into his chickens but could make chickens immune to fresh virulent strains. You can imagine his excitement when he realised that deadly organisms could be treated in ways that would make them harmless without destroying their ability to provoke immunity. Like so many before him, he believed that even his attenuated organisms would produce immunity by depletion from the body of those infected of an essential trace element required for disease. Soon, however, it was discovered that dead organisms were just as good as live ones in producing immunity. It was immediately obvious that the depletion theories, so popular for so many hundreds of years, were all wrong.

With such observations came the dawn for immunology as a science. Robert Koch and his team in Berlin were busy isolating and identifying organisms while Pasteur would take them, modify their virulence, and produce safe vaccines. To honour Edward Jenner, Pasteur deliberately extended the term vaccination (vacca for cow) to include immunisation with any organism that could still produce immunity but had been rendered less dangerous.

It's interesting to note that although Jenner was highly regarded in his own lifetime, wrote extensively about his observations and lived to see his vaccination techniques used throughout the world, he never speculated on the mechanisms by which inoculation could produce protection. Perhaps he had been influenced by a remark that had been made to him by one of his mentors, the famous English teacher and anatomist John Hunter: 'why think, why not try the experiment?' However, things were very different one hundred years later, as more and more scientists observing the work of Pasteur and Koch wanted to know what actually happened in a host, once exposed to an organism, that would make him or her invulnerable to further attacks by the same organism.

Humoral immunity

In 1665 after the great fire of London, Samuel Pepys described in his invaluable diaries an evening when two doctors, Lower and King, demonstrated blood transfusion from one animal to another using a needle specifically designed for the purpose by the great architect Sir Christopher Wren. After the successful demonstration, Lower turned to the friends gathered for the evening and, in an excited fashion, explained that with this experiment he saw an era in which there would be 'the mending of bad blood by the borrowing of blood from a better body'.

Undoubtedly those notes were not ringing in the ears of the German scientists who, in 1890, discovered that immunised animals produced something in their blood which neutralised the deadly diphtheria toxin. They observed the same phenomenon when experimenting with the bacteria that produce the disease tetanus. One can now only imagine the excitement and trepidation with which they rapidly 'borrowed blood from a better body', in this case their

An 1896 drawing by Dr Paul Ehrlich illustrating his concept that certain cells in the body would be capable of recognising something foreign. With remarkable accuracy he predicted, and depicted in this diagram, that any one cell of the immune system would be capable of recognising only one antigen. In the diagram the black characters hooking onto the cell were meant to be diptheria organisms.

horses, and administered this material to children with diphtheria. The results were dramatically good, especially if given during the early stage of the disease. Whatever it was they were administering, it was soon called anti-toxin and then antibody to broaden the concept beyond bacterial toxins. With 'humoral' substances to chase, it was time for chemists to take up the challenge presented by these observations.

It was obvious that antibodies were not substances made only in response to exposure to toxins or even bacteria. Antibodies could be made to harmless substances. Much of the credit for early successful studies on the nature of antibodies is given to the remarkable scientist Paul Ehrlich, whom we met in the last chapter. We've discussed the extraordinary conceptual leap that he made when he realised that cells could be pre-programmed to recognise antigen. But, not knowing anything about B cells, he was convinced that every cell in the body could make antibodies. Ehrlich moved on to

Dr Paul Ehrlich would have said 'I told you so', had he been able to
see an antigen-presenting cell with the electron microscope. Here it
is presenting something foreign for inspection to a T lymphocyte
(*foreground*).

cancer research and to the development of chemotherapy for a
number of conditions, notably syphilis, but it was his theories on
antibody formation that established for posterity the genius of his
intellect.

Cellular immunity

With the discovery of antibodies, most scientists at the turn of the
century thought that the complete solution to immunology was
within their grasp. However, there was a vociferous minority who
insisted that specific cells in the body were equally important, if not
more important than antibodies. The chief protagonist for cellular
immunity was the brilliant Russian zoologist Elie Metchnikoff (1845–
1916), who was strongly influenced by the theories of Darwin circulating in the 1860s and 1870s.

In a famous and spontaneous experiment, he recognised the

importance of cellular defences in the general scheme of inflammatory responses. He related the story of his famous experiment in his
autobiography. In 1883, Metchnikoff and his family were relaxing
at the Straits of Messina. One afternoon when the rest of the family
had gone to the circus, he was looking through his microscope at
a transparent starfish where he could visualise the incessant wandering of its cells around its body. Suddenly, the thought that such
cells could play a role in defence flashed into his mind.

Previously, the observation that cells within the body of simple
animals could sometimes be seen to contain foreign matter had
been interpreted as a phenomenon resulting from the invasion of
the cell by an organism, and thus was regarded as deleterious. Now
Metchnikoff came up with the idea that certain cells may actually
be actively swallowing an invader in an attempt to destroy it. In his
garden in Messina was a little tangerine tree already decorated for
Christmas. From this he took some thorns and introduced them
under the skin of some 'beautiful starfish as transparent as water'.
After a sleepless night he was able to observe that, as he had predicted, the mobile cells of the starfish had swarmed to and subsequently engulfed his thorns.

Metchnikoff developed this observation into a cellular mechanism of defence and became famous and controversial in so doing.
While many others claimed that they had made the same observation
before he did, and indeed had noted similar phenomenology, it
was Metchnikoff who really developed the idea of an active cellular
defence. The next year Metchnikoff observed that a tiny transparent
animal, *Daphnia*, would not be killed by the spores of a certain
fungus if blood cells attacked, engulfed and subsequently destroyed
these spores. He showed the same phenomenon in rabbits and
actually at this stage introduced the term 'phagocytosis', literally
'swallowing cells'. He demonstrated that phagocytic ability was
shared by two distinct cells in the body that we met in the last
chapter, namely the polymorphonuclear leukocyte ('polys') and
the monocyte which matures to become a macrophage. It was
Metchnikoff who established that these cells could move from blood
vessels into tissues by moving through pores in the blood vessel
walls, as they were called upon to attack antigens.

As Metchnikoff developed his theories, he so impressed Louis
Pasteur that the latter convinced him to join his team in Paris. Pasteur
himself, and most of the immunological world, were at the time far
more interested in antibodies than they were in Metchnikoff's
observations. Who needed cells with phagocytic ability when it had
been shown that antibodies could kill bacteria? One can only imagine
the heated debates that must have raged in Metchnikoff's laboratories at the time.

Who was right, Metchnikoff or Ehrlich, wondered the scientific world. We know both were right of course and two English scientists, Drs Wright and Douglass, tried to bring the opposing schools together after their demonstration that antibody-coated organisms were preferentially swallowed by 'polys'. But in 1908 the arguments for supremacy of cellular or humoral immunity were still raging, so the Nobel Prize for Medicine committee diplomatically decided that Metchnikoff and Ehrlich should share the money. Only in the last thirty years have these important arguments been settled once and for all.

PART II

TAMING THE WARRIORS

4

Pregnancy, Nature's version of transplantation

CATARINA had been married for eleven years when I first met her. As is the case with many young couples, she and her husband had not wanted children immediately. Initially, horses were more important than children. Catarina was an outstanding equestrian representing her country at the Olympic Games. After three years of married life, however, she had decided to start a family. She stopped taking contraceptive pills and jubilantly informed her husband three months later that she was pregnant. Healthy and relaxed, she looked forward to motherhood with intense excitement.

Catarina's first pregnancy lasted ten weeks. She lost the baby easily, with little discomfort; not after a fight with her husband, not after a fall, not even after a horse ride. She was having a dinner party for a few close friends when she felt a trickle of blood down her leg and some crampy pains in her stomach. It was all over very quickly.

She and her husband were bitterly disappointed but not alarmed. Thousands of healthy women have miscarriages. However, three more miscarriages followed. On one occasion she managed to take the pregnancy to twelve weeks but she usually lost her babies between the eighth and tenth week of her pregnancy.

The toll from her disappointments was considerable. She became depressed, she lost weight, she became more introspective. Her husband was as much concerned about his wife as he was about the elusiveness of paternity.

One obstetrician said that perhaps her cervix was too relaxed. He advised her to become pregnant once again, stay in bed for the entire pregnancy, and allow him to put a stitch into her cervix after she became pregnant so that the baby could not possibly fall out. She did all three of these things and lost her fifth fetus after nine weeks. (The obstetrician, by the way, was correct when telling her that some women lose babies because of problems with the cervix, but this was not the cause of Catarina's problems.)

Another doctor speculated that the reason she was losing her babies was that they were abnormal, genetically imperfect. He had often examined miscarried specimens and found them to be abnormal. But it seemed unlikely that five babies in a row should have been rejected for this reason.

When I met Catarina, who was Chilean, she assured me that she could have literally purchased a baby in a matter of weeks for ten thousand dollars in Santiago. However, she ached for her own baby.

Catarina brought her problem to America—to Providence, Rhode Island, to be exact. She had been advised that there was a Chilean-born but naturalised American obstetrician who was interested in women with Catarina's problem. She came, he listened, then he phoned me and said, 'I have Mary's "twin sister" here in the office and want to run a few simple tests. But if the results are normal, will you please check her out?'

I was only too pleased to so promise, as our Chilean–American obstetrician and Mary had aroused my immunological interest in the problem that faces women who spontaneously and repeatedly abort their fetuses.

The 'Mary' of our phone conversation was a 28-year-old nurse with flaming red Irish hair who had only just delivered, albeit one month prematurely, an otherwise healthy, red-haired girl, the spitting image of her mum. This was her first successful pregnancy: seven previous conceptions had terminated spontaneously. Mary's problem was that she was too close to her husband. Was Catarina's problem also caused by the same strange set of biological circumstances?

One is not long at medical school before learning that a woman has to be close to her male partner to become pregnant. The closeness problem suspected here was clearly not physical.

As it turned out, we were correct in our assumptions about Catarina. She and her husband were third cousins and their histocompatibility profiles were remarkably similar. Before we finish this story, however, we need some more background information.

Lust, love and lymphocytes are inextricably interwoven into the complicated tapestry that determines the survival of the species; we will concentrate here on the role of lymphocytes. As we look in detail at the immunology of conception and pregnancy, we will see that Nature has developed many mechanisms for perfecting and protecting the single most important thing we can do: reproduce ourselves. There is no room for having all our biological eggs in the one basket here.

With orgasm, the woman contracts her vagina to help the thousands of sperm cells, so generously donated by her lover, move to the mouth of her uterus and more importantly, to those small canals known as the Fallopian tubes that run off from each side of the uterus. Conception without orgasm is possible, of course, but more difficult. Hundreds of sperm cells equipped with wickedly vibrating tails swim against the tide to move upstream so that they can enter the Fallopian tubes. The man has therefore impregnated the woman with foreign material. (Note that 'self' is not lying in these Fallopian tubes.) Immunologically those thousands of squirming, pushy sperm cells are just as immunologically abhorrent as would be gonococcal bacteria. Surely the woman will not fail to reject them!

But if the woman does reject those foreign sperm cells, unceremoniously disposing of them, she will never be fertilised and the species will die. She could accept sperm cells that carried genetic information identical or nearly identical to her own, treating them in a privileged way as 'self', but this would not advantage the species; experimentation is Nature's rule. The woman must give a selective advantage to the sperm cells from someone who is very different from her; Nature is indifferent to the fate of cells that look like those of our potential mother. On the other hand, *not* to reject those cells would surely require a suppression of the woman's immune capacity, which would be dangerous. There is no point in getting pregnant and then dying of pneumonia.

The vaginal lining with its rich blood supply is in contact with this foreign seminal fluid and cells for some time. Given that foreign protein to which one is repeatedly exposed should generate an increasingly vigorous response, *why* do women (usually) fail to reject sperm?

Deep in the testicles, cellular 'factories' produce hundreds of thousands of sperm cells which, when ready, go to the prostate gland. The prostate is part of a man's sexual apparatus. It produces the enriched support fluid in which the sperm cells are suspended. This seminal fluid has wondrous properties, not the least of which is its ability to block inflammation. It is very largely responsible for blocking an immunological reaction to the sperm cells and other injected proteins that would otherwise provoke an immunological response in the vagina. How it does this is still not perfectly understood, but it seems likely that there are chemicals similar to prostaglandins in the fluid, and we know that these chemicals can stop inflammatory reactions.

After foreign material has been launched into the vagina and blocked any local reaction, using the immunological soothing balm that is seminal fluid, many sperm cells will have made it into the Fallopian tubes. The cells break free from the seminal fluid as they swim upstream in locally produced fluids, for they all wish to penetrate an ovum, the little egg produced by the ovary. Their antigenic (foreign) potential is displayed to the local immune system in the Fallopian tubes and yes, it does react to the challenge. The more foreign the sperm cells, that is the greater the genetic difference between the man and woman, the more the potential mother's local immune apparatus is likely to be activated.

However, the immunological response in the Fallopian tubes helps rather than hinders fertilisation. With thousands of invaders, the response made by the woman's immune system is not fast enough to destroy all the cells. All that is needed is for one and *only one* sperm cell to meet the ovum, penetrate its membrane and intertwine its male genes with the female genes therein, in that most loving of embraces that actually sparks life.

The ovum is the ultimate proponent of monogamy. After fertilisation, her outer protective membrane is no longer penetrable; the door is slammed shut. All the unsuccessful candidates are then destroyed and rejected. When this happens, as is usual with any sort of inflammation, there is a degree of local swelling in the Fallopian tubes. As a result, the Fallopian tubes' diameter narrows and the passage of the tiny fertilised egg, which has now become all-important and is already beginning to divide, is significantly slowed. This is very important; the fertilised egg might otherwise tumble back down the Fallopian tubes into the vagina and be lost.

Slowing the passage of the fertilised egg is important for another reason. The destination of the fertilised egg is the wall of the uterus (womb), and this organ must have time to get ready for the guest who plans to stay for nine months.

Rats do it differently, but we tumbled on the secrets outlined above in studies of these invaluable partners in our search for scientific knowledge. The rat has a uterus divided by a membrane into two separate 'wings'. Scientists took rat sperm cells and injected them into one wing of the uterus. The rats experienced an inflammatory reaction only on the injected side, proving that sperm was really antigenic and that immune responses could occur in the womb. Subsequently, when the animals were allowed to inject sperm cells naturally and a pregnancy occurred, it always occurred in the wing of the uterus that had been previously stimulated by the scientist's injections. The immunological response in the womb turned out to be a vital part of the mechanism needed to establish a pregnancy.

From the above, it will not surprise you to learn that mice that are deliberately inbred to produce a colony of laboratory animals that are genetically very similar are less successful than are wild strains in their attempts to fertilise each other.

We have already discussed the concept of our biological trademark: protein flags on the surface of every one of our cells that declare each of us to be individual. An individual's membrane 'signature' represents an almost unique creation. We have discussed the fact that we use these markers to help us differentiate 'self' from 'non-self'. Our immunological system reacts to the virus in the throat, compares it with our trademark, realises the difference, and attacks.

When those trademarks of 'self' enter someone else's body the recipient reacts violently, unless by pure chance they are perfect replicas of that body's own markers; a very unlikely occurrence. To a large degree the violence with which we treat other people's cells is graded by the extent to which they differ from ours. At least eight major and very many more minor protein flags are involved in this system. If two people are identical, except for one major flag, the immune reaction provoked will be less intense than if they are totally dissimilar. (This concept is explained in more detail in the chapter on transplantation.)

The more dissimilar the cells of a man and a woman, the better for the genetic mixing we have discussed. We now have the ability to examine, in the laboratory, cells from a couple in order to determine just how different or similar they are in this histocompatibility (tissue compatibility) sense. You may not be surprised to learn that, when this was done with a number of childless couples without obvious cause for their infertility, where the mother had experienced repeated miscarriages, many were genetically closely matched.

When we mixed cells from such couples in a test tube and let them fight it out, we found a very weak response to each other's 'foreignness'; normally, a battle to the death ensues. This is exactly what we found when looking at Mary's and Catarina's problems: each had close genetic compatibility with her husband. (Figure 9.)

If this is true, however, why did Catarina have to go through twelve weeks of pregnancy before her miscarriage? Well, by dint of a lot of sexual industriousness and the sheer numbers of sperm cells involved, a pregnancy under circumstances of genetic compatibility can occur, if less efficiently than with other couples. But the fact of Catarina's repeated miscarriages suggested that immunological responsiveness was important not only in getting a pregnancy under way, but even more important in maintaining it.

Once that fertilised egg buries itself into the wall of the prepared uterus (implantation) and hooks itself, via the burrowing of its primitive umbilical cord, into the mother's blood supply, the battle

Figure 9. The genetics of fetal survival

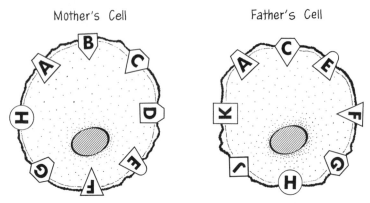

Display of **SELF** ANTIGENS too similar — rejection risk

Display of **SELF** ANTIGENS not similar — success likely

for survival is just starting. The baby that looks (genetically) too much like its mother is in trouble all the way.

If you think about it for a moment, you will realise that an established pregnancy is the ultimate transplantation. Sitting in its mother's uterus is not a kidney or a heart or a liver, but an *entire human*. Half the genetic complement is its mother's, but the other half is its father's and that is immunologically objectionable. If after the pregnancy, or even during it for that matter (although it's a little hard to arrange), some of the baby's skin is grafted on to mother's skin, it will be promptly rejected: we know this from animal experiments using inbred identical strains that can supply us with a living animal identical to one developing in the uterus. When a baby is born, the mother's blood is full of antibodies against those paternal trademark antigens that the baby now carries and that are dissimilar to her own. In fact, we use donations of such blood to help us type an individual's genetic profile. In this respect a woman who has had six children by six different fathers is a biological treasure, for her blood is full of antibodies to a very broad range of histocompatibility antigens.

It is therefore obvious that we must discuss and then dismiss one of the myths about motherhood and realise that superficial appearances are deceptive. We are always seeing the image of a contented mother with a Mona Lisa smile looking benignly at her swollen abdomen, hands resting lightly on the tumour that she is apparently so willing to accept. Down in the depths her body is trying its best to reject that paternal parasite. It is likely though by no means satisfactorily proven that, mysterious to relate, the very fury of her attack on the fetus allows it to survive. How could a continuous immunological response to a developing fetus protect it, rather than destroy it?

To explore this concept and speculate on the mechanisms involved we must introduce two new characters to the story. One, who is only remotely involved, is that great seventeenth-century scientist Sir Isaac Newton; the other, who is indeed very intimately involved in all of this, is the immunologically intelligent baby.

One winter's day Newton was skating on a frozen pond with a friend and, in a jocular fashion, pushed him away (playfully shoved him may be more likely). As he watched his friend slide on the ice, he noticed that he himself went backwards also. On the frictionless ice, his passive friend had displaced Newton as much as Newton had displaced him. Newton raced for a stick, put it on the ice and the two stood toe to toe on either side of this soon-to-be-famous stick of wood. Newton pushed and the two skaters moved away from the stick. As Newton had predicted, the distance they travelled was equal. The harder Newton shoved his friend (who must have been a patient meek soul), the further they moved away from each other. The distance travelled by both, however, always remained equal. One can imagine Newton racing around the ice, screaming at everyone who would listen, that 'For every action, there is an equal and opposite reaction!' or something close to that. Now this story, much loved by physics teachers, may be a little fanciful for both men would have to have been of identical weight and shape if the story was true, but the concept is important to our discussion.

The weapons of the immune system consist of inflammation-producing cells and regulator cells that control the former and ensure that any response is appropriate. The *stronger* the immunological attack that is launched, the stronger the dampening influences produced by the immunoregulatory cells.

There is a slight variation on the Newtonian theme in the immune response. If both 'go' and 'stop' signals were equal all the time, nothing would happen. Therefore, the reaction is more like two tug-of-war teams, with one (attack) team having a few more muscle men initially. Soon, however, it loses this advantage when the other (regulatory) team recruits more help and both teams come back to the starting position once again. Both teams are acting simultaneously; the result is only a matter of balance. What we are looking for in our pregnancy story is a balance situation in which the immunological response against the baby gives an advantage to the suppressive forces.

Experiments suggest that if mother and baby are genetically similar, relatively weak suppressive forces are generated with the result that the mother's immune system continues slowly but persistently to reject her baby. How might the 'attack team' be weakened and the regulatory team be strengthened during pregnancy?

The raging of the mother's lymphocytes against the baby may be hindered by three major factors that could tip the balance in favour of the baby: the mother's powerfully stimulated regulator cells exert a 'go easy' influence on her aggressor cells, the wall the baby has built around itself defends it from aggressor cells, and the baby's own immune system helps suppress the mother's T cells that could endanger its survival.

By ten weeks of fetal life, the baby's immune system is beginning to explore the environment in which it finds itself and gets ready for defence. What does it find itself up against? On the outside we have the mother, all love and devotion, knitting bootees, satisfying one-time-only excusable cravings and being thoroughly spoilt because of her ordeal. Inwardly, she attacks her child; when she retches in the morning, she is showing her real biological feelings about the growth down below. (My wife finds this prose far too sexist and challenges me to find a woman with the time to knit bootees! I know that; I'm a new age man just trying to make a point.)

The vulnerable little baby must be separated from the mother by a series of membranes constructed to wall it off from an intensely hostile environment. At one point (the placenta), these membranes are organised to allow certain blood elements and maternal nutritional factors to be filtered across to the baby. Unless those membranes are breached, the mother's angry T cells can't get at the baby. If the membrane is destroyed, a miscarriage will result.

Nature, however, supplies babies with an instinctive defence mechanism of their own which helps diminish the danger that is all around. The baby's immune system allows all the young regulatory cells to secrete their suppressor chemicals; as no battle is going on inside the developing baby at the moment, the baby can afford to be immunosuppressed. These chemicals are sent across the placenta into the mother to tame her T cells.

The cells perform their task. This does place the baby at risk of being overwhelmed by an infectious agent should one manage to cross the placental barrier at this vulnerable time. It is more important to worry about the mother's aggression, however. Fetal self-help in this fashion may not be enough to save our would-be baby if other mechanisms are not in place, but it may be the additional suppressive force that makes all the difference between survival and rejection.

This survival move on the part of the baby can be of great help to certain mothers. As we will discuss when considering auto-immune diseases, those horrible affairs where our immune system attacks *us* (for example, in the case of rheumatoid arthritis), the basic defect in such situations is one of regulation. Victims of these diseases lack sufficient regulatory chemicals to block autoaggression. When a woman with such a disease is pregnant, the baby may float enough immunoregulatory substances across the placenta and into the mother to actually suppress the autoaggressive tendencies she has developed which are causing disease. She will bloom during the pregnancy, only to have her problem recur twenty-four hours after she delivers her child.

Another hazard must be faced by male babies. The majority of fetuses spontaneously aborted are male. Mothers can actually be driven to make an extra effort to reject their baby if it is male. Why? Because males proudly display their sex by means of a biological trademark never, of course, displayed on female cells and therefore always foreign to mothers. Presumably in the majority of cases the immune system of a pregnant woman is persuaded to accept the 'maleness' antigen (tolerance) but the induction of such tolerance is obviously difficult. Maleness is a risk factor for fetal survival.

Fathers determine the sex of their babies. Their sperm cells may be either female or male, while the mother's eggs carry only female genes. When a father's sperm 'selects' a son, the father is sentencing his offspring to an additional immunological hazard.

It is of considerable relevance to the theme of this chapter to learn that women living under substantial stress may experience a moderate to major degree of immunosuppression. The result is that they are less able than usual to attempt rejection of their fetuses. Perhaps it is not surprising, therefore, that in times of stress more male babies are born. This was very well demonstrated during World War II when the birth rate for live males soared. By the way, the male marker makes it slightly more difficult to transplant a male kidney into a woman with kidney disease. These concepts and the effects of stress on the immune response are dealt with in detail later.

Pregnancy, the most astonishingly perfect example of adaptation, allows a 'transplanted' body to survive inside an immunocompetent woman. As you can imagine, immunologists are trying to develop the knowledge and skills necessary to apply similar methodology to prevent the rejection of transplanted hearts, lungs, livers, etc., and of course for the treatment of those all-too-common autoimmune diseases.

As we mentioned earlier, mothers make many antibodies against the paternal antigens possessed by their babies. Antibodies, as we have seen, can cross and indeed must cross the placenta and enter the baby's circulation if, at the moment of birth, babies are to have some protection from the hordes of bacteria that assail them. Why don't the antibodies directed against fetal tissues harm the baby? It seems that within the placenta is a very clever sponge arrangement. Here are expressed strongly (visibly) a host of paternal antigens. Antibodies heading for the baby will be absorbed by the 'sink' and only good antibodies will cross into the fetus (that is, those that will not react with the baby's tissues).

The placental unit is also capable of secreting hormone-like agents. Of these the most interesting is known as PAPP (Pregnancy Associated Plasma Protein). PAPP is very important for the maintenance of a normal pregnancy and, fascinatingly, its release by the placenta occurs only when there is an immune response to the fetus. PAPP seems to amplify the function of those immunological cells that down-regulate the aggressor cells. Nature is determined to have a lot of 'fail-safe' techniques operating at once to protect her most valued experiment: the unique genetic mixture.

Back now to childless Catarina. We explained all the above to her, and gave her the results of the test we had done on her cells and those of her husband. The degree of genetic similarity between the two fell within the range we were suspicious about. There was a good chance she was successfully rejecting her babies.

Catarina was advised that she had a reasonably good chance of having a baby if she was willing to take a small dose of a cortisone-like drug throughout her pregnancy. Cortisone can, among numerous other effects, suppress immunological responses. There were minor risks to her and her baby with the approach, but we were confident that they could be handled without too much fuss.

So it proved. I'll bet her son, by the time of this writing, is already a fine horseman.

This is not the approach that would be used now, a few short years later. Work on the problem has progressed rapidly. Women in Catarina's position are being 'immunised' with their husband's tissues before they become pregnant. Injecting cells and extracts from one's husband's tissues into the skin and bloodstream on a number of occasions can increase a woman's immunological re-activity to the minor differences that do exist. The results in these early days of this form of research are encouraging. In one series, 78 per cent of women previously unable to complete a pregnancy because of compatibility gave birth to normal children.

5

Human attempts at transplantation

THIS book celebrates the wonder that is the healthy human body. Arguably the most sophisticated of Nature's creations, our bodies function with a precision, indeed a perfection, in no way approached by the most marvellous of our own creations. We are the most intelligent of creatures and can therefore analyse and appreciate the gift that has been given to us to clothe our souls. The same intelligence, however, tells us that we are not perfect. One of our imperfections is youth. Oh, young bodies are close to perfection, but they are so often guided by intelligence *sans* wisdom. As a result, beautiful bodies are wrapped around telegraph poles and damaged by inappropriate diets and generally abused in the name of good times and freedom. Would that maternal wisdom, like maternal antibodies, could cross the placenta and top up our young until they could supply their own!

It was lack of wisdom that led two young sisters to abuse their bodies with a poison that brought them to my attention at a time when they were holding on to their lives by the most tenuous of threads. Susan and Marion were fifteen and fourteen years of age respectively at the time. They were school girls who lived on a farm in the north of Connecticut.

These girls should have been healthy, and Nature and their parents had done a good job with them; then they started sniffing gasoline. This is not a rare problem; the sniffing of dangerous aromatic substances from glue to gasoline in order to experience pleasurable release from reality is increasing.

As so often happens, a tangle of circumstances allowed the girls to drift towards their deadly addiction. The family farm was not doing well. Oil prices had soared and this small farming unit was heavily mechanised. Only with the latest in farming machinery could the girls' father make a profit; even with good equipment, he needed to work from dawn to dusk to make ends meet. So it was that, somewhat reluctantly, the girls' mother went back to work in a nearby town as soon as she felt her children were able to look after themselves for an hour or so after school. The girls had four younger siblings, two boys and two girls. They were healthy and not involved with the older girls' problems.

On the property was a large barn in which tractors and other mechanical devices were garaged and it was in this barn that Dad kept his large drums of gasoline. Sue later told me that she remembered having enjoyed the smell of gasoline since she was a child and that the barn had always been a special place for the children, a sort of warm, unreal refuge for playing and fantasising. Thus I suppose it was not especially surprising that Sue should take the cap off the cans of gasoline housed there to enjoy the aroma that filled the air.

Unfortunately, on one fateful day, she lent over the drum and actually inhaled the aromatic fumes deeply; why she could never tell. She could relate, however, the marvellous effects that the inhalation of these fumes had upon her. It made her feel 'so good'; cares disappeared as worry was displaced with a giggly lightheaded feeling. She inducted Marion into the sniffing club and soon it became their habit to come home each day from school and head straight for the barn and their 'high'. This they were to do for three to four months, and their tired and no doubt preoccupied parents did not begin to suspect that anything was wrong.

The first sign of trouble came when Marion started to bruise easily. The merest bump of thigh against table would lead to a nasty bruise; she became covered in them. In retrospect, the mother was to tell me, she had noticed that both girls had been listless for a couple of weeks before the bruising episodes.

An alarmed mother made an appointment with the family doctor, who ordered some blood tests. He told Marion and her mother to come back in four days to discuss the results, but within twenty-four hours he was on the telephone telling them that something very serious had happened to Marion's blood. The doctor explained that the major problem appeared to be an extremely low platelet count.

Platelets are cells produced in the bone marrow which circulate in our bloodstream primarily to help blood to clot efficiently. When a blood vessel is damaged even slightly, the pressure within the vessel associated with blood being pumped so forcefully around the body makes it very likely that some blood can leak from the damaged artery or vein into the tissues. Therefore, no matter how tiny the breach in the vessel, it is rapidly plugged so that precious blood cannot escape.

Damaged blood vessels secrete a sticky substance to which platelets adhere. They in turn effectively plug the break, then they activate the clotting factors that are present in blood. A clot occurs around the break in the vessels. This will dissolve slowly but only after the vessel wall has healed itself completely.

Normally we have about 250 000 platelets in every drop of blood. Marion's count was down to 4000. But she had other problems as well: the cells that help antibodies in the fight against bacteria, i.e. the neutrophils, were also much reduced in number. Needless to say, young Marion did not connect this problem to her gasoline sniffing. A very concerned mother and family doctor had the child seen immediately by a hematologist, an expert in blood diseases. After listening to the story and examining the child, the specialist immediately admitted Marion to hospital.

That same night, after her shower, an alarmed Susan displayed a number of developing bruises to her incredulous parents.

Sue joined her sister in hospital, for the abnormalities in her blood were identical to Marion's. Given two children with the same problem, their physicians very soon started looking for some shared exposure to a toxic substance to explain the girls' condition. In so doing, they unravelled the gasoline-sniffing story. Gasoline fumes have long been known to have the potential to destroy many of the cells we find circulating in our bloodstream, so the cause of their abnormalities was obvious even if the prognosis was not.

The gasoline vapors, containing dangerous chemicals, had been inhaled into the girls' lungs, whence they were readily absorbed into their bloodstream. Once in the bloodstream they were easily delivered to the girls' bone marrow. The delicate mechanisms responsible for the education of so many vital cells in the bone marrow were poisoned. Sometimes with supportive measures such as blood and platelet transfusions, time can be bought to allow the marrow to recover from the toxic effects of the vapors. Sometimes hormones may help in the process. None of these approaches helped Sue and Marion and the girls were seriously ill when I first met them.

When it became clear that they would die before their bone marrow could recover (presuming it could ever recover), it was obvious that what was required was a successful bone marrow transplant operation; that is, a gift of marrow cells from a healthy person. Once transplanted into the bloodstream of the girls, these cells could dive into their marrow spaces and repair the damage.

Both mother and father volunteered instantly but just as quickly we assured them that neither would be suitable. The girls needed marrow cells that would not be distinguished from their own marrow cells. Why? Because if the cells were different, one of two consequences, both fatal, would occur.

If the children's own T cells were intact (and they were; the gasoline had not affected them), non-identical marrow cells would be ruthlessly attacked and no engraftment (take) of the donor cells would occur. If we suppressed the children's T cells with drugs (which we could do, but it would be dangerous) the non-identical cells that had been transplanted might kill the children. Marrow contains many T cells that actually reside there and exert a major influence on the production of all the blood cells made in the marrow, not just the B cells that make antibodies. These marrow T cells could 'recognise' the children as foreign and 'reject' them, attacking many tissues simultaneously.

The disease that would result is for obvious reasons called 'graft versus host' disease. The donated T cells would roam around the body attacking the skin, brain, liver and intestinal tract first, but eventually all organs would fall before their attack. A death from graft versus host disease is a miserable one. No, the girls had to have identical marrow or they were doomed.

Their parents had each been responsible for donating 50 per cent of the genetic information that had been translated into a Sue and a Marion. The reason for the 50 per cent split is important. All genetic information is encoded on chromosomes; think of songs (genes) on a tape (chromosome). Chromosomes are in fact paired structures (two strips of magnetic tape wrapped around each other). When a germ cell is formed, i.e. a sperm cell or ovum, only one of the two entwined chromosomes (50 per cent) is carried along. For this reason the children could not be identical, in a genetic sense, to either their mother or their father.

In the nucleus of each human cell are twenty-three pairs of chromosomes. Each pair is recognisably different from the other and so geneticists can identify each of them. They are given numbers to identify the first twenty-two pairs (1–22) while the twenty-third pair, which determine the sex of an individual, are, reasonably enough, referred to as 'sex chromosomes'. When it comes time to form a new human being, one chromosome from each of the twenty-three pairs will be donated to the new offspring by both mother and father.

If each of the mother's twenty-three genetic programs (chromosomes) is split into two equal lots called W and X and each of the father's into two equal lots called Y and Z, it is obvious that, for any given chromosomal pair, all the couple's children must consist of one of four possible genetic formulae: WY, WZ, XY or XZ. (Figure 10.) With each pregnancy there is an equal chance that any of the formulae will turn up for each pair of chromosomes. Thus three consecutive children in a family could have the same formula or could all be different. While that would be a matter of chance, what is certain is that if there are five children in a family any particular genetic pairing must be repeated at least once.

Sue and Marion were being plied with blood, steroids, platelets, antibiotics and prayers. They had one hope: each needed to find one sibling with the same genetically programmed tissue profile as herself.

The genes for the eight major biological 'trademarks' (self or histocompatibility antigens) and a myriad of minor ones that pepper the surface of our cells are located on chromosome pair number six. Susan and Marion needed a sibling who had inherited the same combination of maternal and paternal histocompatibility genes as themselves.

As things turned out they were indeed fortunate children; each had a sibling who was a perfect match. Susan's was brother Paul, ten years old; Marion's was baby Rachel, only four years old. There were ethical considerations, of course, in using the sisters' siblings at such a young age, but the parents, physicians and the Institute's Ethics Committee agreed to the propriety of the desperate measures being made to save the girls.

The donor children were anesthetised and large bore needles were inserted into their hip bones to allow the precious marrow to be extracted. The cells obtained were washed, diluted and injected intravenously into the two desperately ill children. After injection the marrow cells race around in the circulation but spill out of the blood as they pass through the marrow to take up their new residence in the previously poisoned spaces. It never ceases to amaze me how cells can know exactly where they want to live, but the homing instincts of all sorts of cells that live in specialised tissues within our body are unfailing.

After this form of transplantation it is always touch and go for the two weeks before the marrow starts to produce new cells; but, happy to report, these girls recovered completely and their siblings came to no harm as a result of their generosity. The family is now united as never before and the two young ladies are much wiser. I doubt that they will ever have so much as a puff of a marijuana cigarette.

Now, except for the case of identical twins, the situation just described is about as good as one will get in the transplantation business. While you work within a family grouping, variations in the histocompatibility (or transplantation) antigens are limited; once

Figure 10. The generation of antigen-presenting molecules and
immunological identity

W, X, Y and Z are different combinations of A, B, C and D locus genes
on chromosome Pair No. 6

PATERNAL NUCLEUS   MATERNAL NUCLEUS

chromosomal   chromosomal
strands   strands

GENES for
antigen-presenting
molecules

Two types of   Two types of
SPERM CELL   OVUM CELL
(each containing 23 chromosomes)   (each containing 23 chromosomes)

W+Y   **W+Z**   **X+Y**   **X+Z**

Four possible recombinations for chromosome Pair No. 6

you break away from the family group the odds of two people sitting next to each other on an aeroplane being identical in this sense are about 200 000 to 1. Consequently if you are in hospital waiting for a kidney transplant, your chances of having your 'mate' brought into the emergency room almost dead and having a card in their wallet saying 'In case of my death please use my organs' are very slim indeed.

Before discussing organ transplantation let us consider in a little more detail these biological trademarks that make transplantation so difficult.

People who are to have a transplant are 'tissue typed'; that is, their biological trademarks, present as membrane-bound proteins, are characterised. With the help of computers and sera from women who have had many babies, there are now bottles of testing material that contain antibodies to all the different trademarks in our community. These markers are given names. On chromosome number six there are four places (loci) where the genes that produce these things reside. The loci are called A, B, C and D. In the human community there are very many different genes that could occupy each locus. Only one gene will be present at each locus in any individual, but remember that chromosomes are paired and therefore there will be eight genes in all involved in the major histocompatibility system.

This means that humans inherit one A, B, C and D set from each parent.

We can place human cells from a potential organ donor or recipient into tiny wells in a plastic tray and suspend them in a small amount of fluid. We can then add to each well a drop of antibody known to react with a particular histocompatibility antigen. As we usually use human white blood cells (leucocytes) for the task, the system is often referred to as the HLA or *h*uman *l*eucocyte *a*ntigen system. If the added antibodies bind to the cells in a well, then the cells will clump together and fall to the bottom where they will be observed as a small white dot. One of the eight antigens has therefore been 'typed'. So you may end up with a profile that looks like this: Mr Smith's HLA type is A3, A24, B8, B27, C2, C7, D2, D4. (Figure 11.)

A perfect match, when it comes to organ donation, will have all the same eight HLA markers that you possess and display. In addition, he or she must have the same red cell group of markers (those of the better known ABO system). Where can you find such a match? Outside the family circle your chances are poor indeed. That is why in the early days of transplantation a lot of 'living-related' organ transplantation was done. Naturally this was restricted to kidney transplantation for here we have a situation where there

An artist's depiction of the DNA helix which contains the genes that make us what we are. (Courtesy Lawrence Livermore National Laboratory)

A photograph taken of a living baby inside its mother's womb. The baby's immune system is well-developed by this stage and is contributing to its own protection by minimising any aggressiveness displayed by the mother's immune system to the foreignness in her womb. (From *A child is born*, Lennart Nilsson, 1965)

Top: A dissection of a 12-week-old human fetus that had spontaneously miscarried shows clearly the bio-lobed thymus gland sitting on top of the big blood vessels coming out of the heart. It is here that the miracle of our immune system is created.

Below: The product of the thymus gland is a T cell, which uses its 'feet' to move rapidly through the tissues in its constant search for invaders. Many viruses may die of fright when they see this monster descending upon them.

A macrophage (in this case an antigen presenting cell) reaches out for an antigen about which it is suspicious. The cell will pick up the bacterium and show it to an inducer T cell to determine whether it is self or foreign.

Left: A human B lymphocyte seen binding bacteria (coloured green) to surface receptors that allow that special cell to recognise this specific antigen. The cell will now divide to form plasma cells and secrete antibodies that can attack these bacteria.

Below: At a lower magnification, the ability of macrophages to extend their antigen trapping arms (pseudopods) is readily demonstrated.

Top: Some macrophages are involved in swallowing and killing antigens. Here we see a macrophage activated by T cells or antibody on the green bacteria, actually swallowing bacteria one by one.

Below: An activated macrophage throwing out dozens of tentacle-like pseudopods to mop up globules of oil (yellow drops).

Top: Two round T cells have attached themselves to and are now attacking a cancer cell.
Below: T cells have the capacity to extend long probe-like structures from their surface to pierce and kill cancer cells to which they have attached.

The large cancer cell in the middle of this picture will be no match for the two T cells that have fixed themselves to its surface and will attack while calling for help from other T cells in the vicinity.

Figure 11. The cellular production of antigen-presenting molecules and immunological identity

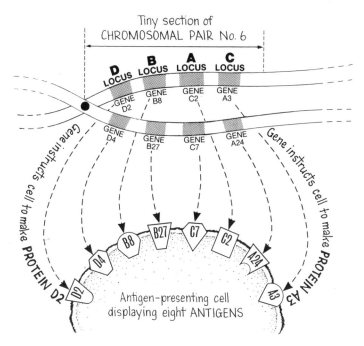

is one organ to spare. It is not too easy to talk family members into giving you a liver or a heart.

You do not have to be associated with a 'living donor' program for long before you become convinced that the immunological advantages are far outweighed by the disadvantages associated with the human drama involved.

To understand what I mean, put yourself through the following scenario. Your brother, five years your senior, is dying of kidney disease. Only a new kidney can save him; he is a kind, productive man with a dependent family. You are healthy and the only one in the family whose HLA type coincides with that of the sick man. Your brother hated to approach you to ask for such an incredible favor but, urged on by his wife and your parents, he put the question to you: 'Would you be willing to have a major operation to allow one of your two healthy kidneys to be removed so that it could replace my dead ones?'

All eyes are on you. What can you say? You are not happy about it, of course. It is a big operation. Things occasionally go wrong with surgery, don't they? You would be left with only one kidney and what if something happened to that, then you would be in a pretty fix! But you love your brother. The family want you to give him his chance. Things will never be the same if you say no and he dies. (A number of donors have told me that unavoidable pressures made it impossible for them to feel good about the selflessness of the act involved. They felt robbed of the satisfaction that comes with being quietly generous.) Anyway, you go ahead with the operation and your brother has a new kidney. Imagine the feeling of all concerned if six weeks later the transplanted kidney is dead and the surgeons are back in again pulling out your former, now useless kidney. Your sacrifice has come to nothing.

Unfortunately, this can happen. While 80 to 90 per cent of so-called perfectly matched kidneys survive and indeed flourish, this is not always the case. The wound or the organ itself may become infected, the delicate hook up of the kidney to blood vessels and ureter (the tube that carries urine from the kidney to the bladder) may run into trouble, or the recipient's immune system may reject the kidney after all.

The immune system can sometimes react to a slight difference that we have not picked up in our tissue typing program. This latter event needs a little explanation. There are undoubtedly 'trademark' antigens, of which we know little. With the exception of identical twins we cannot be one hundred per cent certain that two individuals, even family members, are perfectly matched. With families we can be 90 per cent sure and that is the state of the art. So it is that a sibling kidney may be rejected and the storms that burst when this sort of thing happens within a family are torrential. The donor is frustrated that his or her magnanimous gesture, with its anguish and discomfort, has failed. The recipient is overwhelmed by guilt at having rejected the sacrificed organ.

Because of the emotional tangle and because most patients with renal failure do not have a living relative who is a perfect match anyway, transplantation units have been forced to proceed with their work after accepting two compromises: they must harvest organs from the legally dead (cadaveric donors), and they must suppress the immune system of the new organ's recipient. Transplant teams try to get the best match possible for their patient but, in the real world, the immune system must be partially crippled for the transplanted organ to survive. The danger is easy to see. If you cannot reject the incompatible kidney you may not be able to reject the next virus that 'transplants' itself into your body.

What happens when a transplanted organ is attacked? It is a horrible thing to watch, I can tell you. The alarm-sounding T cells recognise certain HLA proteins displayed on cells within the transplanted organ and its blood vessels. The alarm goes off and B and T cells swing into action, destroying the graft completely.

The immune system has a memory of elephantine proportions, as we know. Should a second transplant be attempted with tissue that resembles the first organ in any way, the graft can actually be rejected before the surgeon finishes stitching the new kidney into place. The kidney can swell up and turn black before the horrified eyes of the medical team.

There is nothing new under the sun and therefore nothing new about humanity's dream of replacing old, worn or diseased parts with young, healthy alternatives. There is a famous and very ancient painting of the saints Cosmos and Damian performing a transplant on a rich nobleman. A well-to-do man of stature needed a new leg and the donor, a black slave, is depicted in the painting in his now 'one-legged' state. There is a smile of intense satisfaction on his face at having been lucky enough to be asked to donate one of his legs (after signing the appropriate informed consent sheet, of course). The black leg looks to be in good condition, attached to the thigh of the nobleman, and there are absolutely no signs of the recipient being immunosuppressed. (Naturally, saints can control the immune system better than we can.)

The rest of us, however, must use powerful immuno-suppressive drugs—or paint—to pull off such a trick. One of the big scandals of modern immunology involved a New York scientist working on ways to make white mice accept the transfer of skin from black mice. Pressures demanding success in the highly competitive world of academic medicine led him into a fatal trap for young players. He faked his success by painting a black square on the back of his white mice and hailing the 'hybrid' as a triumph for medical research. He was discovered and it checkmated his career.

Every day, thousands of transplants are done as doctors and patients alike accept the compromises discussed above. A recent case can illustrate much that is involved. Eleven-year-old Carrie urgently needed a new liver. A year earlier, happy, average Carrie had the misfortune to be involved in a serious car accident. It was the last day of the Labor Day weekend and the family was racing up the New Jersey turnpike towards New York, in heavy traffic and deteriorating weather conditions.

A car swerved recklessly into their lane, much too close for comfort. Carrie's father braked, perhaps overreacting, and as a result the car spun, bounced, tumbled and stopped.

Both the parents and Carrie survived. Mother and father were wearing seat belts, Carrie was not. Her small body careened around the interior of the frenzied car, both bouncing and breaking apart.

She awoke in an intensive care unit concussed, aching all over and reluctant to breathe as broken ribs protested. In the trauma her spleen, nestling under her left diaphragm, had ruptured and poured blood into her belly. Fortunately surgery had been in time to stop exsanguination but she had lost more than half of her blood volume.

None of this had any direct bearing on her need for a new liver. She could and did make a complete recovery from those dreadful injuries. What did Carrie more harm than the car accident, however, was the blood transfusion she was given to replace all the blood that she had lost as a result of the accident.

It was unbelievably bad luck that little Carrie was given a bottle of blood that was contaminated with a virus that can cause hepatitis (inflammation of the liver).

There are at least three hepatitis-producing viruses. Hepatitis A is a virus that enters our mouth, usually placed there by dirty fingers which pick the virus up from feces. It is often called 'infectious hepatitis', a silly name as many other forms of hepatitis produced by other viruses are even more infectious. Hepatitis B is a virus one picks up either from blood, blood products or infected sexual secretions. It is spread in a manner that is identical to the spread of AIDS but it is far more infectious. At the time of Carrie's accident, donated blood could be screened for the presence of both hepatitis A and B to ensure that recipients weren't inadvertently infected with either virus. But the third hepatitis virus which spreads very much like hepatitis B could not then be detected in blood. At the time it was known as non-A non-B hepatitis; it is now called hepatitis C for the responsible virus has been found and characterised. Usually it causes a mild transient inflammation of the liver and recovery follows. Not always, however. For Carrie the infection had flourished in her weakened state and destroyed too much of her liver for long-term survival to be possible.

Carrie was accepted by the liver transplant team and the hunt was on to find a liver. Her cells were HLA typed and her profile fed into a computer. Any potential liver donor who, of course, would have to be involved in their own personal tragedy, would be screened so that the liver went to the best match waiting anywhere in the country.

No one thought there would be a chance of finding a perfect match. Carrie would be given one that was the best available but she would have to have her T and B cells blunted.

As expected, one person's tragedy was to be another's salvation. A call came from Tennessee. In an intensive care unit lay an eighteen-year-old girl shot in the head by a jealous boyfriend. Her brain was dead. The rest of her would soon follow. Distraught parents had given permission for organ harvesting. A team of surgeons from

Carrie's hospital raced to a waiting company jet, kindly and not uncommonly donated for the mission in hand. When they arrived three other teams would be there. One team from California wanted the girl's heart, another team wanted the kidneys and pancreas and the third team would eventually get a chance to harvest the corneas of her eyes.

This sort of macabre but essential scavenging has become possible because of the widespread acceptance by the medical, legal, philosophical and theological communities that death of the brain is all that is needed to declare the death of a person. No longer must the heart stop beating and the chest stop rising before the harvesters can, with gratitude and appreciation of the sensitivities of all involved, extract life for the dying from the dead.

The liver was not too big for Carrie; fortunately the donor had been particularly small. In an eleven-hour operation Carrie's old liver was flung aside and the new organ placed into its new home. The surgeons triumphed and Carrie had a chance. She was given a drug called cyclosporin, a sophisticated T cell poison. Unfortunately it can be toxic to kidney and liver cells and must be used with the greatest of care. However, when administered with the appropriate skill, it can stop rejection with an acceptable degree of toxicity. But the state of the transplantation art is still far from ideal.

What we need to do of course is to master the immunological manoeuvres that allow a pregnancy to survive. We must learn to make the immune system of an organ recipient accept a new organ as part of 'self'—but continue to fight anything else that is foreign. Long-term immunosuppression is associated with high infection risks and an increased chance of developing cancer for reasons that will be explained later. Tolerance induction must be the way of the future.

In examining the immune system, you may remember, we discussed the remarkable fact that each and every lymphocyte is programmed to recognise one and only one specific antigen. If all those cells that can recognise a certain organ could be eliminated or paralysed, a graft could survive in an otherwise immunocompetent recipient. We can induce specific tolerance to an organ in a mouse or rat in this manner, but we cannot do it instantly. It takes days at least. With human transplantation, as soon as an organ is available it must be transplanted.

Research along a number of different lines seems promising. We are getting better and better at preserving organs in tissue culture conditions. If we could keep a kidney or liver alive and well for three to six weeks in an incubator before needing to transplant it, we could find the ultimate match for that organ, attempt to produce tolerance to that tissue in a prospective recipient and decrease the foreignness of the organ. It seems that with time in tissue culture, organs lose much of their HLA profile.

We know that T and B cells are at their most vulnerable to drugs when they divide. They must divide as part of their attack response to antigens. If we could develop drugs that would kill only those T cells and B cells dividing after an antigen challenge, we could eliminate all the cells capable of rejecting the organ. Such a mechanism is called clonal deletion (a clone is a family) and there is no doubt that it will become a reality.

We can now activate special suppressor cells that will reduce the viciousness of aggressor cells that want to attack the liver or kidney or other transplanted tissue.

I want to return to the subject of bone marrow transplantation; important things are happening here that are revolutionising the treatment of one of the most lethal of diseases, leukemia. As usual we will illustrate the newer approaches by describing a case history.

Twenty-three-year-old Kay is a college student majoring in music. She is of Japanese–American descent; looking Oriental and acting like an American. She presented herself to her campus medical office because she was unusually tired and weak. The pressure of examinations could not explain adequately her feelings, and especially the breathlessness that she was getting when walking up a flight of stairs. She was pale but otherwise looked well.

A routine blood count was performed and told the story. Kay had developed an acute form of leukemia. What does that mean? Leukemia is a cancerous expansion of white blood cells—an uncontrollable, unwanted and very dangerous proliferation. The chapter on cancer gives a much more detailed account of the drama that leads to cells misbehaving themselves so disastrously. It is important to understand that one of the hundreds of billions of T cells in Kay's body had become a renegade; only one cell is needed to develop this condition. The now cancerous cell divides incessantly and is soon crowding the spaces where T cells live and travel. Blood, lymph nodes, spleen and bone marrow fill up first, then the T cells spill out into the lungs and other tissues. In Kay's case they were also occupying part of her brain.

Now, this is a real medical emergency. There was no time to worry about what treatment might do to normal cells and their infection-fighting capacity. If those malignant cells were not killed or at the very least hindered from their headlong rush to divide, there would be no Kay to worry about. Consequently she was rushed into hospital and, that very day, given intravenously five anti-cancer drugs known to be particularly effective against rapidly dividing cells. Normal cells in our bodies that must divide regularly will be damaged by these drugs. The cells most affected will be those that produce our hair, the cells lining the intestinal tract and, most dangerously, the normal cells in the bone marrow that produce for us platelets, red blood cells, B cells and the polymorphs and monocytes. All these cells are already in trouble anyway because the leukemic cells are crowding them out, competing more than successfully for local nutrients.

Despite all this intensive treatment, Kay's malignant T cells continued to do their damage. We made the situation worse, not better, as we had not helped her cancer but damaged normal cells.

There are different forms of leukemia, depending on which of the leucocytes turns nasty. Monocytes and B cells can become leukemic. T cell leukemia is one of the worst forms of the disease and the results with Kay were unfortunately not unusual. The plan formulated to save her involved three risky 'ifs'. If we could find a suitable (not necessarily perfect) donor, we could try and kill *all* of Kay's cancer cells with doses of drugs and radiotherapy that would also kill *all* her normal marrow cells. We might have eliminated the cancer in this fashion, but to survive Kay needed a transplant of normal cells that would once again supply her with the essential elements of blood. If a perfect donor could not be found, one as close as possible was necessary to minimise the risks involved in this sort of procedure. Help was needed from the computer. We would also use new techniques to take from the donated bone marrow as many T cells as possible. If we could get rid of every last cell there would be no danger from graft versus host disease. The fastidiousness with which we approach this T cell elimination is terribly important, as animal experiments have shown that it can take but one T cell to kill a helplessly immunodeficient mouse.

Kay was lucky with the computer; a man in England was willing to travel to America to give her his almost identical marrow. Five of the eight major antigens matched and Kay was prepared for her 'one chance' ordeal. Her body was treated with massive doses of anti-cancer drugs and she was irradiated. She was nursed in a specialised sterile room, equipped with sophisticated air conditioning that ensured that air that went out did not return, while air that did come into the room was treated with ultraviolet light. Everyone entering the room was as clean as was practicable. Doctors and nurses showered and entered the room masked, gloved and gowned. The donor arrived, met Kay and her family (the heart-warming part of this sort of adventure), was anesthetised and the donation proceeded. One hundred and forty-two times the surgeons inserted needles deep into the bones of his hip to aspirate from the depths those precious marrow cells needed.

Once obtained, the cells were rushed to a sterile laboratory where an attempt was made to remove all the donor's T cells. For some reason, T cells have a characteristic that makes them stick to red blood cells of sheep (and only sheep). We added some sterile sheep red blood cells to the marrow and many of the T cells present clumped together with the red cells. We then spun the whole preparation in a centrifuge and a large number of the T cells in the preparation fell to the bottom of our tubes because they were heavy now that they were attached to the red blood cells. Carefully, we aspirated the top layer and then added some extracts from peanuts which, of all things, are known to clump T cells. We spun the preparation again. For twelve hours we repeated these steps over and over again until less than one in a hundred of the cells left in the marrow appeared to be T cells. It was not perfect but it was the best we could do.

The T-depleted cells were transfused into Kay. We gave her more drugs to cover the possibility that a few T cells in the donated marrow might have been ready to attack her. We gave her large amounts of antibodies obtained from normal blood. We kept everything sterile and waited. (It takes a month before we can judge success or failure.) Kay needed infusions of normal people's platelets and polymorphs. She needed lots of sophisticated antibiotics. The blood transfusions we gave her were first irradiated to make sure that no live T cells were present in the transfusion.

Kay's graft took and she was well. The leukemia may still return, however. Of course we hope it will not, but if we left alive even a few leukemic cells at the time we were preparing her for the transplant then the disease would recur. However, she had her chance; something she would not have had with the same condition even a few years ago.

Kay's operation and general expenses cost about $100 000. The job is technically demanding and very labor-intensive, needing a great number of doctors and nurses with special skills. We must hope that our ability to manipulate the human defensive system will soon allow us to handle these conditions with far less danger and expense.

It may surprise you to learn that of all the transplantation procedures, heart transplantation is the easiest and most successful. This was not always so, but there have been remarkable advances in this work. Transplanting hearts and lungs simultaneously, which unfortunately we often need to do, remains less satisfactory though it is improving all the time. Kidneys, livers, skin, bone marrow, hearts and eye tissue are regularly and successfully transplanted. Pancreatic transplantation (which theoretically could cure diabetes) is not as yet successful, but the research into this form of therapy is proceeding well.

Nervous tissue (nerves and the brain itself) is notoriously difficult to transplant and is likely to remain so. It is not the immunology that is so difficult here but the problem of connections. Imagine a table covered with spaghetti. A sharp knife divides all of the segments into two. The two halves are then separated and presented to you with instructions to join up all the pieces so that the original configuration is renewed. Such a task would be easy when compared with joining up the many millions of elements that make up our nervous tissue.

While we have noted many of the problems associated with transplantation, we must remember that today it is saving numerous lives. In Sydney not long ago a wedding was held that was more than a little unusual. Both the bride and the groom had undergone a heart transplant operation successfully. After they were declared man and wife and embraced each other and their parents, they turned to embrace the parents of the two young people whose hearts beat inside them. I am sure the loss of the two people who had donated those hearts was made more bearable at that moment.

PART III

THE DEFEAT OF THE WARRIORS

6

The topic of cancer

What is so intrinsically disturbing about cancer? Everyone knows it is a process that can kill, and so we humans, constantly if subconsciously concerned about the brevity of life, are naturally frightened of something that is so often responsible for our demise.

One in four of you reading this book will die of cancer. But is the knowledge that a tumor may kill us a good enough explanation for the dread that is conjured by the term 'cancer'? After all, more of us will die of heart problems than of cancer, yet the thought of a heart attack, although distressing, is more tolerable than the thought of cancer.

Perhaps in that sentence we have stumbled upon the reason why cancer is so feared. We know we can survive a heart attack, we may indeed live with it, but cancer? How many people do we know who have been cured of cancer? In fact many people are cured of some forms of cancer, but little publicity is given to such advances.

I doubt, however, that the perception that death will certainly follow the development of cancer is responsible for its reputation as the most feared of diagnoses. As is so often the case with physicians, my understanding of people's attitudes towards cancer was considerably broadened by one of my patients.

Jennifer was an excellent nurse who had worked in our outpatient department for many years. Forty-nine years old, the mother of four, and the caregiver to an aged mother, she had always been healthy apart from some chronic but not debilitating bronchitis.

One day, however, she confided to me that she was concerned because she had coughed up some blood three mornings in a row. There was little else to tell; she had no pain, no deterioration in well-being although she admitted to having lost some weight in recent months. I arranged for her to have an X-ray examination of her chest. Already advanced cancer, starting in the bronchial tree and progressing to eat its way into her lungs, stood out in bold relief from the normal structures of the chest so clearly displayed on the picture obtained.

Of course, it is harder to deliver bad news to a colleague than it is to a stranger and I am sure you will understand that such episodes are emotionally charged. After we had discussed the matter for some minutes Jennifer asked whether she could see the X-ray film, not doubting the information, of course, but instantly summoning the defiance that humans can harness to defend their psyche. She stared at the film for a long time after I had explained that it would not be possible to eradicate the growth surgically. The silence was heavy. Eventually, after what seemed like minutes, she turned to me.

'It's not the picture on the screen that is so devastating to me,' she said quietly. 'It is what lies ahead for me and my family. That's what I see when I look at that X-ray. I know what dying from cancer will entail.'

From this and similar conversations, I believe it is the connotation of a protracted battle with a high chance of defeat that frequently colors the diagnosis of cancer with great, indeed unwarranted fear.

Cancer is a doubly frustrating condition for the clinical scientist. Failure to help patients in their struggle with cancer has, until recently, been shared with the failure to understand the grossly disordered biological processes responsible for this suffering; all this at a time when other complex medical problems are being rapidly solved. Fortunately, all that is changing rapidly and thus the tone of this chapter can definitely be one of optimism.

At this point, you may be wondering why cancer is being discussed in a book about the immune system. The answer is simple. Certain cancerous cells can, albeit with difficulty, be distinguished from normal cells. We have every reason to believe that lymphocytes can recognise these differences. We also know that lymphocytes can and frequently do kill certain tumor cells. The questions therefore that immunologists must face are these: Is clinically advanced cancer the result of a failure of our immune systems? Are our immune systems charged with the responsibility of constantly screening self to detect cancerous changes in bone, breast or bowel, etc.? If so, is cancer an immunodeficiency disease? Should all cancer cells be recognised as dangerous by our immune systems, or are some clever enough to be indistinguishable from self and thus capable of tricking the most perfect of immune systems?

These are the concepts that we must explore. Understanding the answers to these questions would provide not only a breakthrough in our knowledge of cancerous growth but new and logical ways to approach the treatment of malignancy.

To be logical, we must first explore those events that trans-form a once normal cell into a renegade, disobeying all the regulatory signals it has hitherto obeyed. Once we understand why the cell has so drastically changed its character and function, we can explore its interaction, or lack thereof, with the immune system.

Jennifer developed cancer in a fraction of a second. At one moment she did not have cancer, at the next moment she did. In that split second, the normal functioning of one cell was permanently disarrayed. In that moment, perhaps months or even years before clinical disease developed, her fate was settled. In her case one cell somewhere among the billions of similar cells that lined her airways (bronchial tree) took the malignant approach to its future biological role.

It divided and divided, producing an ever-expanding family of identical cells with identical attitudes towards control. With abandon these cells spread and invaded, damaging normal tissues as they ruthlessly pursued their quest for immortality. At the most fundamental level, that is what cancer is all about—immortality. Only the failure of the cancer victim to sustain the nutritional requirements of the cancerous cell's growth frustrates these tumors' intention.

Increasingly, scientists are able to put single cancer cells in a test tube inside an incubator and observe their apparent immortality. As long as they are fed they live, they multiply. Not so normal cells; their mortality in such artificial systems is obvious within days.

We understand that normal cells in any part of the body have, as an integral part of their genetic makeup, clearly laid out instructions for growth and differentiation (development of a specific function) and division (replication of self). Each and every normal cell is under the tightest of control mechanisms. The cell is programmed from its conception to its death; very definitely, the latter is pre-programmed into the cell. It will divide a finite number of times, then it will die. The simultaneous death of a critical mass of cells in a vital organ will lead to our death. As we age, cells that have the capacity to repair tissues and even repair damaged genetic material die. We are welcome guests of our biological environment, but only for so long.

On the other hand, cancer cells have broken loose from the shackles of self-imposed mortality. They have turned off the bio-logical timer inside their nucleus that would tell them when to self-destruct. The irony is all too obvious; in achieving their chance for immortality, they accelerate the death of normal cells that surround them and ultimately in so doing they destroy themselves. We now know that as we humans age, cells rebel and become cancerous much more easily. We also know that every cell in our body has the potential for malignant change with the exception of red blood cells. Red blood cells don't have a nucleus and why this fact protects them from cancer will be obvious as we proceed.

Cancer is thus a disease process in which one cell undergoes an internal rearrangement of its instructive material so that it no longer lives by the laws of ordered biological development and demise. It stimulates its own growth and replication. It loses its biological death wish and necessarily invades and spreads into both adjoining and remote corners of the body as it reproduces itself endlessly; and in so doing produces damaging mass effects.

How does such a disastrous turn of events occur? Two factors must be considered together. First we will explore the concept that all cells have the potential to become malignant, then we will look at what is known of triggering factors that may impact upon a cell and unleash its tendency to indulge in malignant behaviour.

Look at the back of your hand. Does it look the same to you as it did a month ago? It probably does, but it isn't. Many of the cells you see there, neatly glued together to make skin, were not present a month ago. Much of our body is continuously dying and being replaced in a vital process imperceptible to us in our day-to-day life.

This need to shed and repair puts us at increased risk of developing cancer. Normal cells are turned on and told to divide and, having done so, are then very definitely turned off. The complexities involved in this signalling put us at risk should the system falter and the turnoff signals be ignored.

However, before discussing these things, we shall return to the story of the nurse, Jennifer. To confirm a diagnosis and determine the type of cancer in her lungs, a tube was manoeuvred down her throat and trachea into her bronchial tree. Using warm saline her airways were lavaged, and the cells washed out from deep in her chest were examined under the microscope. Their malignant nature was readily identified. After consultation with radiotherapists, surgeons and physicians skilled in the poisoning by chemicals of tumor cells, it was decided that radiation therapy offered the best chance of slowing the spread of her disease. Bravely, Jennifer commenced her battle against cancer. The scenario she had anticipated became reality with unerring accuracy, until one remarkable departure from the normal script occurred.

Her cancer was mainly confined to the upper portion of her right lung. Eventually in its outward push it reached that part of the lung closest to the chest wall. The lung there is lined by a thin filmy layer called the pleura. (Sometimes it becomes infected and when you take a deep breath it stretches and hurts; that is called pleurisy.) The inside of your rib cage is lined by pleura also, and the layer over the lung and that on your chest wall move easily over each other when we breathe. An oily liquid lubricates their surface, so normally these movements are frictionless.

Jennifer's cancer, which had started from her airways, burst from her lung into this pleural space. Now when she tried to breathe, air would move along the cancerous track into that space, which filled up like a balloon expanding. The pressures collapsed the other part of her right lung and, as you would expect, she felt pain and breathlessness. Worse was to follow. Bacteria from her airways settled in her pleural space and an abscess formed at that site. It extended into the cancer-ridden lung.

Jennifer shivered and perspired as fevers racked her body despite the antibiotics we gave her. For ten days she was suspended on a tightrope between life and death. Jennifer, however, was tough and survived to continue her fight with cancer. But what cancer? Remarkable to tell, as the abscess settled down to be replaced by scar tissue, her tumor shrank and then disappeared from view. Three years later as I write these words, and two and a half years beyond her date with death, she is well and working and appears to be free of tumor.

A miracle? Well, certainly miraculous in the sense of being an unusual turn of events, but perhaps the miracle was wrought by her immune system. Lymphocytes might well have been the minions of the Almighty in saving this worthy lady in a most unusual fashion. An extremely important consideration concerns the delineation of the mechanisms that could have cured her. We will return to this subject later.

Before we continue our discussion of the inner working of cells, we should define a few terms to ensure that what follows is readily understandable. The study of the heart in health and disease is called cardiology; the study of the cell that has become cancerous is called oncology ('onco' from the Greek *onkos* meaning 'mass' or 'tumor'). A doctor who specialises in cancer is an oncologist.

The concept of malignancy is not a medical one alone; malignant is the opposite of benign. Both terms are used frequently when describing swellings (tumors) found in the body. Not all tumors are cancerous expansions, for they can be benign and therefore of little concern.

All of which brings us back to the most important discovery in the field of cancer research in the past twenty years—oncogenes: genes that can cause cancer.

In 1910 in New York City a young scientist, Dr Francis Rous, was studying cancer in animals at the famous Rockefeller Institute for Medical Research. His work received some publicity and as a result a most important meeting occurred. An astute farmer was troubled because some of his Plymouth Rock hens were developing tumors that would eventually kill them. The farmer decided he would consult the bright young Dr Rous about his observations and took one of his affected hens to the Institute. Rous was fascinated because these 'cancers' seemed to be infectious; too many of the farmer's hens were infected for the cancer to be random.

Rous got to work and was soon able to show that if a small piece of the tumor was taken and implanted in another hen of the same strain, similar cancers developed. In a series of now quite famous experiments, Rous was able to show that the cancer-initiating substance was smaller than a cell, smaller in fact than bacteria, for he could still produce cancers after passing the tumor tissue through the smallest of the then available filters. Rous postulated that cancer might be caused by a virus.

What we are talking about is in no way similar to the manner in which viruses may cause the common cold. In that situation viruses take up residence in, say, the nose, multiply and get themselves attacked by the immune system, which wins, but not without a lot of suffering. Your nose becomes the battlefield for the biological war.

In the cancer context we are suggesting that viruses, which are nothing but collections of genetic information, insinuate themselves into cells and change their programming system in such a way that they proliferate in the manner described earlier. A number of viruses can do this and many have been discovered and studied in the animal world. Those studied most thoroughly are, interestingly enough, viruses that belong to the same family to which belongs the virus that causes AIDS.

How do viruses turn a respectable, well-behaved cell into a killer? This is where the oncogenes come in. Certain viruses include in their genetic repertoire genes that are capable of stimulating malignant growth in invaded (parasitised) cells. These will be interwoven with the other genes present so that the victimised cell can carry out its new master's bidding.

But why would a virus wish to turn its host cell into a cancer cell? Cancer cells constantly divide and it is during division that viruses most effectively reproduce. Needless to say, the virus cares not for the fate of the invaded cell.

There is still a missing link to be discussed that bridges the gap between the virus and the cancerous behaviour. Genes, as we have seen, instruct cells to make a specific product. They supply blueprints for the formation of specific proteins; that is, chemicals that influence biological function. The implication here therefore is that proteins, produced by an infected cell in response to the message delivered by oncogenes, can actually *cause* cancerous growth. The virus Rous discovered can certainly do just that.

Having discussed this, we must immediately point out that there is a major problem with this notion (viral oncogenes triggering cancer) as an explanation for all malignant growth. Most cancers, especially in humans, cannot be related to viral infection at all. This puzzle only started to take better shape with the recent and most significant discovery that oncogenes can be found in normal human cells not infected with viruses. (Figure 12.)

This sensational discovery has ruined a number of hither- to prestigious hypotheses. Oncogenes in normal cells! Has nature gone mad? Millions of animals, both human and otherwise, die each year from cancers occurring in so many tissues. Surely such a fundamental design flaw should have been rooted out of our biological systems by this stage of the evolutionary process.

A more calculating and less emotional look at Nature's priorities partially answers the question: we must not live forever if the species is to survive. In the case of us humans, Nature could hardly be expected to have anticipated that so many of us would be sedentary, obese and hooked on cholesterol and alcohol, and therefore depart ahead of time from heart attacks and other diseases. Cancer could be seen as Nature's final solution to the hazard that is longevity. We know, for example, that if men live long enough, the majority will develop cancer in their prostate glands.

Thus we have oncogenes occasionally being delivered by viruses, but other cells seem to be able to get into trouble by activating their own oncogenes, then failing to control them.

The oncogene story, however, is even more fascinating than this account would suggest. These genes are present in normal cells and many if not all of them are owned by the cell. They are not bad genes dumped there by a passing virus. In a fascinating turn around, it seems that oncogenes actually 'infect' viruses. While the evidence of such happenings has been derived mainly from animal studies, recent observations of human cancer make it likely that malignancy in human animals is, in at least some cases, an infectious affair. Some forms of leukemia (a cancer of white blood cells) are almost certainly associated with a cancer-producing infectious process. Here is an example of how such events might occur.

Meet Richard, a tired, middle-order executive who, as we are introduced, is hanging on to the support strap as a suburban train jerks him home from work. His day at the office was a bad one, and he is looking forward to a cold beer with his wife, to whom he can

Figure 12.   How normal cells may become malignant

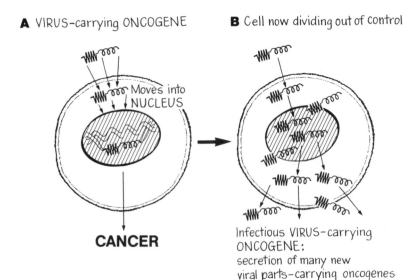

pour out the frustrations of the day. A multitude of thoughts race through his mind, but he is not thinking about the cell at the back of his throat that has become malignant. In two months, it will result in a small tumor that will touch his vocal cords. In six months he will first notice a little hoarseness. In twelve months he will be subjected to necessarily mutilating surgery and will have no voicebox at all. Here's hoping he survives. But all that is in the future; a more immediate biological drama is about to unfold.

Enter character number two in this theatre of life. Samuel is swaying as the train lurches. He is hanging on to a strap three places away from the one clutched by Richard. Samuel is back at work today for the first time in a week, as he has been recovering from an upper respiratory tract infection. In the crowded train carriage Samuel, to his embarrassment, is taken over by the irresistible urge to sneeze. He tries to shield his nose but an explosive sneeze occurs; not a soul seems to notice.

With that sneeze six million viral particles are released into the air. Some will settle on the floor, others on clothes and newspapers; some will be swirling in the air that Richard quietly inhales as he waits for his journey to end.

One of those viral particles lands on the surface of the cancerous cell at the back of Richard's throat. It burrows through the cell membrane and makes for the cell's nucleus. Here is a haven in which it will temporarily settle while it makes more of itself. Soon the cell is making more viral particles that will eventually burst out of the cell, ready to infect other cells locally or to be coughed out into the environment, looking for a fresh host.

In the particular cell that has become home to Samuel's virus, there is already a problem. The cell's oncogenes have activated a growth pattern that is cancerous. As the cell makes viral particles (which are, in fact, viral genes) they can pick up an activated oncogene, hard at work in this cancerous cell; that is, the new viral particles being produced have added an activated oncogene to their genetic makeup and this they will take with them to the next cell they infect. When they infect that cell with their passenger oncogene, they could initiate a malignant change in that cell. In such a manner, cancer can be 'infectious'. Next time Richard coughs in the train he will expose others not only to Samuel's virus but to activated oncogenes as well.

This turns out to be the fuller explanation of the cancer in hens studied by Dr Rous all those years ago. The virus he found did not cause the cancer; it just carried the cancer-activating signal from one hen to the next. Virally induced cancer can thus follow infection with a virus that possesses its own oncogene, or simply carries a cancer-promoting gene, 'donated' by a previously infected cell.

There is no doubt that this viral-mediated threat is an important one, but it is not the major way that cancers develop.

To examine the next step in the unravelling of the cause of cancer, we need to return to the apparent enigma presented to us with the discovery that normal cells possess oncogenes. At first scientists regarded these oncogenes as time-bombs: the genes would sit in the cell in a quiescent fashion until either some intrinsic biological timer said 'fire' or the cell was disturbed by a process that would prematurely trigger the explosion that would lead to cancer. In this view of the cellular drama, oncogenes can only be looked upon as genes that Nature has designed for destructive purposes. New information, however, puts the oncogene problem into better perspective.

Oncogenes are not intrinsically bad genes. They do not sit in cells with nothing to do but wait for the day when they will initiate a tragedy. The truth is that they are constantly playing a role in the most important activity of any cell: self-replication.

Alcohol is not evil, but we all know how 'malignant' can be the effects of uncontrolled overindulgence in this drug. 'Control', 'discipline' and 'appropriate' are all words that conjure up the connotations associated with the harmless consumption of alcohol. And so it is with oncogenes. When they are controlled all is well; when they are not, cancer results.

To understand this part of the story we must ask what is known about the 'normal' function of oncogenes. All the genes, as we have said repeatedly, instruct cells to produce proteins that have a biological function. The proteins produced by oncogenes are vital for replication and therefore the growth or repair of our tissues.

In 1975 a well-known scientist interested in cell replication summed up this aspect of cellular life in this way: 'the most extraordinary attribute of living organisms is their capacity for precise self-replication, a property that can be regarded as a very quintessence of the living estate'.

Professor Lehningen was not talking about the propagation of a species. When a man and a woman produce a baby, that is not self-replication; rather it is the creation of unique newness. We are discussing the replication of self—the 'replacement of skin on the back of the hand' concept discussed earlier. It turns out that oncogenes are essential for the orderly process of cell division necessary for a cell to reproduce itself. Such a process is known as mitosis. Only when something goes wrong with oncogene performance does cancer develop. For this reason oncogenes were, in reality, badly named and of course have had a lot of bad press as biological villains. They should have been called mitogenes.

So, we can put the cancer story into perspective. A cell is only one tiny component of a mighty system. Genes constantly issue instructions to the cell to produce something vital to the mass effort of the organ (move that leg, pump that blood, produce that insulin, etc.). At a precisely *ordered* moment in the cell's hectic life, regulator genes activate oncogenes and suppress other instructions. The oncogenes swing into action and the cellular mechanism involved in one becoming two proceeds apace.

With divisions safely accomplished, oncogenes are switched off by another set of regulatory genes, often located next to the oncogenes on a certain chromosome. If an activated oncogene is divorced from its control mechanisms (picked up by a virus, for example) or if its control mechanisms are disturbed, orderly division is lost and cells are told to continually replicate. They divide and divide again. As they continue in this fashion, a tumor (mass) is formed and a cancerous growth with all its inherent hazards is born.

A most important question for cancer scientists can therefore be posed. What are the factors that can activate oncogenes, disturb their regulation and thus promote the development of cancer? Much progress is being made in this vital area. It is certain that external factors are not always necessary for the disordered regulation of cell division to occur; things can and do go wrong inside the cell with no help from the outside world. But many, perhaps most, cancers involve derangement of oncogene control by environmental factors, for example asbestos in the lungs can cause lung cancer.

We have already discussed viruses in some detail, but even better studied are cancer-promoting chemicals—the so-called carcinogens. Numerous chemicals can interfere with the DNA message possessed by the oncogene and its controlling forces.

In rats the administration of nitrosomethylurea causes breast cancer by changing the DNA message very subtly. The effects are anything but subtle, however; oncogenes are activated in breast cells and cancer develops.

We live in a 'chemical world': all of us are constantly exposed to naturally occurring and synthesised chemicals, be they in the form of preservatives in food, drugs from the pharmacist's shelf or additives to petrol. The wonder is that, of all the chemicals to which we are exposed, relatively few have carcinogenic potential. It follows then that most cancer in humans is triggered by other factors, or occurs spontaneously. That in no way should diminish our determination to find and eliminate from our environment those elements that do have the potential for causing cancer.

The discussion of cancer is now at the point where we must stop and examine the question of cigarette smoking. The tar, chemicals and nicotine contained in cigarettes are far and away the most dangerous chemical carcinogens in our environment, and to do anything but explore this issue thoroughly would be inappropriate. I will try and do this unemotionally, but it is not easy. Physicians see so much unnecessary suffering directly resulting from smoking that it is hard to be dispassionate about the subject, given our miserable track record in getting people to stop the habit and, even more importantly, to refrain from starting.

You remember Jennifer, of course; lucky Jennifer, as it turns out. Well, she was seldom seen socially without a cigarette between her lips. Her bronchitis was caused by smoking more than thirty cigarettes a day for more than thirty years. The simple inescapable fact is that smoking kills and kills and kills. That tobacco manufacturers should be allowed to glamorise this deadly product is a disgrace in an informed society. Tobacco companies employ smooth, verbally skilled individuals to constantly pour doubt on the scientific community's protestations—which are based on ever more convincing evidence—that cigarette smoking is a health hazard of major proportions. It is very different from the situation with alcohol.

Studies support the concept that moderate alcohol intake is harmless. No degree of smoking is harmless; even one low-tar cigarette a week poses risks that should be seen as unacceptable. In fact, as we will discuss, inhaling someone else's smoke (i.e. passive smoking) is also dangerous.

Why is smoking so dangerous? Ignoring for the moment all the non-malignant hazards of smoking, the fact is that the chemicals associated with tar, combined with the blood vessel-changing properties of nicotine, irritate cells to such an extent that deregulation of oncogene activity is a predictable outcome. If you sniff tobacco into your nose you can get cancer in your nose. If you chew tobacco or smoke a pipe, you are at great risk of developing cancer in your mouth. If you inhale it into your airways, the cells lining your bronchial tree are poisoned day in and day out. Hundreds and thousands of Jennifers find out about tar and oncogenes in the most devastating fashion each year.

Cigarette smoking causes bronchitis that may lead to destruction of lung tissue (emphysema). It promotes the development of stomach ulcers and clots in veins. The latter can break away from walls of veins and race to the lungs or brain, causing terrible damage.

The germ's eye view of our bronchiole tree. Using the electron microscope it is easy to see the complexity of these tubes which take air down into our lungs. *Below*: An even higher magnification view of a bronchus reveals the strands called cilia, which trap dust and other particles which we inhale. Note the T cells waiting in the airways to make an immune response to anything foreign or to infectious agents entering our respiratory tract.

Cigarettes promote the development of varicose veins, dangerously lower the birth weight of babies if mothers smoke during pregnancy and very markedly increase the risk of developing heart disease. Smokers, on average, have 30 per cent more sick days per year than do individuals who do not smoke. The combination of oral contraceptives and smoking increases the risk of a woman over thirty-five having a heart attack 39 times and the risk of having a stroke 22 times. Women who are heavy smokers run a much greater risk of developing cancer of the cervix. Smoking lowers fertility in both males and females.

In most Western countries, smoking is responsible for five times more deaths per year than traffic accidents. In the United States, where men can expect to live beyond seventy years of age, 40 per cent of smokers who use twenty-five or more cigarettes per day die before the age of forty-five. Habitual twenty-per-day smokers shorten their life span, on average, by at least five years; many reduce it much more than that.

If you like playing games with statistics you can calculate that the average smoker shortens his or her life by 5.5 minutes with each cigarette they smoke. Men below the age of forty-five who smoke fifteen cigarettes per day or more are nine times more likely to die of coronary heart disease than men of the same age who do not smoke.

The figures are overwhelming, the scientific facts indisputable. Yet the percentage of individuals who smoke, especially women, is increasing in most countries. Governments can be roundly criticised for their capitulation to the rich tobacco industry. All forms of cigarette advertising should be banned and warnings on packages should scream 'smoking kills'.

Physicians, educators, sociologists and psychologists have totally failed to develop strategies that will significantly reduce the incidence of young people taking up smoking. What twelve-year-old girl cares what her health will be like when she is forty? Perhaps the only hope for the near future is the increasingly common attitude among non-smokers that smoking is indeed an antisocial habit. Expense, bad breath, ash litter, etc. have never deterred smokers but if smoking is regarded by society as an antisocial, disgusting, foolish, non-macho weakness, then we may get somewhere.

The rapidly accumulating evidence that inhaling someone else's smoke (passive smoking) is dangerous may just turn the tide. Sociological change, not medical facts, influence societal smoking patterns. Restaurants, aircraft and the workplace are just some of the commonly encountered spaces in which those who do not care to smoke are affected by the smoke produced by others in the area.

Smoke is an interesting and dangerous substance. Watch a puff of smoke from some smoker's mouth and you will see that the smoke flows can be divided into mainstream and sidestream sections. The latter is likely to drift into your area and therefore be taken into your lungs. Because of its dispersion properties, sidestream smoke contains considerably more of the most dangerous chemicals than does mainstream smoke. For example, in sidestream smoke there is more carbon monoxide, tar and nicotine than is found in mainstream smoke. Three-quarters of the nicotine retained by filter tip cigarettes is released into the air in sidestream smoke. As a result the majority of non-smokers have nicotine detectable in their body fluids most of their lives. It has been calculated that an office worker sharing space with a smoker may inhale the equivalent of five cigarettes per day.

One can go on and on, and certainly the most polite and timid among us must deliver an emphatic 'yes' to the question, 'Do you mind if I smoke?' But we are talking about cancer and it is no exaggeration to say that lung cancer would be reduced by more than 95 per cent if people did not smoke. Not that lung cancer is the only malignancy associated with smoking, as we have seen.

Given the expense, the suffering and the death caused by smoking, we all have a responsibility to remain educated about this matter and to do our part in removing this definite cause of cancer and so many other ills.

Many other environmental factors interact with cells to trigger cancerous changes. Overcooked food can cause bowel cancer (Japanese communities in which only raw fish is consumed have no cancer of the intestinal tract); expatriate Japanese from such areas living in other sites where they eat cooked food have the same chance of getting cancer as do the locals. The hepatitis B virus can precipitate the development of cancer of the liver. The virus that causes glandular fever (infectious mononucleosis) can cause cancer in the throat and cancer in B lymphocytes. Hundreds of other examples could be given.

To summarise, cancer occurs when the process of orderly self-replication is disturbed. Oncogenes are activated either spontaneously (intrinsically) or by chemicals, viruses or other extrinsic factors. If these activated genes are not rapidly deactivated, cell division will continue in an uncontrolled fashion: a tumor will develop. This mass of cells will crush local normal tissue and the cells will break down walls of blood and lymphatic vessels. Cancer cells will then be transplanted (metastasised) to different parts of the body, there to continue their deadly expansion. Vital organs will be damaged and the patient will die.

At last, then, we come to the immunology of cancer. Let's set the scene. A cell has, for one reason or another, embarked upon a malignant course. Is the cell still self or is it foreign? This question has been challenging the scientific community for fifty years or more, as the answer is of utmost importance. If cancer cells are self, albeit dangerous, then there is no reason for lymphocytes to attack and destroy them. If they are in their malignant state, even slightly different from self, then they should be killed. Cancer could then be at least partially blamed on an inefficient immune system.

Fifty years ago scientists took tumors from animals and implanted them into other animals. The recipients' immune systems mounted a vicious attack and soon disposed of the unwanted tumor cells. The researchers claimed, not unreasonably, that cancer cells could be rejected by immune mechanisms and inferred that the donor's immune system was defective. The problem was that the animals rejected the cancer not because it was cancer, but because it was foreign tissue. Transplant rejection rather than cancer rejection was being observed.

While this situation was being sorted out, clinicians had no doubts about the matter. Patients who are immunosuppressed, either by disease or treatment, have a significantly increased risk of developing cancer. Nowhere is this more obvious than in patients who have undergone an organ transplantation. A patient harboring someone else's kidney needed that new kidney for survival; his immune system cannot be allowed to reject the donated tissue. When drugs are used to blunt our immune response to the organ transplanted, the incidence of cancer developing in the patient is increased. Obviously some homeostatic mechanism has been compromised.

From such observations came two related ideas. The first idea suggests that cancer cells must be developing fairly frequently in everyone's body, while the second suggests that the normal but potentially dangerous situation is controlled by competent lymphocytes that recognise a cell's malignant change and then destroy it. All day, every day, lymphocytes carry out 'immunological surveillance' to ensure the early detection of cancer. Today we know that this concept is true for some cancers but not for others. There is not an increased risk of developing all forms of cancers if you are immuno-suppressed. Constantly vigilant immunosurveillance mechanisms for a number of cancers, especially cancers within the immune system itself, are definitely of vital importance.

With the development of our ability to 'stage' an attack by the immune system on cancer cells in a test tube, we have been able to demonstrate that at least three distinct cell types within the immune system can kill tumor cells. A branch of the T cell family, 'cytotoxic' T cells, can attack tumor cells physically, grappling with their membranes and then destroying them. (See photographs in the colour section.)

A second group of cancer-killing cells are called natural killer cells. These are lymphocyte look-alikes, dependent on the availability of interferon to activate their chemical attack on tumor cells. Finally there are K cells, a lymphocyte-like cell (possibly derived from T cells) that can kill (hence the capital K) tumor cells coated with antibody to some component of the cancer cell wall. The antibody guides the K cell to the target.

To kill a cancer cell the cell, metaphorically speaking, has to stick its tongue out at the potential killer cells; there must be something on the surface of the cancer cell that declares its renegade state. In addition, you may remember, T cells at least can only attack when simultaneously they see 'self' in the form of histocompatibility antigens at the same time as they see foreignness. Thus we can only expect killing of cancer cells if they display 'tumor-specific antigens' and a self moiety *simultaneously* on their cell membranes.

A number of cancers do just this and they are killed. Day in, day out, we are ready to kill off new but cancerous cells before they can do any harm.

The problem is that, in certain tissues, tumors may arise that display precious few of these essential 'give away' markers. What's more, they may protect themselves in at least two ways. Firstly, they may hide those telltale cancer markers on their surface and, secondly, they may activate regulatory T cells in the environment around them to blunt the attack against themselves. Pretty clever, you will agree.

There is a familial component in all this cancer immunology. As with so much of biological performance, some of us are better at handling cancer than are others. This variable degree of proficiency may apply to cancer in general or perhaps just to cancer occurring in certain tissues.

Here is a case history to illustrate this. Margaret noted a small lump in her right breast when she was thirty-six years old. It was removed surgically and found to be a cancer. Caught early enough, all cancers that can be removed can be cured. While one can never be certain, however, that a few cells have not escaped, Margaret was still well five years later and so considered one of the lucky ones.

At forty-seven years of age, a routine smear from the mouth of her womb showed an early stage of cancer. Again the surgeon removed malignant tissue to save her. At fifty-one she was enjoying good health, as she had been since that operation. Recently, however, she had noticed some blood in her stool. Not visible blood, but blood that she could detect by using a chemically impregnated card that reacts to it.

Why was Margaret so compulsive in seeking blood in her stool?

Her mother had died at the age of fifty-two from cancer of the colon. Her two aunts had also died of cancer before their sixtieth birthdays. One had a tumor in the pancreas and the other cancer in her colon. Margaret's grandmother had died of cancer starting somewhere in her genital tract. Margaret's sister had breast cancer and had not been as lucky as Margaret; she was alive but the tumor was in her liver.

Cancers plague some families in a manner such as this and, while not particularly common, it occurs frequently enough for us to realise that genetically inherited influences can predispose generations to cancer. As blood in the stool is often a very early sign of cancer of the bowel, Margaret had been advised to check her stool in the way described. With the detection of the blood, a colonoscopy (an examination of the colon with a colonoscope, a flexible tube that features fibre optics to allow one to look around corners) was performed. An early cancer was found and removed by the instruments attached to the colonoscope. Margaret battles on.

There is evidence to suggest that the propensity to cancer development, shown by Margaret's family, may also be inherited by individuals rather than families.

We have already seen that the second time an antigen is encountered the stronger will be the body's immune response to that particular substance. Once sensitised, immunological memory supplies a much higher level of protection. If cells are taken from a tumor and put in a test tube, and then T cells are taken from the blood of a healthy person picked at random, not much happens immediately. The T cells are not sensitised to the cancer. They have never seen such tissue before.

But with certain tumors, if T cells are taken not from the proverbial man in the street' but from a healthy and close physical associate of the patient with cancer (not necessarily a family member), things may be quite different. The T cells of lovers, flatmates, family members living in the same house or other close associates often rapidly attack the tumor cells obtained from their close contact. One obviously tantalising explanation is worthy of much more research. Perhaps all these people with sensitised T cells have met and defeated the same cancer in their own bodies, or they have 'seen' and become immune to the cancer-triggering chemical or other cause that is now displayed on the surface of their friend's tumor cells. The available evidence strongly suggests that individual performance in the face of a malignant challenge varies. Some of us are far more resistant to cancer than are others.

Despite this, immunologists are not prepared to accept the theory that when cancers take hold and spread an *a priori* failure of the immune system is responsible. Dangerous cancers can occur in anyone and escape immunological attention because of the extremely poor display of cancer and self antigens on their surface. Besides, the immune response can be foiled by tricks that the tumor cells can generate.

The story of Jennifer's miraculous recovery is by no means unique, although such occurrences are unfortunately rare. When pathologists take some of the secondarily infected tumor tissue, as in Jennifer's case, they find that, in the furious immunological attack on the bacteria, innocent lung tissue and not-so-innocent tumor cells in the area of the struggle have been killed. The cancer cells are caught in the biological crossfire.

Because of these observations, my unit became involved in deliberate attempts to mimic the circumstances surrounding Jennifer's cure. Once a cancer in the lung had been localised with computer-assisted imaging, we injected some dead tubercle bacilli (the bacteria that when alive can cause tuberculosis) into the middle of the cancer. We had immunised the patients with this preparation two weeks earlier. A reaction occurred in the tissue with T cells pouring in, but the battle we had hoped for did not occur. In some way that we do not understand the tumor was able to manipulate the immune response in that area so that the T cells that came in were 'turn off' not 'turn on' cells. That is why Jennifer's story is so unusual. She could get killer cells into her tissues when the bacteria invaded. Most cancer patients cannot.

To summarise: our immune systems are capable of recognising cancer cells in many tissues much of the time. They do this constantly as malignant cells frequently occur in our bodies. Suppressing our immune system markedly increases our risk of getting cancer. Some people are better at handling cancer immunologically than are others. Some tumors are much harder to detect than are others; they could fool anyone's immune system. They may be very hard to kill as they either do not display telltale surface antigens needed to excite our cancer killing cells, or they hide their antigens or suppress the immune system. Cancer is a formidable foe.

The following sections present some interesting and useful facts about different types of cancer. After that, we will look at the treatment of cancer.

Breast cancer

Breast cancer will be diagnosed in more than 120 000 women in the United States in any one year. For women between their thirty-fifth and forth-fifth year, it will be the major cause of death. The incidence is highest in Caucasian women and lowest in women from the Indian tribes. The incidence is similar in most Western countries but lower in the East. Oriental women who move to the West assume the risks of other women living in that area. The causes of these differences are unknown.

The risk of dying of cancer of the breast becomes greater with each year lived, except for an unexplained plateau around fifty years of age. Women whose periods started early in life or ended after the age of fifty-five are at greater risk than women with a more typical menstrual history. Irregular periods are associated with an increased risk of cancer. If a woman has her first child after the age of thirty, her risk is three times that of a woman who has her first baby at eighteen years of age.

This form of cancer does tend to run in families. If a woman has a mother or a sister who develops breast cancer, she is three times more likely to develop it than if she did not have this familial incidence. The risk is heightened further if a woman had a sister who developed cancer before menopause.

Other factors that increase the risk are diets high in animal fats, obesity and radiation to the chest in the form of X-rays and from atomic bombs. There was a marked increase in breast cancer among Japanese women who survived Hiroshima.

Prevention is definitely the best approach to this form of cancer. Ninety per cent of women find their own cancer but too often their discovery is accidental. Regular, skilled self-examination is the proven best weapon. Women after their fortieth year who belong to a high-risk category should have X-rays of their breast (mammography) annually, as this is a reliable tool for most women and can now be done with extraordinarily low doses of radiation.

Many women with breast cancer have malignant cells with membranes on which are receptors for the female sex hormone, estrogen. This hormone, once bound to that receptor, stimulates the growth and spread of these highly malignant tumors. Drugs that block interaction of the hormone and the cancer cell are proving very worthwhile.

Technology has been developed to readily tell whether a patient's particular tumor cells are using sex hormones for growth or not. Anti-estrogen therapy can be given if the cells are dependent on this hormone and, if that fails, more drastic measures can follow such as the removal of ovaries in pre-menopausal women and of the little adrenal glands that sit on top of the kidney. The ovaries and the adrenal glands both produce sex hormones.

For small tumors diagnosed early, surgery or radiotherapy are recommended. For tumors that are spreading, more radical surgery may be needed together with radiotherapy, anti-hormone therapy and cancer-killing (but very toxic) drugs. With local tumors, survival rates five years after diagnosis may be expected to be between 40 and 80 per cent. Even with the best available treatment, a five-year survival rate of 10 per cent is all that could be expected for cancer that has spread beyond the breast.

Today, breast cancer is managed better than ever before but it is still a major health hazard for women (and also for 900 men per year in the United States). One can only end this section by urging every woman to be ever vigilant and thoroughly trained in the best methods of breast self-examination.

Lung cancer

For reasons we have mentioned earlier, no cancer is more distressing to discuss than lung cancer. The disease would all but disappear if people would *stop smoking*. In the United States, more than one hundred thousand men and fifty thousand women develop this malignancy each year. The incidence is rising dramatically in women, who are tending to smoke more at a time when men are smoking less. It is tragic that any graph showing the rising incidence of lung cancer and breast cancer in women demonstrates that the title of leading cancer killer of women will change in the next few years, with lung cancer becoming the most common form of fatal malignancy for women.

Death rates from lung cancer for both sexes are doubling every fifteen years. For men over the age of thirty-five, this scourge is the leading cause of death by cancer. Most cases occur between the age of fifty-five and sixty-five years, but thousands of 35 year olds die from lung cancer every year.

Perhaps the most sobering statistic for those few readers who will still smoke, having read the earlier parts of this chapter, should be this: at the time of diagnosis the disease is incurable in 70 per cent of cases. Survival of five years with this form of cancer is achieved by only 8 per cent of patients.

Lung cancer is, in reality, bronchial (airway) cancer and it starts when cancer-causing agents are inhaled into the airways. The cancer develops slowly but symptoms associated with this growth develop even more slowly. Sixteen per cent of patients are diagnosed as having lung cancer by a routine chest X-ray; the majority of other patients present themselves after coughing up some blood or because they have developed a nasty cough. As we have said, it is too late for a cure in 70 per cent of these cases.

Most patients with lung cancer are immunosuppressed by the disease and that, of course, facilitates its spread. We have excellent evidence that smoking, apart from stirring up oncogenes, disturbs the normal surveillance mechanisms found in the airways and for this reason smoking is a double hazard.

Apart from smoking, the only other numerically significant cause of lung cancer is asbestos. Inhalation of asbestos particles into the lungs can cause the disease in an alarming percentage of exposed individuals. We have no way of eliminating the indigestible and irritant fibres once inhaled. For this reason there is a massive effort in most countries to make sure that asbestos, used as a fire retardant in so many buildings, is completely covered. Unfortunately, many cities have ordinances that demand the removal of all asbestos from public buildings. The performance of this work is extremely hazardous and may cause many more problems than would occur if the asbestos was left alone and very good maintenance techniques were pursued to prevent its fibres leaking into the air.

Bowel cancer

Roland was fifty-six years old when his bowel habits changed. He had always had a tendency towards being constipated; now he was noting frequent days when his stools were, for him, surprisingly loose. He felt well and was not unduly distressed about the symptom. About two months after the onset of his changed bowel habit he put on a pair of pants and realised that he had lost a significant amount of weight; they looked decidedly baggy. He was puzzled. His appetite was good and he felt he was eating as much as ever. Still, he did not think the situation warranted a trip to his family doctor.

Three months later he was still losing weight and had some discomfort in the lower part of his belly; not serious, but nagging. It was the blood he passed one day with his stool that finally fired off alarm bells in his mind. His doctor could feel the cancer in his rectum with his finger, so low in the bowel had it developed.

To give him a fighting chance, his rectum was removed by a surgeon who simultaneously diverted his bowel away from his rectum, so that it could empty through an opening made in the skin of his abdomen (a colostomy), but all too late. The cancer had spread to his liver and he died within a few months.

Cancer of the large bowel and rectum is one of the commonest forms of the disease. In the United States 5 to 6 per cent of all men and women will develop this tumor. The incidence of this form of malignancy and the survival of patients after surgery has not improved in the last forty years. Newer approaches such as immunotherapy are promising and much needed.

The major and appropriate effort being made at this time concerns the identification of substances we eat that may cause cancer, foods that we could eat that might prevent cancer and ways of protecting the bowel from dangerous chemicals. Other urgent matters that need pursuing include ways of screening the entire population over fifty years of age for early cancer, and the identification, for closer scrutiny, of those individuals who have a higher than normal risk of developing cancer.

A most fascinating and potentially useful observation has been made by scientific studies of bowel cancer in Africa. Where fibre content in the diet is high and stool bulk accordingly large, there is a much lower rate of cancer than is found in areas where little fibre is consumed. The theory that has been generated (but awaits formal proof) suggests that fibre (wheat bran and fibre from citrus fruits are the best sources) increases the bulk of non-absorbable waste in the bowel which understandably wishes to get rid of it. Transit time through the bowel is therefore hastened. Potential cancer-causing chemicals that may have been ingested are not allowed to linger and communicate with oncogenes. There is also some evidence that some chemicals with the potential to cause cancer are actually bound to fibres and eliminated from the body with them.

Whilst on the matter of diet, there is no doubt that high fat diets (containing, particularly, saturated fat) increase the risk of colonic cancer. In Japan, cancer of the bowel was an extremely rare disease until they adopted the bad eating habits of the Western world. As their cholesterol shot up, so did their incidence of bowel cancer.

One of the more relevant and interesting observations of late concerns the geographic clustering of cases of bowel cancer in areas where the trace element selenium is lacking in the soil. It would be a wonderful break if adding selenium to our diet (just like adding fluoride to our water for teeth) prevented or minimised the incidence of bowel cancer.

If the entire population could be screened annually for cancer of the bowel the occurrence of the incurable form of the disease would all but disappear. Unfortunately this is not economically feasible, even in Western countries. Unlike lung cancer, this form of cancer grows slowly. Between the start of the cancer and the development of symptoms, and certainly before its spread, a period of two to five years elapses. If cancer is detected by a routine examination, i.e. before symptoms develop, 80 to 100 per cent of patients are cured by simple surgery. The question thus is, how do we screen populations for this problem?

First let us identify groups at highest risk. To start with, we must say that everyone over forty years of age is at risk (one in twenty-five will develop this form of cancer in the Western world). Those patients with inflammatory bowel disease such as ulcerative colitis have a higher risk. Strangely, women who have had breast cancer or genital cancer have a considerably higher risk of developing bowel cancer than women who have not had these problems. Patients with little protrusions from the bowel wall called polyps are at risk and should be watched carefully. People with this cancer in the family have a four times greater chance of getting the disease.

Having identified high risk groups, how do we screen them for cancer? The most promising technique for mass screening utilises hemoccult (hidden blood) cards. These cards are impregnated with a chemical substance exquisitely sensitive in detecting blood in stool even if it is present only in trace amounts. If every person were to regularly test his or her stool for the presence of microscopic amounts of blood, thousands of lives could be saved. Not that the test is foolproof by any means. Not all cancers bleed while they are curable. What is important, of course, is that the majority do. Patients must refrain from eating meat, chicken and fish for twenty-four hours before they test their stool and they are advised to eat a lot of roughage during the period before testing to make it more likely that an early cancerous lesion will be irritated and bleed.

Despite the problems associated with this test, at least 50 per cent of patients with positive tests have cancer, and 86 per cent of those people have curable disease, which indicates the importance of pushing on with research into this promising approach.

Apart from hemoccult cards, the detection of cancer requires an examination of the bowel itself. All in the high risk groups mentioned above may like to discuss with their doctors the usefulness of having an examination of the bowel with an X-ray and/ or sigmoidoscopy every two years or so.

Remember, bleeding, change in bowel habits (constipation or diarrhoea), lower-belly discomfort, nausea and vomiting, and weight loss are the symptoms of bowel cancer.

Cervical cancer

Issa Bella is a tall and once beautiful woman of the Pearl tribe of West Africa. She is twenty-four and works as a prostitute in St Louis, a pathetically poor but populous city on the coast of west Africa north of Dakar. To find clients, she mainly works the dance halls around the town, which are extremely popular night spots, as West Africans love to dance and do so extraordinarily well. One is particularly appreciative of their skills when one listens to the difficult rhythms they prefer. Issa Bella had been working since she was fifteen years old. West Africans age rapidly, but this chronologically young woman was ageing even more rapidly than is usual in this part of the world. She could even have passed for someone of forty years in the West.

Her remarkable French doctor introduced me to Issa Bella when I visited St Louis while working in Dakar. Marcel, the doctor in question, and his wife Lisette ran a blood bank and clinic for patients with sexually transmitted diseases. Marcel was alarmed at the amount of cancer involving the cervix that he was seeing in young African women, particularly the prostitutes. Here was Issa Bella at twenty-four years of age with a large malignant ulcer on her cervix. Marcel was convinced that cancer of the cervix was being caused by a virus that was presented to the genital tract during intercourse.

A few anatomical details are needed at this point. Around the entrance to the womb (uterus) is a small, very muscular passageway. This guardian of the inner sanctum is the cervix. It keeps things in the uterus that should be there (such as babies) and lets things out that should be let out (such as the menstrual flow). The cervix projects downwards into the vagina like pursed lips. As such it is very much in communication with anything that comes into the vault of the vagina. The cervix is lined by a delicate membrane of cells that often become malignant, giving rise to the condition known as cervical cancer.

Issa Bella, already in her tenth year as a prostitute at the age of twenty-four, took no precautions. She had suffered numerous and repeated sexually transmitted diseases. She was very poor despite being busy; prostitutes charge only between forty cents and one dollar in these small towns where the competition is fierce. She certainly could not afford to use the pill.

She had had two pregnancies; her first child miscarried, her second was born and welcomed into her family but died of malaria at the age of two. The period following the second pregnancy had been a rough one for Issa Bella. Her uterus became infected and the Fallopian tubes were seriously damaged, effectively sterilising her. Now at twenty-four she had a horrible cancer in her cervix. Marcel thought, correctly, that such a woman could be a valuable subject for a research project that would attempt to investigate the cause of cervical cancer.

For many years epidemiologists have been saying that the risk of developing cervical cancer is markedly increased in any woman who begins her sexual activity at a young age, and is directly related to the number of sexual partners experienced.

You may remember from the chapter on pregnancy that seminal fluid has properties that can suppress immune responses around the cervix. It is possible that seminal fluid could blunt such an attack by T cells trying to pick off cervical cells that have just become malignant. Certainly cancer in this region is practically unknown among women such as nuns, who lead sexually inactive lives.

However, the more likely explanation, and one that would encompass the risks associated with promiscuity, would emphasise that the more sexual partners a woman has the greater are her chances of being exposed to sexually transmitted viruses such as the herpes virus or, another that has been incriminated recently, the papilomavirus. Certainly the virus that causes genital herpes and is sweeping the world, the herpes simplex virus Type 2, is more commonly found in the cervix of women with cancer than in others.

This form of cancer is very prevalent in women of Latin America and Africa. It is more prevalent among the socio-economically deprived of the world and in women who have had multiple pregnancies. The two factors are often related, of course. One warning that is now acted upon comes from studies showing that female children, born to mothers given female sex hormones during pregnancy, have a much higher incidence of cancer of the cervix than normal when they become adults. Fortunately, studies have clearly demonstrated that cancer of the cervix is not related to the use of a contraceptive pill.

Serious consequences of this cancer can be avoided by its early detection. Regular (every second year) 'Pap' smears (named after Dr Papanicolou, who described the usefulness of this approach) in which a scraping of the cells from the cervix is examined microscopically to look for malignant changes will prevent incurable disease developing unnoticed. If the cancer does develop it will announce itself with small amounts of bleeding after intercourse, a discharge or heavier than usual monthly bleeding. The American Cancer Society looking at the cost–benefit ratio of Pap smears has recommended that women twenty years of age or older, but with no symptoms, and those under twenty if sexually active, should have a Pap smear annually for two consecutive years and at least one every three years until the age of sixty-five. Women at higher risk should have yearly smears.

Melanoma

Our skin is a truly marvellous organ. Not only, as was pointed out in the Alan Sherman song, does it 'keep your insides in', but it acts as a primary defence against infection. Unbroken skin allows inside only what it wishes to allow inside.

Unless you happen to have black skin, there is no doubt that you are foolish if you deliberately expose your precious skin to the rays of the sun. Skin, as opposed to its owners, hates sunlight. It shrivels and cracks, ages and protests, but still more and more people expose more and more skin to the sun. Dermatologists find tanning to be offensively ugly; how can people deliberately spoil something as perfect as unexposed skin?

The most serious consequence of exposing skin to sun is a particular form of skin cancer known as melanoma. Here under the carcinogenic influence of sunlight, pigment cells in the skin have oncogenes activated and a tumor that is arguably the most dangerous of all cancers is born. All the cells in the skin are rapid dividers even when healthy; skin cancers can multiply and spread very rapidly.

Harmless pigmented 'growths' on the skin are called moles, and many people have hundreds of these tumors scattered around their surface. The fact that we are used to seeing pigmented spots on our skin may make us fail to notice the arrival of the cancerous variety.

In the Western world, the incidence of deadly melanomas has doubled in the last ten years and shows no signs of slowing. If you are fair-skinned, have blue grey eyes and expose your skin to the sun in bursts (the weekends-only exposure at the beach habit), you are at most risk of developing a lesion.

This cancer responds very poorly to even the most potent anti-cancer drugs, and laughs off radiotherapy. Some melanomas can spread to every corner of the body and are then incurable; early recognition followed by surgical excision is the only worthwhile strategy. This should be easy, as the cancer is there for all who look with an informed eye to see. Melanoma is a medical emergency and removal as quickly as possible is essential.

This is a tumor that our immune system can recognise and spontaneous cures do occur, but all too infrequently. Horrible sight or not, we should all inspect all of our skin frequently to look for the following 'telltale' signs that should have us running to our doctor's office:

- Any pigmented spot on your skin that has either an irregular border or a lack of uniform color (that is, has more than one shade noticeable) must be removed. The important colors that are signs of malignant melanoma include shades of red, blue or *white*. Cancerous lesions can be uniformly colored and then they are usually bluish black, bluish grey or bluish red. These must be removed.
- Any pigmented spot that changes significantly and rapidly in size or color or bleeds must be removed.
- A spot that becomes itchy or painful must be removed.

Chances of surviving from melanoma can be assessed by examining the thickness of the cancerous tissue once it has been removed surgically.

Males and females who have a poor degree of tolerance to sunlight (that is, who develop sunburn after even short exposures to the sun and who tan poorly) have a very high chance of getting melanoma and should not take the risk. In the long run they will not enjoy the results of repeated sunning anyway.

More women than men get melanoma, but it spreads faster in men. Melanomas developing on the chest, back or abdomen tend to be worse than those developing on the arms or legs. Detected early, the cure rate for melanoma is 80 to 100 per cent. With any spread, however, only 10 per cent of patients will be alive five years from diagnosis. Immunotherapy, as we will see, may add significantly to our ability to obliterate this cancer.

The treatment of cancer

We live in an age when purveyors of alternative medicine advertise blatantly that they can cure cancer with everything from apricot pits to caffeine enemas. This is a particularly tragic form of fraud, as it preys upon the fears of those people with extensive cancer who cannot be helped by the currently accepted strategies of the medical profession. Medical science seems close to improving our ability to manage many forms of cancer, and it must be stressed that great strides have already been made with the conventional approaches to the treatment of cancer now to be described.

Surgery can be curative and therefore the best approach to tumors that are accessible to skilfully wielded scalpels is removal. If the cancer has not spread beyond the area excised surgically, then treatment of it can be expected to be 100 per cent successful. The best chance of a surgical cure occurs in those cancers that announce their presence early in their development. Skin, breast, stomach, bowel and uterine cancers are some of the tumors that can be cured by surgery if detected early enough. For this reason there is an understandable emphasis in preventative medicine, on regular checks for early symptoms and signs of malignancy. Even if surgery is not curative it is often best to remove the bulk of the tumor so that it will not interfere with a local and vital function by, for example, obstructing the bowel. After removal of the main mass of the tumor other 'mopping up' procedures can be used.

Sometimes the new machinery available for the delivery of radiotherapeutic beams can deliver sufficient radiation with such precision that this form of therapy can be curative and, indeed, may be the first line of therapy. Often, however, radiotherapy is used for palliation: slowing the growth of a tumor and reducing the pain associated with an infiltrating growth that is eroding sensitive nerves.

Radiation destroys cancerous (and normal) cells by damaging their chromosomes. As a result they lose their ability to divide. When they attempt to do so they become so genetically disorganised that they die. The more rapidly a mass of cells is trying to divide, the more sensitive will that mass be to the effects of radiation.

Major problems associated with radiotherapy include getting enough radiation to the tumor without damaging surrounding tissues and, even more importantly, protecting vital healthy tissues such as bone marrow, as even small amounts of irradiation could damage delicate young cells necessary for our survival. You will remember that the bone marrow is responsible for the production of red and white cells and the clot-promoting cells known as platelets.

The final conventional approach to the management of cancer

utilises chemotherapy. Here we administer drugs either by mouth or intravenously and wait for these toxic chemicals to be delivered via the bloodstream to the tumor. The advantage of this approach is that in most cases it should be possible to get the drug to every cancer cell in the body. The problem is that normal cells in all tissues will be exposed to the toxin as well as the cancer cells. Hence scientists have developed a collection of cellular poisons preferentially taken up by cancerous cells.

There are cells in our body that quite normally divide rapidly but, unlike cancer cells, do so in a controlled fashion. Normal or not, the drugs used to kill rapidly dividing cancer cells will penetrate these normal cells and kill them. The cells lining the intestinal tract and bladder, the cells in our bone marrow and the hair follicles are some of the most frequently affected normal cells. If you see children or adults attending a cancer clinic you cannot help but notice that many have lost their hair.

Chemotherapy can cure some forms of cancer, especially some forms of childhood leukemias, but most often chemotherapy produces a remission (freedom from symptoms) for variable lengths of time and in that way prolongs life. The art of the chemotherapist is to prolong life which has an acceptable quality. All chemotherapists long for the day when their skills will no longer be needed.

Today, as we have discussed in the chapter on transplantation, our ability to perform marrow transplants allows us to push chemotherapy further than ever before. If the patient's marrow is unavoidably damaged in poisoning the cancer cells, then rescue is available, if risky. Ultimately, however, chemotherapy is not the solution to the cancer problem. What is? Certainly immunomanipulation holds the most promise at this time, and it is this that we will now discuss.

We now believe that cancer is perceived by Nature to be a threat to the species when it occurs (as unfortunately it does all too often) in the very young. Cancer was designed by Nature to develop in the elderly. We wind down our immune activity in later life and the incidence of cancer soars; all very orderly. Before it is cancer time, however, our immune system can and does protect us in a number of ways.

While we know a good deal about cytotoxic T cells, K and NK cells (discussed earlier) we have recently become intrigued by the observation that most if not all T cells, no matter with what antigen they are preoccupied on a day-to-day basis, can be activated to attack malignant cells. It is as if measles-recognising cells, together with all their brothers, have a second instruction delivered to them in the thymus—to kill measles virus or whatever they have been taught to recognise, but in addition to help out by joining in the attack on any cancer cell they may see.

What do all these T cells see when looking at cancer cells? We do not know. Observation is ahead of explanation at this point but the observations are worth understanding.

Imagine this situation. A man has a melanoma found on his chest; the surgeon removes it but studies show that the tumor has already spread to the man's liver. Unless the cells there are killed, he is doomed. Would that we could concentrate hard, summon up T cells and despatch them to the liver to kill the melanoma cells! Our patient, unfortunately, shows no signs of doing anything immunological about his perilous situation.

If we take his all too complacent T cells out of his body and put them in an incubator with some interleukin 2 (the hormone-like agent that T inducer cells secrete to activate killer T cells), the cancer-recognising property of the lymphocyte may well become active. After a few days in the incubator, reinfusion of these cells may have immediate and dramatic effects. The stimulated cells race like silver bullets to cancer cells in the liver and kill them.

We do not know if this phenomenon, induced outside the body by interleukin 2, occurs naturally in healthy people and whether this stops them from getting cancer. Such may be the case, but the phenomenon described and so clinically useful could be a totally artificial one. In favor of the latter concept are observations that the administration of interleukin 2 to patients, in an attempt to make their cells kill cancer cells, is not successful as the doses needed to achieve this are too toxic. Of course, in the normally functioning body, very high doses of interleukin 2 may be effective and safely released only in those compartments where it is needed.

Thus it is that the observation, that T cells removed from the body and cultured with interleukin can kill tumors on reinfusion, has done two things. Firstly it has given us a potentially very valuable new tool to use against cancer. Research into the machinery needed for removing large numbers of T cells and safely culturing them for days and then returning them to a patient is well advanced and clinical trials well under way. Secondly, however, the observation requires us to look at normal subjects and see if the actuation of most T cells against malignant cells is a natural phenomenon. If it is, we need to know what signal the cancer cell, presumably unwittingly, gives to trigger such a response. Another extraordinary property of these interleukin 2–stimulated cancer-killing cells is that they do not need to see self antigens before they kill.

This is well past the theoretical stage. Patients with melanomas, bowel cancers and tumors of the kidney, for example, who have had cancer racing through their bodies have had it disappear after the reinfusion of their lymphocytes treated with interleukin 2. To date we can say that in *some* there has been a relapse with time, in others no tumor is visible eighteen months after the completion of therapy. The potential of this approach is encouraging.

Another area of equal if not greater excitement in the cancer immunotherapy world concerns the use of monoclonal antibodies to attack cancer cells. Let me explain in a not too fanciful story set five years hence.

Nancy looked at her chest X-ray as the immunosurgeon explained the situation to her.

'This white mass you can see here on the right side of your chest is cancer caused by your *pathetically* antisocial smoking habit,' he said. Nancy knew he was right, of course. No longer did nice people smoke, but she just couldn't help herself.

The surgeon continued, 'Look here, Nancy, the tumor has reached the stage where it has certainly spread around your body. Conventional surgery cannot cure you, but immunosurgery can.'

The surgeon skilfully removed Nancy's lung in much the same way as he would have done years before, but then the new technology took over. While an assistant closed up Nancy's chest, our surgeon left the operating suite and entered an adjacent laboratory. On a bench in this room was a cage containing eight mice; they would save Nancy's life.

Our immunosurgeon carefully cut some of the cancer tissue from the lung he had removed. He placed this cancerous material into a machine that disrupted the tissue into single cells, which were then washed in a special fluid that supplied them with nutrition. Our surgeon then drew up the cancer cells into a syringe, affixed a needle to its end and approached the cage of mice.

The mice got to work immediately, or at least their immune systems did. Lymphocytes raced into their skin to look at this obnoxious tissue newly placed there. Some cells looked at the cancerous cells and responded to the distinctive antigens they saw. B cells made antihuman antibodies and T cells geared up for an attack.

Other lymphocytes said 'Airway tissue' and responded to the distinguishing antigens that they had recognised. B cells made anti-airway antibodies and T cells geared up for an attack.

But other lymphocytes recognised not only human airway tissue but markers found only on cells developing in a malignant fashion. These markers were the product of oncogene activity and other genes that might have been activated. We know that no other cells in Nancy's body will have these markers; they may be Nancy and not totally foreign, but they are tumor-delineating. B cells made antihuman antibodies and T cells geared up for an attack.

Two weeks after her operation Nancy was all but recovered from her surgery but was still faced with the need to get rid of the cells not surgically extirpated. Two weeks after her operation, the mice had killed the tumor cells that had been removed. Now living in their spleens were B cells that had made and were still making antibodies to those differentiation antigens that distinguished Nancy's tumor cells.

The immunosurgeon returned at this stage and gently put the mice to sleep and removed their spleens. He put these organs in his tissue masher and single cells in the millions were harvested from the spleens of the mice. The cells were washed and placed in a test tube, which was carefully sealed. At the end of this exercise, the immunosurgeon rested and held the tube up to the light. Too small to see with the naked eye were the spleen cells now resting in the nourishing liquid. Somewhere in there were B cells that could make antibody to Nancy's tumor.

Even under the most favorable circumstances, B cells will live only for a few days in a laboratory. How, then, will our new breed of cancer doctor find among all the millions of cells present in the test tube the particular B cells that can make antibody to Nancy's tumor, and nothing else? Even if a researcher finds them, how can he or she separate them and keep them alive long enough to get such little cells to make enough antibody for harvesting and injection back into Nancy to kill her remaining cancer cells? Easy, and in a way poetic justice; it will be done, thanks to the abilities of malignant cells themselves. Cancer cells will allow these mouse antibodies to kill Nancy's cancer.

Remember, we discussed the fact that cancer cells are immortal; put them into a test tube and feed them and they will live forever. Mice, like humans, get cancer of their antibody-producing cells (plasma cells). This form of cancer is called myeloma. When malignant plasma cells are put in a test tube inside an incubator they live forever, not for four days, like the normal B cells. Plasma cells are factories that make antibodies—two thousand of them in every second. You will recall that individual plasma cells make only one antibody molecule; there is only one model produced by each of these factories. The antibody produced by *one* cell and its identical progeny (clones) is called a monoclonal antibody.

If you take a malignant cell and glue it with polyethylene glycol to a normal but shortlived B cell, the genetic information that has been activated within that B cell moves across into the plasma cell. On its arrival there it activates these immortalised factories, which begin to produce massive amounts of the antibody that the B cell was trying to make.

By taking the B cells from the spleens of the mice that had successfully killed Nancy's lung cancer cells and then gluing them to cancerous plasma cells, an immortalised 'hybridoma' is formed that will produce buckets (literally) of antibody to the antigen or antigens the B cells had recognised as cancer-specific.

B cells from the friendly mice are glued to plasma cells. Each new cell is put in a little fluid in a separate compartment and allowed to continue multiplying. After a few days the immunologist and a team of helpers sample a little of the antibody being produced to see if antibody from a particular fusion reacts with Nancy's cancer cells, samples of which were kept at the time of surgery.

Hundreds of antibody samples from the various hybridomas are tested. A clone is found producing antibodies that will react to the differentiation antigen or antigens on Nancy's lung cancer cells. The cells producing this precious antibody are isolated and the rest discarded. Soon a large volume of fluid containing pure antibody is produced; that is, monoclonal antibody to something only displayed within Nancy's body on her cancer cells. When injected into Nancy, the antibodies will bind to these malignant cells and nothing else.

Now, if that were all, it would be a great story—but our immuno-surgeon can do better than that. He knows that antibodies are specific but cannot kill cancer cells very well. They can find tumors better than anything else, but they cannot kill as well as can some other agents. Our immunosurgeon smiles as he prepares a poisonous antibody cocktail for Nancy's cancer.

Remember the tragic story of the ruthless terrorist who wished to dispose of a certain jumbo jet full of innocents? He gave his loving girlfriend a briefcase filled with explosives instead of the money he had promised her, instructing her to get on a specific plane. He then sat back and waited for his foul act to kill all the passengers, including his fiancee. All he required of her was that she should get on the correct plane; the explosives would do the rest.

Nancy's immunosurgeon had similar ideas and abilities to those of the terrorist just described. He called in his chemists, who took the monoclonal antibodies that had been prepared against Nancy's tumor cells. Antibodies consist of long chains of amino acids with binding specificity at one end. To the other end the chemists attached firmly, chemically, three killers.

The first to be locked on to the antibody was the toxin Ricin. This is the most powerful poison known; once it binds to a cell, that cell will die. (It has been a famous poison ever since a KGB agent used it to kill a Bulgarian diplomat. The sharpened tip of an umbrella was dipped in Ricin and the unsuspecting fellow was jabbed in a crowd. He collapsed and died within seconds.) Besides the Ricin, the immunosurgeon asked the chemists to couple some Chlorambucil, a highly poisonous anti-cancer drug, to the antibody. As well, some radioactive iodine was added. This isotope can be made so that it irradiates lethally but only for a very short distance of one to two cells.

Now the monoclonal antibody was ready to work. Here was an

antibody that could recognise with exquisite accuracy Nancy's cancer cells, and *only* those cells. The antibody would deliver the three 'assassins' right to the target. No other cells would be victims; no cancer cells could hide.

Nancy was brought in and the mouse antibody, loaded with the cancer-killing agents, was injected into her veins. The treatment was repeated on consecutive days and, apart from a few shivers and chills, there were no side effects. The cancer cells died and Nancy was cured. To be super-cautious, the plasma cells making the precious antibody were allowed to live. Should the cancer return, these same antibodies could be used again.

Fanciful story? Only a little. Monoclonal antibodies to differentiation antigens of human melanoma, breast, colon, ovary and lung cells have been made and used in humans. They have been tagged with chemicals and isotopes. Monoclonal antibodies labelled in this way have cured animals of cancer. We are only just beginning to develop our clinical expertise with humans. Nevertheless, it is quite accurate to say that the immunotherapy of cancer is now a reality.

It is certain that the treatment of cancer will be revolutionised. Perhaps our immune systems are at fault when cancers develop; perhaps they are not. In either case it seems certain that our immune systems are only too willing to help us win this most important battle for a body very much at war.

7

Dealing with
AIDS

I T is 1969. A ten-year-old black child walks across the rolling hills of the fertile plains near his village in the Mengo district of Uganda. Even the most casual observer can see that this boy is ill, wasted with the peculiar large belly of the severely malnourished. Very large lymph nodes have deformed his neck. He is limping. On his left foot is a reddish-brown nodule that is ulcerated and bleeding quite severely. It is obviously very painful. Other nodules of a similar nature, perhaps twenty in all, are on his body, although these are not ulcerated.

His mother has taken him to the tribal herbalist, who has tried a few different medicines. None have worked. The child's health is deteriorating and more purplish nodules have appeared on his skin. The tribal doctor is an experienced man and although he has never displayed to his charges the slightest doubt about his omnipotence, he knows his limitations. He has seen many similar cases recently and thinks that this child will probably not survive the summer. He informs the parents of the inherent wickedness of this child (which explains his inability to help) and tries to find a more suitable case for his talents.

The child, of course, is not wicked; rather, he is the victim of a terrible new disease spreading ever more rapidly across tropical Africa. He has been infected with a lethal virus that can destroy his immune system. Eighteen months earlier, he was given a blood transfusion after becoming very ill from a vicious attack of malaria. Many red blood cells were destroyed after his infection with this parasite and a severe anemia developed.

How could the tribal doctor know that the blood given to the child was donated by a man himself destined to die from the ravages of a virus circulating within the cells of his bloodstream? The ten-year-old child we are discussing has subsequently had his immune system destroyed by this same virus. As a result, he has become an easy victim for a particularly nasty form of a 'cancer-like' illness known to us in the Western world as Kaposi's sarcoma (KS) and visible in the skin of the boy as the purplish nodules mentioned. (See photograph in colour section.) In 1872 Dr M. Kaposi, a Hungarian specialist in skin diseases, wrote a paper that told a horrible story. He described in detail a young man who developed reddish-brown nodules, initially on his feet, which spread to his hands and then, ever more rapidly, over all his body. Kaposi commented on the peculiar sponge-like feel of these nodules and the fact that with time, as he stood by helplessly, the nodules, especially those on the patient's face, changed color, becoming bluish-red. His patient developed a hectic fever, lost weight and, as his strength failed, suffered bloody diarrhoea. He died coughing, drowning from blood-filled lungs. Kaposi organised an autopsy and as the internal organs of the dead man were exposed, the same reddish-blue nodules that peppered his skin were found to have proliferated in his liver, lymph nodes, lungs and many other sites. All Kaposi could do was report the strange facts to his colleagues.

For nearly eighty years of this century, Western physicians interested in cancer saw enough KS to come to one firm conclusion. The most aggressive and lethal form of this rare disease occurred in patients who were immunosuppressed; that is, a weakening of the immune system seemed to predispose them to the development of this disease.

Thus KS was noted to occur in some patients who had had a kidney transplant. Such patients must be given drugs to poison their T cells so that they cannot reject their new kidney. The administration of these drugs must balance the risk of rejection against the risk of overwhelming infection. Infections are all too common when the balance is not quite right and, in this setting, a patient may develop KS or indeed a number of different cancers. Stopping the immunosuppressing drugs in such circumstances has sometimes been associated with recovery of the immune system, which is then capable of rejecting the KS.

In the United States in 1981, only two cases of KS were reported for every 10 000 cases of cancer. While KS remained rare in the Western world, however, the aggressive form of this disease had become much more common in parts of Africa. Indeed, in the fifteen years prior to 1981 there was a tenfold increase in the incidence of this disease in many countries of Africa.

KS was appearing among the black population, with very few cases being reported in the Indian or white populations of countries such as Uganda. In its epidemic form, KS mainly attacked the young, most victims being under twenty years of age. We now know that during the early 1970s the disease was prevalent in Tanzania, Zaire and Angola and cut a path across the tropical girth of Africa.

Some doctors and missionaries asked why such a rare disease usually associated with severe immunosuppression (at least in the Western world) was occurring so frequently in Africa. No one could answer the question; few people were really interested. At the time no one dreamed that the strange epidemic being reported was the start of the scourge now known as AIDS. Indeed, AIDS was discovered in the United States and only after much detective work was its origin traced back to tropical Africa.

At the Center for Disease Control (CDC) in Atlanta, Georgia, epidemiologists (medical detectives) and other specialists monitor, by means of reports coming to them from hospitals and doctors all over the country, the infections that trouble the population of the United States in any given week. In April of 1981 scientists at the CDC noted two strange reports, one from New York and one from Los Angeles. From each city cases were reported of homosexual men who had developed severe pneumonia caused by the organism known as *pneumocystis carinii.*

Pneumocystis carinii is a strange organism. It is neither a virus nor a bacterium but it belongs to a group of microbes known collectively as protozoans. We have already discussed some members of this family, such as the organisms which cause malaria and African sleeping sickness and also a disease commonly suffered by humans who live in close contact with domestic cats. *Pneumocystis carinii* is not one of the more powerful members of this family. It poses no threat to the individual with a normal immune system, whose T cells readily destroy this agent. It frequently takes advantage of immunosuppressed states, however, and then it can cause severe, even fatal, infection of the lungs. The organisms can often be found deep in the trachea or windpipe of normal humans, as if in taking up residence there they are hoping for an immunological disaster that may allow them to swoop down into the lungs where they may grow into tiny cysts (hence the name). The lungs of people infected by these organisms develop a severe pneumonia.

Within two months the CDC had heard of many more cases, all occurring in gay men. A number of these gay men had not only this peculiar form of pneumonia but also Kaposi's sarcoma. The CDC now believes that the first two cases of AIDS occurred in 1978 and 1979 in the New York City area. Both cases involved gay men, who both developed Kaposi's sarcoma. Very rapidly physicians began to ask why two serious consequences of immunosuppression should be visited upon gay men.

The young men who were being reported as desperately ill with KS and severe pneumonia had previously been reasonably well, with no known serious diseases. For lack of specific knowledge, it was said that they had Acquired an Immune Deficiency Syndrome (a syndrome is a collection of symptoms and signs that suggest an identifiable illness). Thus the term AIDS was born.

AIDS and the nature of things

Recorded history documents clearly enough that the human race has several times been devastated by plagues. Catastrophic infections killing thousands to millions tend to occur every so often in the microbiological scheme of things. To have an epidemic, i.e. an infection sweeping through an apparently defenceless population, one of two conditions is necessary. The responsible organism must be a new arrival in a particular area or have so changed its characteristics that it can no longer be recognised for what it was. Under these circumstances there would be no reservoir of resistance in a given population, no 'herd' memory. If an army marching into town meets well-organised pockets of resistance in the form of freedom fighters who have previously encountered the invaders and know a thing or two about their methods of attack, the predators will at least be slowed down and weakened. If no resistance is forthcoming however, a relieved army may become wilder, more reckless and evermore savage as it sweeps down on defenceless citizens.

No species, as we discussed in an earlier chapter, is locked into a design that will ensure its demise. Gene rearrangements can occur as a cell divides, and any new arrangement which allows an organism to flourish will soon become a prominent feature of those members of the family that survive.

Now, we humans carry out, on average, great genetic experiments two or three times during our lifetime and, to produce a new genetic prototype, we need a partner. The experiments of course produce our children and on some days we are certain that the world is a better place for our efforts while on other days some doubts creep in. Micro-organisms, however, reproduce very rapidly, perhaps dividing thousands of times in a very short period. The chance that some of the millions of variations on a theme (mutants) so produced will confer a survival advantage is high. While other members of the family die, these mutants survive. Most of us know how rapidly bacteria can become resistant to a given antibiotic. Bacteria that were rapidly killed by penicillin in the 1950s are now not troubled by the drug. They have actually developed a gene product that neutralises penicillin.

Seen in this context, i.e. in the natural order of such developments, the AIDS epidemic is nothing more than the latest in a neverending series of 'plagues'. However, while we wonder what developments will occur to trouble us in the centuries ahead, we are in the midst of a life-and-death struggle with what is arguably the most dangerous virus yet to evolve—the Human Immunodeficiency Virus (HIV), now known to be responsible for the AIDS epidemic.

HIV is a member of a particularly nasty family of viruses, known collectively as retroviruses. Until fifteen years ago, we thought the members of the family troubled animals but not humans. Veterinary scientists knew that these viruses could cause severe brain damage to horses and sheep, produce leukemia and damage the immune system in cats, and produce cancer in other animals.

Retroviruses are RNA viruses, that is they have their genetic programs written in this language rather than the DNA used by the creatures they wish to invade. This is a significant problem for retroviruses. Like all such micro-organisms, they are an incomplete life form and not having a cellular structure of their own, they cannot reproduce unless they take up occupancy within a living cell. Here they must insert their genetic program ('How to make more of me') into the computer (nucleus) that houses the genetic programs of the parasitised cell.

We talked in an earlier chapter about the nucleus inside a human cell. Here is collected, in one geographically distinct organised entity, all the genetic programs needed to make an individual a unique person. More than 400 000 genetic programs, each capable of directing the production of something—a hormone, a tissue, a protein, etc.—are clustered along the forty-six chromosomes present.

You can compare the nucleus in a cell to a computer. Stacked next to this computer are 400 000 hard disks, each of which contains a biological program, but only a restricted number are playing simultaneously in a given cell. Let's use this computer analogy to explain how HIV has become so dangerous, as we look at the properties of the virus responsible for AIDS.

Retroviruses and T cells

You may remember my earlier anecdote about a Californian car service centre that featured a large sign which read, 'Virus is a word used by doctors to mean your guess is as good as mine'. It is of course true that of all the micro-organisms that cause disease in humans, viruses have been the most difficult to defeat. Antibiotics are useless against viruses, and you are all too well aware that medical science cannot even cure the common cold.

When RNA retroviruses enter a cell, they need to insert their genetic (computer) program into the cell's computer; but, continuing the computer analogy, their program is written in the equivalent of *Apple-talk* while the cell can only read *IBM-compatible* material. In other words, the viral program and the computer are incompatible. The only solution for the virus is to rewrite its genetic program into a format understandable by an IBM machine.

In biological terms, this means that the viral RNA must be translated into DNA once the virus is inside a human cell. Retroviruses have 'learnt' from many millennia of experimentation how to do just that. They carry along with them a chemical (enzyme) known as *reverse transcriptase*, capable of translating RNA into DNA. The 'retro' in the name (*retro*—to turn around) is derived from this capability.

In the last fifteen years, it has become obvious that members of the retrovirus family do indeed cause a number of serious diseases in humans. T cells in humans can sometimes be embroiled in that serious malignancy called leukemia. The latter term is applied to cancer developing within any of the white blood cells which normally circulate in the bloodstream. One highly malignant and therefore serious form of the disease is one which develops following the infection of T cells with a retrovirus known as the Human T cell Lymphotropic Virus type 1 (HTLV 1). This virus can so upset the regulation of growth in T cells that they multiply out of control. The same virus can also infect cells of the nervous system, particularly in people living in the tropics for reasons that are unclear but are probably related to genetic factors. The virus can then produce a serious form of paralysis. A slightly different version of the retrovirus HTLV 1 known as HTLV 2 may also be associated with the production of a cancer in B cells. It is interesting that in animals retroviruses can cause destruction of the immune system, or cancer, or destruction of nervous tissue. Enter on to centre stage the human immuno-deficiency virus (HIV), which can do all three. HIV is indeed a special foe, a virus among viruses, a fascinating but frightening addition to the disease-producing capability of retroviruses. Just what makes it so special?

Now, lend me your imagination for a while and join me in a fancy in which we pretend we are retroviruses trying to come up with strategies that would enable us to invade human cells and reproduce ourselves efficiently, while evading the ever-vigilant immune system. Well, for starters, we know that we have to get into a cell and carry out the RNA-to-DNA trick and have the invaded cell turn into a factory producing more of us. We know that human T cells are going to recognise that an invasion is under way. To prevent this from happening one solution would be to kill the person infected within a few days, before their T cells can get organised and attack effectively. But if this strategy was used, how would the virus escape being buried with its victim? No, a strategy is needed which will allow us to find a way of moving into a new host before the original host dies, and that takes time.

How about this for a solution—invade T cells themselves? After all, attack is the best form of defence. Make them reproduce the invading virus, then kill them. As they die, move out of the now useless T cell into an as yet uninfected T cell and repeat the whole process. Eventually, the person infected will not have sufficient T cells left to reject anything. By doing all this slowly, the infected and infectious individual will have plenty of time to pass the virus on to someone else, thus immortalising this strain of the retrovirus family. Well, that is exactly the solution developed by HIV, with a few more tricks thrown in for good measure, as we shall see.

HIV and the immune system

From our earlier discussions, you will be familiar with the concept of an 'alarm-sounding' or inducer T lymphocyte, one of the four distinctive members of the T cell family produced by the thymus gland. These cells express on their surface membrane a 'cluster of differentiation' protein known as CD4. If we find this particular marker on a T cell, we have a fairly good idea of what its function must be.

The vast majority of such cells are involved in the business of initiating a specific immune response to antigen. Now, you will appreciate that at the level of the CD4 lymphocyte, we have all our immunological eggs in one basket. If CD4 cells (T4 cells) do not recognise foreignness and stimulate the release of cytokines, those cells capable of removing invaders from our body remain on the sidelines, undoubtedly frustrated. As we have discussed previously, they require a permissive signal from CD4 cells in the form of interleukin 2 (IL2), and no doubt from many other cytokines, before they can attack. Pivotal to understanding the effects of HIV on the immune system is the realisation that immune function will be crippled if CD4 cells are destroyed.

HIV consists of a central core containing the RNA needed to reproduce itself and the enzyme needed for translating that RNA into DNA—reverse transcriptase. Surrounding the core, however, is an envelope or coat that is the design masterpiece responsible for making this virus so dangerous. The coat is composed of a lipid which fits snugly around the core but is characterised by a series of projections that thrust out from the coat like the spikes on an old medieval hammer. The projections are composed of sugar and protein, a combination referred to as a glycoprotein (gp). Remarkable as it may seem, it is a fact that these projections actually allow HIV to attack CD4 bearing lymphocytes (and a few other cells that sometimes carry CD on their surface).

For millions of years, the CD4 protein has been present on the surface of those T cells charged with firing off an immune response. Part of the molecule is buried in the cell's coat (membrane) while the remainder projects into the space around the cell. The CD4 molecule is functionally important, as it helps to lock an antigen-presenting cell to the T cell as it displays the suspect that it has captured in its purpose-built groove.

HIV has developed projections which are exquisitely accurate mirror images of some sections of the CD4 molecule. Imagine that a CD4 cell has on its surface the most intricate lock you can envisage. The virus has produced and projected from its surface a 'key' that fits into that lock. Thus it is that when HIV bumps into the surface membrane of a CD4 cell, an intricate interlocking occurs that will lead to the death of the cell after it has served the virus's purpose.

It all reminds one of that terrifying piece of micro-nature where the female praying mantis needs the male to copulate with her so that she can reproduce, but has worked out a way of feeding at the same time. Before the sex act is completed she bites off the head of her mate, actually severing nerves that block some inhibitory signals, and in this macabre way actually improves his sexual performance as he dies.

HIV is a praying mantis, in that it will embrace and parasitise a CD4 cell, force it to assist in the reproduction of the virus and then kill the cell. However, we are getting ahead of ourselves.

The projections from the surface envelope of HIV have a head and a tail. The head is a huge convoluted structure covered in sugar and has a molecular weight of 120 000 daltons (for the non-chemists out there, that's big!). The tail, which is buried in the coat of the virus, is smaller with a molecular weight of 41 000 daltons. For convenience, the two portions of the molecule are referred to as gp120 and gp41.

Nature tends to conserve useful molecules and use them over and over again in different situations. Thus, gp41 is not unique to HIV and in fact is found near the outer membrane of a number of viruses. It is so useful because it has the ability to fuse the outer membrane of a virus to the membrane of the cell it wishes to invade.

Imagine a group of a dozen children holding hands and dancing

Figure 13. The binding and fusing of **HIV** to **CD4** CELLS

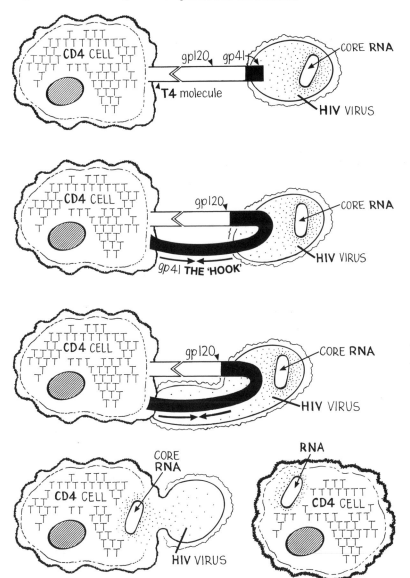

round in a circle. Four more children approach and they too are dancing around, holding each other's hands to make a second smaller circle. In the middle of this smaller circle is a fifth person, not attached to anyone. If this little circle approaches the big circle and two children break into the bigger circle by seizing the hands of big circle children, the two circles will fuse and the fifth person will suddenly find himself in the middle of a now much larger circle. This is how the all-important core of HIV (the fifth person) gets into a CD4 cell. HIV's key to the CD4 cell, gp120, binds to CD4 and then the gp41 molecule joins the two structures together. (Figure 13.)

Once inside the cell, the virus uses its reverse transcriptase to translate its genetic information into DNA. The most efficient anti-retroviral agent being used to help patients today is Azidothymidine (AZT). One of the major actions of AZT is to interfere with the efficiency with which the RNA to DNA translation can take place. By slowing this process down, it is more difficult for HIV to force the invaded T cell to make more virus.

Once a T cell is invaded by HIV, the speed of what happens next is variable. The virus may not do anything for some time or it may proceed to insert its now viral DNA into the T cell's own DNA inside the cell's nucleus. If the virus does insert new genetic information and activate the genes so inserted, then the cell's function will be altered. Eventually, the virus will cause the T cell to become a factory making more HIV, and individual building blocks needed to create a copy of HIV are created in different parts of the cell. AZT and the other related anti-retroviral agents that we have available also interfere with the successful linking together of the individual building blocks needed to make new HIV.

Gradually, the invaded T cell will fill up with new viral particles and these begin the process of leaving the T cell. A burrowing-like process commences, in which the new viral cores will push their way through the wall of the T cell, picking up some of the structures of the T cell membrane to make a new coat for themselves. This entire process in which a virus makes a new coat for itself as it pushes through the wall of a T cell is referred to as 'budding'. In this way thousands of new viral particles will be released ready to attack and invade T cells not already infected. The T cell releasing all this new virus will die during the process. This process is illustrated in the colour section in the middle of the book and Figure 14 illustrates the whole process using our computer analogy.

For every one HIV virion (viral unit) that enters a T cell, as many as a thousand identical copies may be made. Now you can appreciate the unique threat posed by HIV. It can attack the only cells in the body capable of activating defence mechanisms needed to eradicate the virus, and kill such cells after forcing them to make copies of itself.

Now, despite the lethal manoeuvres described above, it is clear that such mechanisms are not responsible for the death of the more than 400 billion T cells circulating in our bodies. Indeed, relatively few cells containing virus can ever be found. Using standard technology, we can find on average only one CD4 cell actually carrying HIV in every 1000–8000. Newer technology, which is able to amplify any viral genetic material that might be in a cell, does show trace amounts in perhaps as many as 1 in 20 CD4 cells, but it is certainly obvious that the extraordinary efficiency with which HIV is able to initiate mechanisms that destroy all CD4 cells involves more than the mechanisms we have described to date.

When a parasitised CD4 cell is making copies of HIV, an excessive amount of gp120 and gp41 is produced, a bit like an automobile factory getting a little disorganised and producing six headlights for every car. The result of this munificence is the appearance of gp120 on the surface of HIV-infected T cells. Now the cell has not only CD4 poking its head out into the environment but gp120 as well, and that's bad news for any non-infected CD4 cell which passes by. Such a cell coming in contact with the membrane of an infected T cell is likely to have its CD4 molecule and the gp120 on the surface of the infected cell fuse, and thus the spider has trapped another victim in its web. The gp41 associated with the gp120 fuses the two cells together. Now we have a non-infected cell that's been forced to become one with an infected cell. Indeed, this process can go on and on and sometimes we see one infected T cell trapping 500 non-infected T cells by this method alone. (Figure 15; first method.) This of course improves markedly the ability of HIV to kill CD4 cells but there's more to the story than even that.

Our immune system does object to the presence of HIV in our bodies and reacts. We make antibodies to various parts of the virus and functioning CD4 and inducer T cells order killer T cells (T8 or more correctly CD8 cells) to attack gp120 and gp41. Unfortunately, the critical portion of gp120 needed to bind to CD4 T cells is so cleverly hidden by sugars that we don't attack this binding site effectively with either antibodies or killer lymphocytes. We do, however, attack other portions of the viral envelope.

When an infected T cell is ordered to make gp120 and gp41, not only does excessive production lead to a display of these molecules on the surface of an infected cell, but such cells actually secrete these characters into the environment, where they float dangerously in this body fluid or that. Again, use your imagination to consider the events that occur when a passing healthy CD4 cell encounters circulating gp120. The latter will bind to the healthy

Figure 14. The invasion of lymphocytes by **HIV**; replication in and destruction of **CD4**

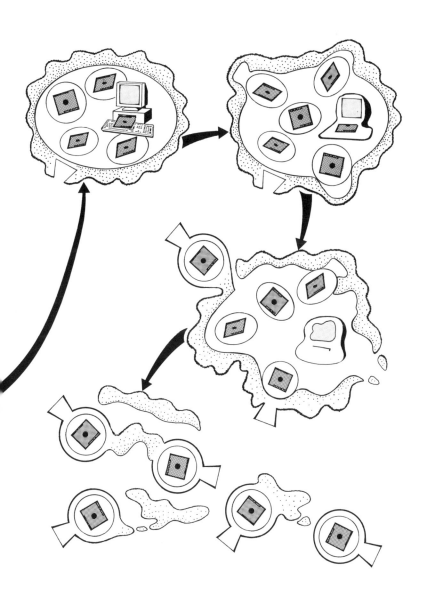

Figure 15. Two indirect methods used by **HIV** to kill **CD4** CELLS

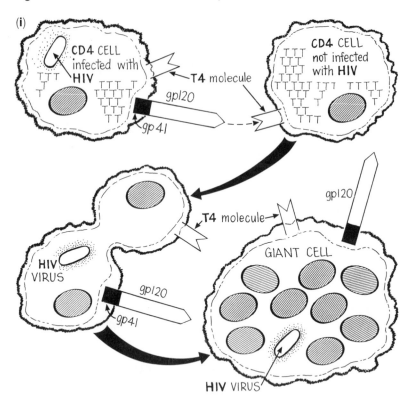

CD4 cell, thus making it a target for killer cells hunting around for infected T cells. The killer cells looking for gp120 will not be able to distinguish an infected from an uninfected T cell, and thus will kill uninfected CD4 cells displaying a harmless piece of the virus on their surface. (Figure 15; second method.)

At least one other mechanism may be of great importance. The human immunodeficiency virus may not have learnt to place gp120 on its surface just to bind to the CD4 molecule on T cells. Some of the protein structures of gp120 may mimic histocompatibility antigens (HLA antigens), particularly D-locus antigens. This will make it all the easier for T cells to attack cells binding gp120. You may need to refresh your memory at this stage with a flashback to our chapter on the organisation of defence.

You can now appreciate that HIV has developed many structural features which ensure that the immune system of any human host

(ii) Normal **CD4 (T4)** CELL destroyed by antibodies, **NK** or **T8** CELLS because it bound secreted gp120

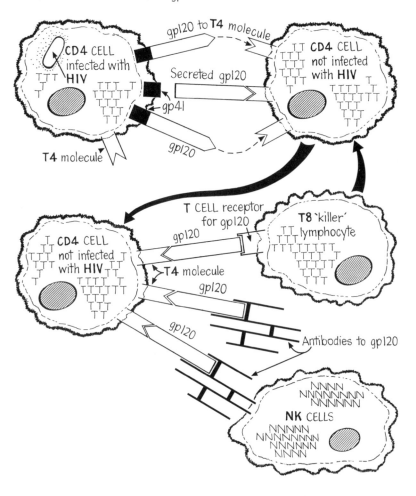

will ultimately be destroyed. The various mechanisms involved are best understood by linking the text to the diagrams supplied in Figure 15.

It is quite likely that other mechanisms yet to be discovered also help HIV to directly or indirectly destroy our CD4 cells. Because of the huge number of cells involved the destruction takes time and indeed we now know that, on average, it takes 9.2 years of infection with HIV to totally cripple our immune system. Before we look at the consequences of that dreadful development and then quite rightly spend much time talking about avoiding infection, let's reflect for a moment on the biological facts presented above. To begin with, we are obviously dealing with a deadly virus with a unique ability to destroy the human immune system. There is no doubt that it will be no easy task to develop a cure and it certainly won't happen in this century. Similarly, it does not look as though we will have a vaccine available to prevent infection for many years, although I am confident that such a vaccine will be developed eventually. The inescapable conclusion from studying the biology of HIV is that, at this stage, the importance of a worldwide effort to stop individuals infecting each other with this virus cannot be overestimated.

The development of AIDS

Quite a few departments within the human body feature a little spare capacity. We can live quite successfully with one lung or one kidney and even half a liver. Perhaps in a few million years, we might develop a second heart which would be a useful improvement on the old model. We have, in our youth, an abundance of T cells and thus the destruction of quite a few of these cells may produce no visible harm. But as with any army of any size that is constantly having its numbers depleted, there must come a point in time, a threshold, where trouble develops. Now, once there are simply too few T cells left to protect us, not only from HIV but many other infectious agents as well, we refer to an infected individual as having Acquired an Immune Deficiency State (Syndrome)—AIDS. Currently, a review of those known to be infected ten years ago suggests that over that period 67 per cent of infected individuals develop AIDS. While that's an extremely grim statistic, it also means that 33 per cent of people do not and much research is under way to try to understand better the resistance shown by this minority.

It has been surprisingly difficult to educate the media and the public about the difference between being infected with HIV and developing AIDS. As you can now appreciate, AIDS can be thought of as the ultimate consequence of losing one's long drawn out battle with HIV.

Staging the infection

We divide the struggle against HIV into four categories. About three to four weeks after infection, a flu-like illness may develop. This is often quite definite but hardly remarkable. Occasionally, shooting pains in the legs, for example, suggest that something out of the ordinary is happening but it all lasts for too short a period of time to provoke much action. What is happening in this Category I stage of the disease?

After infection, the virus has a few weeks to have its way with us before we marshal any sort of adequate defence. The virus invades T cells and multiplies rapidly. In the bloodstream you can find whole virus and portions of the virus, particularly an excessively produced protein from the core of the virus known as gp24. About three weeks after infection, we produce our first antibodies to the virus (sero-conversion) and our T cells swing into action releasing interleukins and the like. The virus dives for cover, hides and slows down its reproduction. At this time the chemicals produced by the immune system, in response to infection with the virus, produce the flu-like illness.

As things become more peaceful those infected, who are now of course infectious, may be totally unaware of the drama going on in their body and the danger they pose to others. This long period of good health enjoyed by infected individuals makes HIV particularly dangerous, as there is plenty of time for one person to infect many others. We refer to the asymptomatic phase of the illness as Category II infection and characteristically it lasts for six to seven years after infection.

Behind the scenes there is a lot of immunological activity going on to slow down the multiplication of HIV and the damage it can cause to our immune system. Our appreciation of this fact in the last few years represents a most important breakthrough. Until recently we thought that HIV 'went to sleep' (latency) for a few years after infection, before awakening, becoming aggressive and killing T cells at an ever-accelerating rate. The virus does possess genes which when activated tell it to either multiply or rest; however, that is only part of the story, and probably a minor part at that.

We now know that antibodies and killer T cells (or CD8 cells) attack the virus when they find it. Of course, this can lead to some of the innocent bystander damage we discussed earlier but the virus is definitely kept in check. Of particular interest has been the discovery that some CD8 cells release a soluble factor that interferes with the ability of HIV to multiply. At this writing, the factor has not been characterised but it is not one of the chemicals known to be released from T cells.

These discoveries have stimulated research into the discovery of a vaccine to give to people already infected with the virus, in order to strengthen their initially successful immune response which at least in part is responsible for them maintaining good health for so long. The converse is of course of vital importance—what goes wrong and what happens to allow HIV to escape from these protective mechanisms?

While a leopard may not be able to change its spots, HIV certainly can. The proteins associated with the envelope (products of the virus's genes) constantly change. Remember that a given T cell, out to destroy the virus, can only recognise a small portion of the envelope. After recognition, cells with that capability multiply (immunological memory). Thus, as the years go by in which the virus constantly attempts to escape such T cell surveillance, only those viral 'variations on a theme' that do *not* lead to the virus being killed will survive. Increasingly, the viruses remaining in the body of an infected individual are those that have so changed their structure that they are no longer recognised by T cells. Now the killing of T cells becomes more efficient than the killing of virus. Infected individuals become more infectious and the virus they transmit to someone else is a particularly nasty one. This is why individuals infected by someone close to developing AIDS may themselves develop AIDS well short of the average nine to ten years.

For all of the above reasons, biologists have been carefully studying all the variants of the coat of the virus they can isolate in an attempt to find a constant backbone—i.e. protein arrangements that are always present. There is currently much excitement in this area, for in a vital part of the envelope, known as the V3 loop, the mutations are restricted. Six variations cover approximately 85 per cent of the isolates. (Figure 16.) During natural infection our T cells are not much interested in the V3 loop, but if a vaccine containing these proteins enhanced T cell aggression against this conserved region then our protection would be much improved. For HIV, an intact V3 loop is essential if it is to infect CD4 cells.

Within a year or so of becoming infected with HIV, many individuals develop swollen lymph nodes (glands), those strategically placed battle-stations we discussed earlier. This is where our immune system prefers to fight its battles. Recent evidence suggests that CD4 cells are dying quite rapidly within lymph nodes while the circulating pool of such cells remains stable. This means that we should, if possible, intervene before the blood CD4 count starts to fall significantly. In the 60 per cent of patients whose nodes become enlarged, frantic activity is taking place. Here virus is concentrated and T cells are crowded together. The passage of virus from one cell to another is facilitated. However, here also we have our best chance to kill infected cells.

HIV does not infect B lymphocytes but does stimulate them to turn into plasma cells and produce antibodies. You will remember that this normally happens when B cells have recognised something foreign that is bound to their surface. Here, however, HIV makes B cells secrete antibodies even though there has been no entry into the body of the foreign proteins that could be attacked by these

Figure 16. **HIV** changes the structure of its envelope (coat) to confuse attacking **T8** CELLS

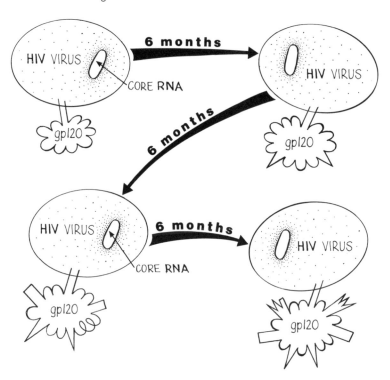

antibodies. It's busy work, unproductive and potentially harmful. Many patients, as their T cells are destroyed by HIV and therefore T cell control wanes, have B cells that actually produce antibodies to their own tissues (autoantibodies). These may produce auto-immune diseases with antibody-mediated destruction of platelets—those little cells in the peripheral bloodstream that make our blood clot—being the most common of such phenomena. Sometimes, the unbridled stimulation of B cells may cause them to become malignant (a B cell lymphoma).

Careful studies have not indicated that HIV-infected individuals with swollen lymph nodes (lymphadenopathy) have a prognosis in any way different from that of individuals whose nodes do not enlarge. Often the glands can be so big that they produce much discomfort and, for a number of my patients, I've had to call for help from surgical colleagues to remove apple-size glands so that, for example, the arm can rest comfortably by a patient's side.

Individuals who have swollen lymph nodes are said to have Category III HIV infection.

With the progression of the disease into Category IV the drama really starts. In this stage of the infection, symptoms and signs develop as a result of either an upsurge in viral activity, not experienced in such a degree of intensity since the first weeks of the infection, or the demise of immune function to that point where organisms, many of which are never harmful to immunocompetent individuals, start to have a field day, infecting and spreading while meeting little or no resistance. Let me give you some real-life examples.

Gary was gay, a musician (and a good one at that), and earned a handsome living playing the guitar with many a band. Gary was also a fighter. When I first met him five years ago we came to the conclusion that he had been infected some three years before his diagnosis, made when he decided that he could live with uncertainty no longer. He was anguished but not surprised at his positive test result, for he had had a number of casual sexual encounters with men while working in Los Angeles for a year three years earlier.

At the time of this diagnosis, there was little evidence of any damage to Gary's immune system. Normally, there are somewhere between 700 and 1000 CD4 cells in each microlitre of blood (a mere drop). Gary's count was 680. I was pleased to note also that his CD8 count was comfortingly elevated at 1900 cells for every microlitre of blood (normal value is less than 500 per microlitre). As we saw above, T8 cells are our major defence against HIV and the number circulating in the blood is elevated in the first few years of infection. Gary had swollen lymph glands but looked and felt well. He told me how determined he was to fight this infection, indeed he was a great believer in mind over matter. We discussed the fact that the evidence does support a better prognosis for those with a positive attitude, for reasons probably related to mechanisms that you will find discussed in detail in the final chapter of this book. I asked him to stop smoking marijuana and tobacco, and he agreed. Tobacco is known to decrease airway defence mechanisms and irritate the T cells there, making it more likely that HIV will multiply in such cells. He ate well and exercised regularly, and the few friends with whom he shared his problem were supportive. Two years ago, although no symptoms had developed, his CD4 count had fallen to 500 which, while not a drastic fall, was worrying enough for us to start therapy with AZT. He tolerated the drug well, experiencing nothing more than a little extra fatigue at night.

Eight years after his infection he came to see me, and all was not well. Despite a good appetite and good food, Gary had lost 6 kg in six months. He felt more lethargic than usual and had one more telltale symptom. Once or twice a week he would wake up in a drenching sweat. So profuse was his perspiring that he would be forced to shower and change his pyjamas. Gary's CD4 cells had fallen to 220 per microlitre, his CD8 cells to 700 per microlitre. It was clear that his particular HIV was escaping from his immune system, multiplying and killing cells which, as they died, released numerous chemicals and produced Gary's symptoms. The condition he was experiencing is commonly referred to as AIDS Related Complex, or ARC. Gary's HIV had experimented and produced a series of mutants able to resist AZT and escape from his CD8 cells. He was rapidly approaching that point when he might develop AIDS. Fortunately, a new drug, Didanosine (ddI), which works in a manner similar to AZT, has antiviral effects against mutants resistant to AZT. Gary's symptoms have settled down on the new drug and again he feels well, but his T cells slowly but surely continue to fall. When last measured, his CD4 count was 150. I have started him on a sulphur-containing drug as prophylaxis against a pneumonia caused by a parasite that very frequently develops at this stage of the disease.

HIV and the nervous system

Ken knows exactly when he became infected with HIV. It was almost three years to the day before he came to see me. Ken is bisexual, married, and has two teenage children whom he adores. Three years before I met him, Ken, who had not had sex with a man for eight years, went to a business convention. A few drinks, a long way from home, and Ken was vulnerable. A night with a stranger followed, during which he had receptive anal intercourse. He returned home terrified, feeling guilty and convinced he had been infected with HIV. He was correct. Three months later, a positive blood test confirmed his worst suspicions. He told his wife the truth; she was tested and was fortunately negative and remains wonderfully supportive. After the initial shock, she told Ken that they would fight the infection together. There was, and is, much love in this relationship.

   Ken is an air traffic controller and indeed has been a senior lineman for eighteen years. He is full of all the tales these professionals tell. Too many planes, new equipment introduced too slowly, accidents avoided only because of the diligence and intelligence of the controllers working under great strain. Ken came to see me because he was worried that his performance at work was deteriorating. Just a subtle business, nothing dramatic but enough to convince him that his judgment was less reliable, his reaction time just a little slower than was normal. No comments from co-workers, just a matter of self-criticism.

We discussed the possibilities. Ken had adjusted well to the uncertainty associated with being infected with HIV but it was certainly a constant source of worry. Perhaps tension and a less than perfect sleep pattern were to blame if Ken's assessment of his performance was accurate and not overly self-critical. But there was another possibility. HIV does cause damage to the brain.

Retroviruses cause disease either by affecting the immune system, producing cancer, or attacking the nervous system. With the development of HIV, all these nasty properties have been rolled up into one particularly dangerous virus. Within two weeks of infection with HIV, it can be found in the central nervous system. It is not transported there by CD4 cells, as we once thought, but rather by those other white cells described earlier—macrophages. A few of these cells do in fact have CD4 receptors on their surface and are thus vulnerable to infection with HIV, but a few that do not have any CD4 receptors on their surface still get infected. Obviously, there is a yet undiscovered second way some cells can be invaded by HIV. There is much that we still need to learn about what happens next. We do know that some strains of HIV are more toxic to the brain than others. We know that HIV in macro phages doesn't rest, as is often the case in T cells, but multiplies slowly and constantly. We also know that chemicals from infected macrophages in the brain can damage certain cells of the nervous system. The results can be subtle or blatant, and independent of any demise of CD4 T cell function.

Often it is the higher nervous system functions that suffer first. Concentration, judgment and appropriateness of behavior under stress may change slightly but significantly and often the only person to be aware of these early changes will be the infected individual. Sometimes, the speed at which the brain is destroyed and a presenile atrophy develops is quite frightening.

Don came under my care in hospital because he had developed a mild pneumonia. He had AIDS but on admission was intellectually sparking. Don was a computer man. He brought with him his own PC, printer and modem. Soon he was hooked into this information source and that and each morning, on our ward rounds, he would show us his latest printout—some new piece of information about AIDS that he had discovered in libraries that lend via satellite. Six weeks later, his lungs were fine but Don was demented. He could not recognise his own mother or form a coherent sentence. His computer screen remained blank beside his bed. A CAT scan of his brain showed that 40 per cent of this man's nervous system had vanished. Don died because his brain died, not his immune system.

Now, Ken, our air traffic controller, had such a responsible position and was himself so responsive to the demands of professional ethics

A CAT scan of the brain of a patient with AIDS shows an overall wasting of the brain tissue, and the presence of two large white spots of infection with toxoplasmagondii.

that objective testing of his brain's 'higher centre' function was required. Fortunately, many psychologists have become interested in measuring, in a scientific and reproducible fashion, how well those vital but subtle functions of the brain are performing. Concentration, the speed and appropriateness of decision making, mental performance under stress, etc. are subjected to neuropsychometric analysis. In looking at Ken's neurological function in terms of day-to-day living and his capacity to perform normally in a way that would be required in most professions, no defects could be detected. But the testing did reveal mild but definite slowing of his ability to rapidly make critical decisions, and his critical faculties tired under concentrated pressure: the sort of thing he would be subjected to during a normal shift sitting atop a control tower responsible for the life of thousands of approaching and departing passengers. Together, we explained the situation to his employer. He should not work in the tower but he could teach, administer, plan, and generally be useful in a number of ways because of his long experience. There was no reason why he should be made to stop work altogether. Currently, we are fighting the decision of his employer to force Ken to take medical retirement, and to deny him the benefits his contract had specified. Three years ago a qualifying clause was added to the entitlement regulations. Benefits would not be available to those who were forced to retire because of infection with HIV. We'll see.

The type of nervous system destruction described above is not related to any immunodeficiency state: HIV itself does the damage. For one and a half million people at this writing, however, so much damage has been done to their precious CD4 cells that they have indeed an Acquired Immune Deficiency State, or AIDS. As the total number of CD4 cells falls below 200 per microlitre, the army is so weakened that many organisms that once would have had no hope of being able to produce disease in a human—because of the ease with which they would be despatched by the immune system— find themselves able to be successful and to take the extraordinary opportunity presented to them. No vigorous defence force is unleashed as they march right in and cause serious tissue damage.

Rose lives in a beautiful small coastal town one hundred and ninety-five kilometres south of Sydney. Eight years ago she had a minor heart attack. Subsequently, dye was flushed through her coronary arteries so that X-ray images could tell her cardiologists just how diseased were those vital arteries required to supply her heart's muscle with oxygen. Three of the major vessels were seriously blocked; a second, perhaps fatal, heart attack was imminent. Surgery was performed, with a vein in her chest (that was dispensable) providing the new vessels, which were grafted around the blockages in her coronary arteries. A new lease of life followed and, a year after the surgery, she felt better than she had in years. Her rejuvenation lasted for six years, when the now 62-year-old grandmother developed a series of vague complaints that a doctor had trouble treating. She complained of lethargy, the occurrence of night sweats and a change in her skin, which seemed to be more oily and subject to itchy rashes and even pimples she hadn't experienced since her teenage years. When he examined her, all her doctor could detect were some swollen lymph glands. Tuberculosis crossed his mind but his tests revealed nothing unusual.

Six months ago, Rose started to lose weight despite a good diet and normal appetite, and night sweats continued to trouble her. Again her doctor was puzzled and told her that she probably had some irritable bowel syndrome and asked a local gastroenterologist to see her. This doctor found no evidence of malabsorption and asked her to return in a few months time for a further assessment.

A month before she would be sent to our hospital for investigation, Rose developed a dry, hacking cough and some breathlessness. Her puzzled doctor ordered a chest X-ray and, as usual with Rose, all was normal. He gave her cough medicine to no avail. A week later, he visited her at home and she was now quite definitely ill. She was breathless and had a fever. Into the local hospital she went and this time her chest X-ray showed definite changes at the bottom part of both her lungs—some form of localised pneumonia. Her doctor, relieved at last to have something to treat, gave her penicillin but her condition deteriorated. A local respiratory specialist was summoned. He was puzzled and on taking a careful history, discovered that Rose had a pet parrot at home. Could an allergic rather than an infectious process be damaging her lungs, he wondered. Bird droppings are known to sensitise some individuals and cause severe inflammation in the lungs. Rose was sent to Sydney for bronchoalveolar lavage, a procedure where saline is introduced into the bronchial tubes to wash out any inflammatory cells present. An analysis of such cells often provides a diagnosis, and so it did in this case.

One hour after receiving specimens washed from Rose's lungs, the laboratory called the ward to say that the fluid was filled with organisms known as *pneumocystis carinii*—little opportunistic parasites that cause just this type of damage in patients who have developed AIDS. Soon HIV antibody tests confirmed the diagnosis and T cell values of 100 per microlitre told the tale of HIV-induced damage. Subsequently, it was discovered that during Rose's cardiac surgery she had lost sufficient blood to require a transfusion and received HIV-infected blood. At that stage, the blood supply could not be screened to avoid such a tragedy occurring. Fortunately, with appropriate therapy, steroids and oxygen, Rose recovered 70 per cent of her normal lung function and at this time is well, as is not unusual for a year or so after a first attack of *pneumocystis carinii* pneumonia. She has handled the shock involved with courage and dignity and knows what lies ahead.

I am telling you this rather long story in order to make a few points. *Pneumocystis carinii* pneumonia is the most frequent first presentation of AIDS and the organism usually announces its presence with nothing more than the production of a dry cough. Treated early, it is almost always easily controlled. As T cell values are often above 100 per microlitre there is still some immune function surviving, and it is not unknown to have an 'AIDS honeymoon' when nothing more of consequence will happen for a year or two after the pneumonia has been adequately treated and AZT introduced. Of course, patients are followed very carefully and remain on anti-pneumocystis therapy.

Rose's story illustrates a number of other points however. Firstly, this case highlights the advantages of early diagnosis of HIV infection. AZT and prophylaxis for *pneumocystis carinii* pneumonia can add years of quality life to a person infected with HIV. Secondly, we can see all too clearly the diagnostic problems associated with a pocketed epidemic. Some doctors treat hundreds of patients infected with HIV, but most treat none and will have trouble recognising their first case. Thirdly, there is the question of 'look-back' programs. All over the developed world, patients receiving blood and blood products were at risk of HIV infection from about 1978 to May 1985 or later, depending on when the blood banking services of individual countries started screening their collected blood for antibodies to HIV. In many European countries, North America, Australia and elsewhere, there had been no particular need to maintain careful records linking specific donors to specific recipients of blood. Hence, when it first became evident that individuals were developing AIDS as a result of a contaminated blood transfusion, it was frustrating to be unable to locate the donor of the blood and find out who else may have received blood from the same source. These days, when one gives blood to a transfusion service, it is not uncommon for three recipients to benefit from some of that one donation. Later in the epidemic, better records were kept and recipients and donors could be traced. However, there are still individuals out there who are infected, don't know they are infected, and not only need help themselves but need to be found so that sexual partners are spared.

Preliminary data from our own studies suggest that post-menopausal women are more easily infected during vaginal inter-course than pre-menopausal women; and we have five cases in Sydney where older men, infected in a manner similar to Rose, that is during open heart surgery, have subsequently infected their spouses despite having intercourse on only a handful of occasions.

There is no doubt that in affluent countries that can afford the luxury, all patients who received a blood transfusion between 1978 and the time when local blood banks started testing for HIV should have an HIV test. The vast majority of individuals tested will be negative, but even though time is running out and many are pre-senting as did Rose, we still believe that, in many countries, hun-dreds of infected individuals are yet to be found.

As T cells fall down to 50 CD4 cells per microlitre, any number of other problems tend to occur and although we are more skilled at managing many of these complications than we were when I started seeing patients with this disease in 1982, much suffering is involved. People live longer in Western countries, provided that there is a National Health Scheme to support the expensive medi-cines patients with AIDS require (approximately $20 000 per year in direct drug costs for each year a patient has AIDS), or that they have insurance or other means of financing that therapy. In countries such as the United States where there is no National Health Scheme, poor black and Hispanic individuals infected with HIV struggle to find adequate care.

The origins of HIV

So dramatic and consistent are the effects of HIV on the human body that it is inconceivable that physicians in earlier centuries who recorded in minute detail exactly what they saw, even if they understood little or nothing about the mechanisms responsible, would have failed to describe AIDS if it had been a common problem in their communities. Indeed, we have every reason to believe that the human immunodeficiency virus in its present form is a new arrival on the scene, perhaps infecting humans for no more than the last thirty to forty years. The first infections with HIV appear to have occurred in southern-central Africa, with perhaps the first recorded case being detected by the examination of serum stored for hepatitis B research in 1959. Uganda, Tanzania and Rwanda appear to be the countries most likely to have seen the initial phase of the human epidemic.

Now, while HIV in its current manifestation may be new, it, like all viruses, has a lineage and examination of this lineage has proved to be particularly interesting.

Take the latest model Buick manufactured by General Motors. I'm sure that there are features about the automobile that would allow the manufacturers to claim that this model is unique. Never before has there been a Buick with features A, B and C. However, if you are a car aficianado and have been following the history of Buick engineering for many a decade you will be able to point out the lineage involved. Sure, they've added A, B and C, but you can see that 90 per cent of the chassis and body of the car have been retained from a previous model.

The same is true with viruses. HIV has unique characteristics that make it the dangerous fellow that it is. The closest known relatives to the virus on earth are retroviruses that infect monkeys. These are known as simian immunodeficiency viruses (or SIV), for some monkeys infected with SIV go on to develop an AIDS-like illness. Of interest, many monkeys infected with SIV do not get rid of the virus but do not get sick. It's tempting to speculate that such monkeys are the survivors from a population of animals that were infected with SIV many a generation ago. Only those animals which for one reason or another were able to resist SIV may have survived.

There are two forms of HIV that infect humans—HIV I and HIV II. The exact lineage of HIV I is unknown. It causes over 80 per cent of the infections that lead to AIDS on this planet and is similar to the simian immunodeficiency virus that can be found in green monkeys in Uganda and Rwanda. But it is not similar enough to be regarded as an immediate predecessor. Thus there is a gap in our knowledge of the lineage of HIV I.

HIV II, however, is very closely related to a simian immunodeficiency virus that infects monkeys in west Africa, particularly in Sènègal and Côte D'Ivoir. Here the lineage is much closer and it is likely that in some way, as yet unknown, HIV II evolved from SIV II, the monkey virus we are discussing. HIV II is not quite as dangerous as HIV I. It may take up to fifteen years after infection with HIV II before AIDS develops, and the transmission from mothers to babies of this virus is less efficient than is the case with HIV I. It is particularly common in rural areas of west Africa. Since we have already found two varieties of HIV it would not be surprising if in the future we find more variations on a theme.

Now we could speculate at length on how an SIV could become HIV but our speculations would remain just that, for we do not have a satisfactory answer to the riddle at this time.

We know that animal viruses do not usually trouble humans and vice versa. As we saw when discussing parasites, all invasive microorganisms have a favourite host and, within that host, a favourite site at which they prefer to take up residence. Dogs do not get measles and humans do not get distemper (although both animals get something very similar). It is entirely possible, but by no means established, that extraordinary circumstances in Africa may have seen animal retroviruses present in the body of young immunosuppressed Africans, who could not eliminate it with the ease with which an animal virus would normally be destroyed by a healthy immune system.

If the virus started its march through humans in Uganda the dreadful deprivations of the Idi Amin regime, coupled with chronic disease, would have facilitated its passage. Indeed, malnutrition and malaria seem very important co-factors and may well have contributed to a less than hostile environment for the animal virus. Thus it may have been allowed to mutate into a form that produces a lethal problem for humans. We know that viruses can gain strength from a sojourn through individuals with low resistance, becoming wilder and more dangerous as they do so. Certainly, some HIV prototypes developed new strengths that allowed them to infect even healthy humans.

How could animal viruses get into humans in the first place? Clearly, ingestion of animal tissues, especially brain and blood, that had not been adequately cooked could have been responsible. Monkeys are eaten in central Africa and frequently their blood is drunk for medicinal purposes. Humans bitten by monkeys carrying SIV could have become infected with that virus with the changes described above following on.

The only animal that can be infected with HIV besides humans is the chimpanzee. It is perhaps of great significance that two such animals killed by hunters in Africa had their blood tested and were found to be infected with HIV. Chimps do not get sick when infected with HIV, but it is at least possible that the virus was present in some chimps in a form that did *them* no harm but caused all sorts of problems for humans once the virus passed from chimps into humans, perhaps in a manner similar to that described above for other infection of humans by monkey tissues.

HIV II is on the move. It spread from Africa to Portugal and then marched up into Europe. It has reached as far as Germany at this writing and sporadic cases have occurred in the United States, Australia and other countries because of the common migration patterns of individuals from western Africa. Most Western countries now test their blood supply for both HIV I and HIV II.

The spread of HIV

The human immunodeficiency virus developed in Africa and stayed there for perhaps twenty to thirty years before turning up almost simultaneously in the Caribbean basin and in Belgium and France. How it got to the Caribbean and why it settled most obviously in Haiti is unknown. Speculations abound, ranging from the transport of the virus by Castro's troops returning from Angola to the idea that poor migrant workers from Africa took the disease to Haiti when they travelled that great distance seeking work in the sugar plantations of that country. We are more certain about the way in which the virus was transported to Europe. Visitors (mainly students) and others attempting to work in countries that had formerly had a colonial interest in Africa took the virus to Belgium and France, and infected local men and women as a result of sexual activity.

From the time the AIDS virus arrived in Haiti, probably early in 1978, the events leading to the establishment of the epidemic in the Western world are far clearer. To understand this, we now need to turn our attention to the way in which HIV can be transferred from one body to another.

We have already discussed the fact that HIV can indirectly and perhaps even directly damage cells within the central nervous system. Infected brain cells, however, will not be passed from one individual to another under any circumstance so that the infection of the brain is irrelevant to the AIDS epidemic. The crucial factor in the spread of HIV is the ability of the virus to infect T4 lymphocytes. Where are there T4 lymphocytes in the body of one person that could possibly find themselves transported to the body of another?

You will be familiar, from the earlier chapters, with the circulation of T4 cells in our bloodstream. The circulation of blood provides a major mechanism for the transportation of T lymphocytes from point A to point B. Thus if blood containing T4 cells that contained HIV were to pass from one person's body to another, infection with HIV could occur.

T4 cells are normally present in the sexual secretions of both men and women. I suppose that, after a few million years of trying to protect the human body from this infection and that, T cells realise that in their patrolling they should certainly pop into the genital regions on a regular basis. Throughout recorded history the careless sexual activity of men and women has facilitated the transmission of infectious agents during sexual intercourse, and these invading micro-organisms need to be attacked by T cells. Whatever the reasons, one finds significant numbers of T4 cells in the seminal fluid of perfectly healthy men and the vaginal secretions of women. If anyone has had a previous sexually transmitted disease that caused a lot of inflammation in their genital region, then it is likely that more T cells than normal will be present. In such situations, sexual secretions could be more dangerous than usual if they are contaminated with HIV. It is estimated that there are 625 million sexually active people on the planet, so the exchange of sexual secretions between bodies is a very common event.

Besides sexual secretions and blood, the only biological fluid that contains significant numbers of T cells in a situation where they could be transferred from one body to another is breast milk. Tragically, young babies being breastfed by mothers who are infected with HIV, particularly if that infection is a recent one, are likely to become infected, presumably because their immature digestive system is not able to inactivate the virus before it becomes absorbed into their bodies where it may then jump into their T cells.

To summarise then, HIV infection results when infected blood, infected sexual secretions or infected breast milk moves from one body to another. There are no other known circumstances associated with infection. With these facts in mind, we can return to our discussion of the spread of the HIV around the world.

It seems quite definite that in the late 1970s many gay Americans visiting Haiti, which had become a favourite vacation resort for homosexual men from many parts of the world, became infected with HIV when they bought sexual favours from the economically deprived local men, who may have been selling themselves for money. Certainly, Americans infected in this fashion transported the virus back to the gay communities of Manhattan and San Fransisco and then in an ever-accelerating fashion to gay communities around the world. Indeed, as we mentioned earlier, although AIDS had been spreading in Africa for more than thirty years before the events we are now describing, the disease burst into the Western world's attention as a result of the infection of homosexual American men. To understand the speed with which the infection spread and the magnitude of the epidemic that resulted, one must clearly note two very significant developments, one biological and one social, which coincided, indeed collided, and created a recipe for disaster.

The biological event was the evolution of a deadly virus transmitted mainly during sexual activity. The sociological event was the 'gay revolution' occurring in major cities such as New York and San Francisco and indeed many others around the world. This revolution led to a new sexual lifestyle that could not have been better designed to disseminate the virus.

While we need to explore these concepts in detail, let us recapitulate at this stage. A virus that could damage the immune system emerged among poor, malnourished and diseased Africans in the late 1960s and early 1970s. The virus was present in considerable quantities in blood and sexual secretions. It was confined to Africa for some time but then burst forth almost simultaneously into Europe and Haiti. From Haiti, it was transferred by sexual activity to visiting gay Americans. They transported HIV back to the liberated sexual atmosphere of San Francisco and New York, and the Western epidemic began.

Obviously, this new and devastating disease occurring in gay men in America made it imperative to examine homosexuality as a co-factor in the dissemination of the disease. If the AIDS virus had continued to spread through the world's gay communities at the same rate that was occurring in the late 1970s and early 1980s, the already horrendous death toll (more than 420 000 gay men have died of AIDS at this moment) would have increased steadily with many more hundreds of thousands of deaths occurring. For this reason, scientists had to draw aside the veil of privacy that usually surrounds people's sexual habits and place the intimate behaviour of gay men under the microscope, in the hope that they might learn more and more about the way that the AIDS virus is spread. Prevention strategies require this knowledge. I should point out the obvious—that when the first cases were discovered, we had no idea of the nature of the infectious agent causing the problem.

It is an undeniable fact that, even leaving AIDS aside, health hazards are visited upon many in our society (both homosexual and heterosexual) who, in seeking pleasure, involve themselves in activity that places them at risk of picking up serious infections while damaging their immune systems. Careless sexual activity and the ingestion of drugs which can alter immune function are obvious examples of what I mean. While the AIDS epidemic has now led most gay men to change their lifestyle, and they are both educated on and terrified of the disease, there is no doubt that their activities, flourishing in the late 1970s and early 1980s, represented a real hazard. Let me state immediately, however, that much of what follows applies equally to careless heterosexual activity.

Seminal fluids can carry infections such as the hepatitis B virus, the cytomegalovirus that causes a mono-like illness or worse, bacteria such as those that cause gonorrhoea and chlamydia, the little spiro-chaete that causes syphilis, and many fungi that can cause severe diarrhoea if allowed to enter the rectum. Last but not least, there is the ubiquitous herpes virus that has infected at least twenty million Americans and may now be the most common sexually transmitted disease.

As millions of gay and straight folk can attest, genital herpes is bad news. Perhaps 20 per cent of the young population of the United States is infected with the herpes virus and the rate of infection is growing rapidly. Men and women can infect each other with this virus. A gay man whose anus becomes infected with the herpes virus suffers from extremely painful blisters in the area. The curse of herpes is that, in one out of every three victims, it does not go away after the first episode but recurs at regular and not-so-regular intervals. Such unwelcome visits can continue for years. While fresh lesions are present, intercourse is unlikely because of pain; but if after an attack sexual activity is resumed the virus may still be present on the genital or rectal surface and ready to move on.

Pregnant women with genital herpes have a terrible problem. Sixty to eighty per cent of their babies will be infected if delivered vaginally. In babies, herpes infection can be fatal. When such a situation is discovered the baby must be delivered by caesarian section.

The reason for discussing this now is to point out that very frequently sexual encounters with someone about whom one knows little or nothing are dangerous and increasingly so. Gay men with many different lovers have nearly all suffered from hepatitis B, syphilis, gonorrhoea, numerous infections with bowel bacteria, fungi and anal herpes. In the period we are discussing, before the AIDS epidemic was known for what it is, many homosexual men, enjoying a liberated lifestyle, socialised late into the night, smoked and used recreational drugs. Of course, a number also used hard drugs intravenously. The result of that lifestyle was that many gay men were chronically ill and might not have had an immune system in tiptop condition when they were unlucky enough to come into contact with the AIDS virus. It is hardly surprising that, in cities such as New York, infection among the gay community spread rapidly. Most of the early men infected with the virus confided to their physicians that they might have had between 500 and 5000 different sexual partners in their usually young lifestyle. Thirty different sexual partners in one day was not uncommon. I stress that gay communities have become far more cautious in the 1990s, for it's unusual to find a gay man who does not know someone who has died of this horrible disease.

Perhaps if we meet one of the young gay victims of AIDS and examine his story in detail, many of the major features of the problem will fall into place. James, lying pale and obviously exhausted in the bed, was only thirty-two years of age but looked twenty years older. He had recently lost his eyesight as a virus infected and destroyed his retina. As a result, his head moved constantly because he needed to localise the sounds reaching his ears. He tried to speak but even this required a physical exertion that made him breathless, causing his speech to be punctuated with gasps for air despite the oxygen being fed into his nose. An organism had infected and destroyed most of his lungs.

His thirty pounds' weight loss of the last three months left him wasted and the skin of his arms, which had so recently been tanned and taut over strong young muscles, was pale and dry. Standing out from this pallor were numerous round purplish discolorations, some rising from the skin in discrete lumps. A careful examination revealed a similar lesion inside his cheek.

Cancerous cells developed in the blood vessels of this man's skin and were now multiplying and migrating out of control: Kaposi's sarcoma. As he attempted to speak, his incoherence and removal from reality became obvious. Mercifully, this patient was only partially aware of his surroundings and situation. He had another organism which, finding no resistance from any infection-fighting defence forces, had invaded his brain to produce the mental changes now so obvious.

We have been discussing the case of a sensitive and intelligent young lawyer. James's practice in a small law firm in middle Connecticut kept him busy during the week, but the weekends were his own. He was the second of three children. His older brother, married with two children, ran a small family business successfully. James had been an outstanding athlete at school. The youngest sibling, a sister, had just completed a degree in business administration and all seemed to be going well for this family.

If any of James's family knew that he was gay, and he thought his mother did, they never admitted it to him. In recent years James, a talented guitarist, had developed a preference for music rather than sport. He was thin and good-looking in a fragile way. He wore thick glasses which made him look more serious and scholarly than he really was.

He certainly did not dislike women. Once or twice he remembered being sexually aroused by a female. However, as early as his fifteenth year, he had realised that he felt the sensations so vividly and frequently described by his older brother much more frequently in the presence of men. By the age of sixteen he realised he could identify his sexual preference for men.

On one or perhaps many Saturdays between 1979 and 1981, he encountered once, or perhaps many times, the virus that would kill him. Being single and a professional, he was now able to encounter similarly orientated men in pleasant surroundings by visiting New York City. Here he considered his sexual adventures to be satisfying, civilised and safer than in earlier days.

In the past he had sometimes felt passionate enough for sex with total strangers, even in a toilet booth. But on this typical day things were very different. He drove to New York in mid-morning and entered a small, unremarkable-looking apartment building and walked up three flights of stairs with ease. He was fit and excited.

The top floor of the building had been converted into what at first looked like an executive-type health club. After using his key to enter the area he was greeted by the familiar sound of male laughter, the hectic sounds of splashing as arms propelled bodies through chlorinated water and the humid, in fact quite steamy, atmosphere of this sunny area into which he strode confidently.

Around the perimeter of the room were perhaps twelve dressing rooms containing lockers and a comfortable chaise for private resting. Louvred wooden doors provided access to these rooms. There were no locks on the doors. Most of the men in the room were naked; a few wore abbreviated shorts or swimming trunks. This was no collection of young gods of fitness, however; all shapes and sizes and a wide range of ages were represented. James guessed from a quick survey of the scene that he knew at least 50 per cent of the people present. He moved to a vacant dressing room, where he changed into swimming trunks.

His first lover that day was an old friend with whom he had experienced sex on many occasions and they moved into the privacy of one of the dressing rooms for their encounter. Others, less inhibited, enjoyed each other while lying by the pool. It is certainly of more than prurient interest that in this first sexual session James not only kissed his lover on the mouth but took his lover's penis and semen into his mouth, and that he kissed with his tongue his lover's anus. It is almost certainly of deadly interest that before the day was over James would have four more sexual encounters, two with strangers, men he had never seen before that day.

During the day he was reminded of a problem he had been facing for two years. James suffered from genital herpes, tiny blister-like sores situated near his anus. They were not at their worst, but nevertheless they were painful. To receive the penises of his lovers into his anus, he used a lot of cream for lubrication to minimise the pain. He used a cream containing cortisone which he had bought without a prescription from his pharmacist.

During these passionate encounters this day, he experienced a number of orgasms. With each of these experienced lovers he had time, as the moment approached, to break open a small capsule containing the drug amyl nitrite, which he inhaled through his nose. The drug made his whole body flush with a warm feeling and when he timed it right this feeling coincided with his orgasm; the intensity of the pleasure was wonderful.

During the sexual highlight of the day one of his lovers, to increase further the pleasure he was experiencing, twisted and pushed his fist into James' well-lubricated anus. James felt pain from the intense stretching that occurred and some of the delicate tissues around the anus tore, causing him to bleed a little, but he willingly accepted this pain because his sexual pleasure far outweighed the physical discomfort involved. By the end of the day five different men had discharged their sexual fluid into his rectum and he had returned the favor for three of them.

James showered and washed himself meticulously, as did the others present. He returned to Connecticut well satisfied with the pleasures of the day, already anticipating further encounters with these men, especially those he had met for the first time. He wished that Robert, the man with whom he had lived for four years, would come to New York and share these experiences with him. But Robert was not interested, did not like to experiment, did not wish to take drugs and simply wanted a quiet, monogamous life.

As James drove up the Connecticut turnpike, his thoughts turned to one of the men he had enjoyed that day. Passionate, certainly performing normally, yes; but for all that, clearly not well. He was surely too thin, his eyes were dull. Had he imagined it, or was this man depressed? And then there was the matter of those two strange purplish-red nodules on his hands. James had never seen anything quite like them.

Well, James is dead and Robert is dying and there can be no other conclusion than that James carried a lethal infection to his faithful partner.

A re-examination of James's activity on the day described illustrates some of the risk factors that contribute to the spread of the disease AIDS. The infectious agent capable of causing AIDS is present in sexual secretions. James took sexual secretions into his mouth and rectum. While skin is almost impenetrable and a superb barrier to infection while its integrity is unbreached, mucous membranes, those smooth, moist filmy linings throughout the mouth and intestinal tract, are just the opposite; they are designed to facilitate the entry of materials into the vital areas of our body. These membranes in our intestinal tract absorb fluid and the nutrients from digested food. Viruses and many other infectious agents penetrate these linings easily. Nature was not foolish enough to leave these areas without protection and we have discussed earlier the special role of the secretory immune system. It is certain, however, that a number of organisms find that our inner skin provides an excellent route for invasion.

To absorb the nutrients obtained from a good roast dinner, the small intestine opens wide the blood vessels that flow into this area. As the blood vessels increase in size, more blood will flow through the area. As a result there will be an increase in the temperature of all the cells around as metabolism is stimulated. Many of these cells will have their membranes stretched, opening tiny pores in the outer shell that will allow the nutritional factors that need to be absorbed and other matters to pass selectively from the intestinal tract into the blood. Once there, these nutrients may be whisked away for immediate use or stored in the liver.

The same increased blood flow and increase in the ease of absorption of chemicals (and, of course, of an opportunistic virus) will occur after the use of amyl nitrite. This drug dilates blood vessels, giving that warm feeling that many feel adds to their sexual pleasure.

It does not take much imagination to see some risk factors for James. He might have taken infected sexual fluid from a man with AIDS into his mouth or rectum and then flushed open his blood vessels, facilitating the ease with which a virus or some other deadly micro-organism might enter his body. When you consider that the surfaces of his mucous membranes were already breached by his genital sores and the traumatic nature of his lovemaking, it appears that James was actually inviting the deadly guest to come inside. The cortisone cream he and many gay men used as an anal lubricant before intercourse would not have helped their local defence mechanisms, as cortisone can suppress the immune system.

So, what have we? A new virus, potentially lethal to humans, lives in Africa for some time then rapidly moves to Haiti then into the gay populations of the United States. At this point we know that the virus is in seminal fluid and enters the body of homosexual victims through the intestinal tract. If the virus can be transmitted sexually to males, what about women?

I knew that American women would not be exempt from the curse that is AIDS very early in the AIDS story. Soon after we started our clinic and research into the disease at Yale, I met an extraordinary couple who performed a terrible and conclusive experiment.

Jane and Barbara were lesbians who had been living together in northern Connecticut for three years. The relationship seemed satisfactory to them, and they assured me it was stable. The couple's biggest frustration in life was their inability to have a baby ('to make our marriage normal') and in this department, but no other, they were willing to admit that men were useful. As adoption was out of the question they came up with a solution that was common, they assured me, among lesbian couples.

Jane and Barbara knew many gay men. They started looking for a suitable genetic father for the baby that Barbara had decided to have (Jane, of course, would be the real father). Blue eyes and blond hair were essential; they agreed on that much. Eventually they decided upon a beautiful young man named Tom.

Jane asked Tom whether he would help them get their much-wanted baby. He was bemused and flattered although, of course, he was not sexually interested. It was arranged that Tom would come to their apartment the following night, when Jane's research suggested Barbara's cycle would be at its most fertile, and masturbate into a dish. The seminal fluid would be aspirated into a small syringe and he was free to go.

Jane had learned that fertilisation was facilitated by meeting with sperm at the moment of orgasm. Therefore she took the syringe with Tom's semen into the bedroom and made love to Barbara. As Barbara's climax approached Jane inserted the syringe as far into her vagina as was possible and injected the seminal fluid. This exact procedure was carried out for six nights in a row, with Tom supplying the seminal fluid nightly.

He demanded and was paid $50 for his trouble on the last three occasions. Barbara did not become pregnant—but she was infected with the AIDS virus.

This case, of course, proved that when men are infected with the AIDS virus, vaginal sex places women at enormous risk of getting the disease. The AIDS virus must be able to penetrate the female genital tract and enter the body, where it can do its damage.

Seminal fluid in the mouth, particularly if swallowed, must be presumed to be infectious; while seminal fluid ejaculated into the rectum of a woman is, from an infectious disease point of view, no less dangerous than it is for men.

After reading this story you will not be surprised to learn that, in a number of countries around the world, women married to sterile husbands are turning to sperm banks for help. Collected sperm from the bank is artificially inseminated into the woman anxious to become pregnant and in many cases such attempts are successful. Many sperm banks pay for donations. Consequently, it is not unusual for money to be the main, if not the only, reason for a man providing some of his sperm cells. Sad to report, in recent years a number of donors have been infected with the HIV virus. As even the most careful history and examination of the donor could not have detected this situation, a number of sperm samples containing live AIDS virus were inseminated into women in many parts of the world. A number have gone on to develop the disease.

If men can infect men and men can infect women, what about the transmission of the virus from women to men?

Hermann was a German engineer working on a project for his company in the United States. The work would keep him in the northeastern section of America for two years. The construction job in which he played an important role was proceeding at a great pace and only once a year could he have time off to return home for a few weeks. Hermann and his family had been through this deprivation before: similar projects had taken him to Asia and north Africa.

Hermann loved his three children and his wife. In sixteen years of marriage he had never dreamed of being unfaithful to her, at least not by *his* definition of the word. Sexual relief with prostitutes was quite another matter.

Sixteen months before I met him, Hermann had arrived in the United States and two months after settling in he had carefully chosen a prostitute. He always did it this way, he told me; find one you like, make sure she is clean and compatible, and stick with her. Regular customers get better treatment anyway. He knew that Priscilla, the girl he chose, was an intravenous drug addict, but weren't they all? He was certainly not about to get involved with the drug scene in any way.

He got on well with Priscilla, who was black; he liked black women. She introduced him to anal sex. He had six sexual encounters with Priscilla over a fourteen-month period. At the end of that time two things happened. In the few weeks before he saw me, Hermann had not felt very well. He had noted swollen glands under his arms and in his groin and he had experienced some drenching night sweats. He knew nothing of AIDS. Two days before coming to see me he had his last liaison with Priscilla and a terrible thing happened: she stole his wallet.

He felt betrayed, then very annoyed and with no sense of embarrassment called the police. They picked up a surprised Priscilla, who had the wallet in her bag, and off to jail she went.

Initially, of course, we did not know what was the trouble with Hermann but we had our suspicions. Sure enough, his T cells had the characteristic alterations that we see in people infected with the AIDS virus. Once the story was known we contacted the prison doctor, who was most co-operative, and Priscilla was sent down for us to check. She arrived in the clinic with her feet and hands cuffed (a little excessive, we thought), was tested and found to be infected with the AIDS virus.

Hermann decided to go home to Germany to await his fate. He lived for another two years. I only saw him once more six months later when he dropped into my clinic unexpectedly. He had returned from Germany, sick and all as he was, to testify against Priscilla. He had his own strict sense of duty. Priscilla had been out on bail and was sentenced to six months in jail but served not one day. She was released on medical grounds and disappeared. By this stage, of course, her medical condition was known; no one wished to deal with an AIDS victim in the local jail.

It is obvious from all of the above that it is a dangerous misnomer to refer to AIDS as the 'gay plague'; the AIDS virus has no sexual preferences at all. In the United States and many Western countries, the reservoir holding the virus was for some time locked away inside the gay community and members of it infected each other.

From the beginning of the AIDS story, however, the opposite has been true in Africa. Here most infections have involved heterosexual activities. The disease continues to spread at an alarming rate in this manner. Recent studies of the way that AIDS is creeping through Africa illustrate the great danger in the spread of the disease among heterosexual people in Western society if any significant reservoir of HIV builds up in that population.

Several million people in Africa are infected with HIV. At least twenty-four African countries are involved. Males and females are infected equally and 90 per cent have no identifiable risk factor apart from heterosexual activity. In countries where the question has been studied, patients infected with HIV have had an average of thirty different sexual partners while those who are not infected with the virus report a figure of four.

The infection rate among prostitutes is very high in many of these countries. Forty-three per cent of prostitutes are infected with HIV in Rwanda, while even higher percentages are being recorded in Uganda and Kenya. In some studies, as many as 81 per cent of the prostitutes are infected and therefore could be spreading this disease. It is estimated that one infected prostitute could spread the disease to at least fifty of her clients in any given year.

One-third of HIV victims in Africa have had at least one other sexually transmitted disease and it seems likely that casual sex and the frequent use of prostitutes is responsible for most of the African cases.

Women in Africa appear to be more readily infected by men than do women in some Western societies. It is considered likely that this results from the frequency of genital and cervical ulcers in malnourished and often diseased African women. Such ulcers would make it easier for the virus to penetrate mucous membranes and gain entry into the body proper.

After the AIDS virus arrived in New York and San Francisco and was identified as a sexually transmitted disease within the gay community, people rapidly realised that this was not the only way the disease could spread.

We must now discuss infected blood. The blood of victims infected with the AIDS virus is just as infectious, if not more so, than the seminal fluid of such people. The blood of people suffering from an infection with the AIDS virus contains T4 cells; T4 cells contain virus and therefore the disease can be spread if blood containing infected T4 cells enters a body.

Thus, soon after AIDS arrived and its association with sexual behaviour was noted, the same syndrome turned up in intravenous drug addicts, hemophiliacs and recipients of transfused infected blood.

My first patients with AIDS contracted as a result of an intravenous drug habit were a husband and wife.

Peter and Jo were not typical drug addicts; apparently they were both successful and happy. Peter wrote a nationally syndicated column telling people how to look after their house plants. His wife Jo was a psychiatric nurse, very much involved in her profession and working full time in an academic psychiatric institute. They were childless.

Jo had started using heroin while she was still at college. She remembers being quite scared of the whole drug scene during college and indeed it was not until her final year that she fell into an ever more common trap. One night after they had made love, her boyfriend told her that he found that heroin made the experience even more intensely pleasurable and urged her to share it with him. She allowed him to inject her with some heroin, which certainly had the effect he described.

For many months they shared heroin after lovemaking and insidiously addiction developed. Eventually Jo broke the relationship with her boyfriend, but not her drug addiction. Shortly after the romance ended, Peter entered Jo's life and she introduced him to exactly the same pleasures and horrors.

At the time I first met them, their drug addiction was under some control. Because of the enormous costs involved in a daily heroin habit, the couple had placed themselves on a regimen which consisted of daily maintenance therapy with methadone (a narcotic drug taken by mouth), which Jo would steal from the hospital where she worked. This kept them reasonably satisfied from Monday to Friday but on the weekends they splurged and went by themselves to a shooting gallery in New York. On Saturday mornings the couple would drive from their rural home in Connecticut into New York City and, in what they admitted was a particularly seedy shooting gallery in one of the poorest parts of Brooklyn, they would buy their heroin.

They were aware of the infectious risks associated with drug addiction. Jo was treating a number of drug addicts and had seen how many had contracted hepatitis B infections because they shared needles with other drug addicts at the time that they 'shot up' their drugs. Syringes and needles are difficult to come by and are used time and time again by drug addicts, who make little attempt to clean them properly. Indeed, modern needles and syringes are meant to be disposable and it is not really possible to clean them adequately.

Jo and Peter avoided these problems by using sterile equipment whenever they injected drugs intravenously. Jo's hospital was the unwitting supplier of the equipment. They frequently took needles, syringes and a bottle of water for injection to the shooting gallery in Brooklyn, where they would buy their drug, suspend it in the sterile water and inject it immediately.

The couple were able to pinpoint with great accuracy the moment in which they met the AIDS virus. Only once, Jo, who was responsible for bringing the equipment, thought she had put it in the car but had in fact left it behind on the dining room table. As a result, when the couple arrived in Brooklyn, now quite desperate for their heroin, no safe equipment for injecting the drug was available to them. In their desperation they decided to gamble and use other people's needles and syringes.

The man from whom they borrowed equipment was obliging but clearly emaciated and unwell. They knew him by his first name as they had seen him on a number of occasions in the gallery, and they were later able to tell me that they discovered eighteen months later that he was in hospital desperately ill with this strange new disease called AIDS.

Jo and Peter suffered a severe flu-like illness that hit them both approximately two weeks after their visit to the shooting gallery. For a week or so they had severe sweats, felt exhausted and even visited their local doctor, who understandably told them they had a flu that was going around and to rest up until it passed. The symptoms passed but the virus did not.

Not for a further year did any health problems descend on them. In the six months prior to seeing me, however, they had developed swollen glands, had lost weight, sweated frequently at night, suffered from attacks of stiffness in the hands on waking in the morning, and had periodic rashes on the back and chest. Peter was more affected than Jo.

In the United States and many other countries, drug use is still a major factor in the continuing spread of the AIDS epidemic. As little as two drops of infected blood containing T4 cells infected with the virus can deliver a fatal dose of the AIDS virus when injected into the bloodstream of another person. Experience has shown that it is much more difficult to modify the behaviour of drug addicts than it is, for example, to change the sexual customs of gay men.

You will now see why AIDS has become such a serious problem

for patients who suffer from hemophilia. This group is suffering most severely from the AIDS epidemic, certainly suffering the most from the problems associated with contaminated blood. This group feels more bitterness and frustration than other victims of the disease. Hemophilia is a somewhat rare genetic condition that affects males only. The defective gene is carried by the mother who, although not affected, may pass it on to a son, who will develop the disease. Most people know of bleeders: people who can bleed for hours, even days, if they suffer the slightest cut. Not all bleeders are hemophiliacs, but most are.

Almost as interesting as the immune system, and designed along similar lines, is our blood clotting system. When a blood vessel is cut or torn in a way that would allow blood to leak or even pour from the breach, an emergency of some proportion is signalled. All the blood circulates through major blood vessels every sixty seconds so it would be possible to exsanguinate remarkably quickly if a major vessel was opened.

The cells lining damaged blood vessels release chemicals that attract cells in the bloodstream called platelets. These cells are made in the bone marrow, and plugging leaks in blood vessels is their biological task. They do this every day for all of us because even if you bump your side on a table, tiny blood vessels would leak blood, causing a bruise, were it not for this mechanism. All of us injure ourselves constantly without even knowing it.

The platelets plug up the leak with their bodies but signal for stronger and more permanent repair work to be started immediately. In the bloodstream are twelve factors called, logically enough, blood clotting factors. These are activated in chain-gang fashion and, when the end of the reaction is reached, a new wall of fibrin is built that can manage until the blood vessel grows its new wall.

Hemophiliacs lack one of the twelve factors: factor VIII. As a result, they cannot repair efficiently even the most minor breach in blood vessel walls. If they cannot make any factor VIII, they are in constant and terrible danger of bleeding to death. Some hemophiliacs can make some factor VIII so the disease has grades of severity.

Severe hemophiliacs have led miserable, boring lives until recent years. Either they were almost literally wrapped in cotton wool to protect them or they battled on, but bled time and time again. Their joints suffered particularly because the joints are, of course, subjected to strains and bumps continuously, and small amounts of blood leaking into the joints would eventually destroy them, causing crippling arthritis.

Scientists discovered how to extract factor VIII from normal blood. Not only could the factor be extracted but it also could be concentrated and packaged so that bleeding could be rapidly controlled by an intravenous injection of the missing factor.

Producing commercial quantities of this factor required a lot of blood and it was soon realised that asking people to donate blood would not supply enough of the precious red stuff for this task. The volunteer pool was simply not big enough to maintain normal blood supplies and make enough blood available for factor VIII production. The commercial companies involved decided that they must buy the blood and so centres were set up where one could sell a unit of blood for cash.

From the outset it was realised that the 'sellers' would, to a large extent, be desperate people and that a number of drug addicts and the like would avail themselves of the ready cash. However, all donors were and are screened by physicians and all blood harvested was, and is, thoroughly checked for the hepatitis virus and every other known problem. The system worked well. The life of hemophiliacs was revolutionised.

Their tragedy, of course, is AIDS. Drug addicts and homosexuals infected with the virus lined up to sell their blood for factor VIII production. The collected blood pooled for commercial use became infected with the HIV virus that no one could detect at the time. Small amounts of the lethal virus were distributed in thousands of vials of factor VIII to the hemophiliacs of the world. On a per capita basis they are far and away the most affected and infected high risk group. More than 70 per cent of the 12 000 hemophiliacs in the United States, for example, have been infected with the virus. Let me introduce you to one of the most remarkable.

Michael was thirty-two years old when I met him, seeking help for a severe cough and difficulty in breathing. He had a high fever and was clearly distressed, but he had one of those irrepressible personalities which made him minimise his suffering. His fiancee, a nurse, was with him; their wedding was planned for a few months ahead. This remarkable hemophiliac had done something no one else afflicted with the disease had managed. From his earliest years, Michael was crazy about flying. Like so many little boys, he wanted to be the pilot of a big commercial jet; an impractical ambition for a hemophiliac but his was a fairly mild form of the disease and he ended up at the age of thirty-two as captain of a commercial airliner.

Throughout his life he had required factor VIII on only a few occasions and he had not received any for many years when he sprained his ankle one day in 1980. He went to his local hospital, concerned that this degree of trauma might lead to a dangerous amount of bleeding into his ankle joint. The ankle was strapped and his physician told him that, though it seemed all right, Michael should have some intravenous factor VIII 'just to be on the safe side'. Michael was doubtful, but eventually agreed. He received a bottle of contaminated factor VIII.

Michael had pneumonia when I first met him and was severely anemic. The pneumonia was the one that so frequently troubles victims of AIDS but the anemia puzzled us. Michael had not been bleeding and our investigations soon revealed that a nasty form of tuberculosis had invaded his bone marrow and was stopping him from producing blood.

For the next nine months Michael struggled with the disease. He was very religious and his faith and courage kept him cheerful, even when he became covered with sores caused by a herpes infection. Amazingly, he died without bitterness.

How do children get AIDS? Like adults, they can contract the disease if they receive a transfusion of contaminated blood or blood products, but this is not the most common way they meet the virus.

Seth was only two when he first came to my clinic, the cute black child of a black mother and a smart but careless black father who is currently in the care of the government for two years.

Seth was 'failing to thrive'. He had big nodes in his neck and a big spleen, and he kept having one infection after another. It took us a few months in the early phase of the AIDS epidemic to work out what was amiss with Seth, but when the penny dropped we wanted to know how this two year old had contracted the disease.

We tested his mother and found that she had an early form of the infection. We tested the father (who was in prison) and he was perfectly well. His mother swore she was no drug addict and we believed her; nor had she had any blood transfusions. What Seth's mother had was a lover who was an intravenous drug addict. He was infected with the AIDS virus and had donated the virus to both mother and baby. She was pregnant when she met this man.

The AIDS virus can cross the placenta, moving from the mother's bloodstream to the baby's developing T cells. That is the way most children catch this disease.

We have already mentioned our new knowledge that the virus is secreted in the breast milk of an infected mother and that a child suckling at the breast can be infected in this way.

These cases illustrate how one can become infected with the AIDS virus. These are the only ways in which you can get infected. You cannot get it by accepting money from a gay man or washing your clothes in a laundromat frequented by gay men; nor from swimming pools, public toilets, cutlery, crockery, etc. It is sexual not social intercourse that is spreading this virus.

The world scene

The World Health Organization is telling us, here at the beginning of 1993, that we have a worldwide health crisis on our hands because of AIDS. More than 15 million people are infected with HIV and by the year 2000, 40 million will be infected unless intervention strategies are successful. During the first ten years of the epidemic, we have seen some slowing of the pace of infection in the Western world but in Africa, and particularly in Asia, the pandemic is gaining momentum. By the end of 1997, 85 per cent of all HIV infections will be in the developing world (to use that hollow euphemism). Today, 10 000 new infections will occur and more of these will be in women than in men. HIV/AIDS is becoming an ever more serious problem for women and their babies. Even healthy women are more easily infected than men, but they become particularly vulnerable if poorly treated sexually transmitted disease or inadequate obstetric care have left them with genital ulcer disease.

In very many parts of the world, women are treated as second-class citizens with very little right to negotiate in a sexual situation.

Currently, we believe that one and a half million people in North America, more than a million in South America, more than a million in Europe, more than six million in Africa and more than a million in Asia have been infected with the virus. To date the brunt of the epidemic has been borne by western and sub-Saharan Africa, as well as countries in the central and southern parts of that mighty continent. Of all the countries in the world, Uganda has been most devastated with perhaps one million of its citizens infected. In Africa today one million children have been orphaned as a result of losing both parents to this disease. By the turn of the century we expect to have ten million orphans worldwide. Many of those will themselves be sick with the disease; others will be left to struggle on without parents, without siblings, and often without an extended family to take care of them.

Tuberculosis is a disease that can be spread from one person to another by social intercourse. Simply being coughed upon by someone who has in their sputum the bacteria responsible for tuberculosis can cause infection. As tuberculosis is raging among HIV-infected individuals in communities where there is much of this disease, ordinary citizens not infected with HIV are being plagued with a new epidemic of tuberculosis. In Africa there are a million more people infected with tuberculosis than would have been the case had it not been for the AIDS epidemic. To make matters worse, a particular form of tuberculosis that is multiplying easily in people infected with HIV is resistant to many of the standard anti-tuberculous drugs. As this form of tuberculosis spreads around the world we will all be at risk.

In southeast Asia, the country where AIDS is spreading most rapidly is India and it is quite likely that by the turn of the century that vast nation will be more affected by HIV than any other.

Currently, Thailand and Burma have very significant epidemics. We know that the disease is spreading rapidly in southern China and that the potential for an explosion of the epidemic in Indonesia, Malaysia and the Philippines must be guarded against. Every twenty-four hours, two thousand people get infected in the southeast Asian region.

While to date, and quite rightly so, we have concentrated on the human tragedy involved with HIV infection, it is very important to look at the socio-economic consequences of this disease. Thailand, for example, a country on the verge of becoming a Second World country, has been devastated by HIV and by the year 2000 will have lost US$9 billion to the scourge. It is particularly important that governments realise the socio-economic disasters that can befall a community affected by HIV. In some African countries even the food chain has been interrupted as some 70 per cent of the truck drivers may be infected with HIV.

The disease is unique in that it affects mainly young adults at the time of life when they should be most productive. A loss of productive years, a waste of education, a loss of taxes paid, a loss of the chance to support education for children who in turn would be more productive: all lead to socio-economic havoc within an infected community. It is vital that the governments of the world, insufficiently alarmed by the invisible epidemic, that is the growing number of people infected with HIV who remain well, understand the need to act now. Unfortunately, humans are much better at building dams after a flood than before the water has tumbled downstream. Also, we are not good at learning from other people's mistakes and problems.

In a number of developing countries, governments regard themselves as bastions of a very conservative society that cannot easily discuss matters such as sexual intercourse, the use of condoms, and the injecting drug behaviour of the citizens. Very often I have found, as I visited countries first in Africa and then in Asia, that the official conservatism is in no way matched by the behaviour of much of the citizenry, which is anything but conservative. Governments must react to the behaviour of people, not the desired behaviour. Recently, I was in an Asian country where the authorities were telling me that the devotion of the people to Islamic principles would protect them from AIDS. In their society, they assured me, very little sexual activity was occurring. It's all the fault of those wretched prostitutes in Thailand, I was informed. Hoping but not by any means certain that after our discussions I would change their minds on certain issues, I returned to my hotel and had a drink with some American businessmen. Four of these men told me that they were in this country to sell spare parts for military hardware purchased by the army. On hearing that I was there to discuss AIDS with various officials they told me how relieved they were to be out of Thailand, for everyone knew that you couldn't use the girls there any more. With a wink and a slap on the back, one of the men told me that the army were fixing up for some local girls to come over and entertain them that night. The behaviour in the bedrooms of that hotel that night would in no way have matched the conservative image presented to me in the morning.

Some Asian countries are still putting too much emphasis on trying to make commercial sex safe, rather than change the image they portray to tourists. Countries such as Thailand, which have magnificent vacation resorts and wonderful beaches and scenery, should be promoting family packages as they attempt to turn the focus of the world away from their flourishing sex industry. Of course, commercial sex workers must be taught to protect themselves and their clients but we live in a buyer-beware climate and governments should not pretend that they can make commercial sex safe. Much educational effort should be spent on convincing men (and yes, women) that commercial sex is becoming an ever more dangerous business. Clearly, people who do have anal or vaginal intercourse with a commercial sex worker would be extraordinarily foolish if they did not protect themselves with a condom, but even when using the best quality condoms accidents can happen. As you are well aware from the material we have already covered, HIV is a most deadly virus that produces a most unpleasant disease. As we look at the epidemic around the world it is important to realise that, overwhelmingly, HIV is spread during *vaginal* intercourse. Eighty per cent of all the people infected to date have been infected in this manner. Only 5 per cent of the epidemic has occurred as a result of anal intercourse, with the majority of other infections resulting from the use of contaminated blood for medicinal purposes or the sharing of injecting equipment containing HIV.

It is extraordinarily difficult to change sexual behaviour. Gay communities around the world have certainly changed because they are educated and terrified, and very many individuals have had personal contact with someone dying of the disease. However, the incidence of gonorrhea and other sexually transmitted diseases has increased among women in Sydney over the last two years, despite our best efforts to educate people about the risks of casual unprotected sexual intercourse. Any country that wants to know how its education program is going needs only to look at the incidence of all sexually transmitted diseases in a community to determine whether the message is being received and acted upon.

I was recently associated with a survey of sexual behaviour among young men and women attending university for the specific purpose of being trained as health counsellors in our schools. Much of the course involved the development of skills that would allow people to teach the young men and women at our schools about the dangers of careless sexual activity. An anonymous survey of a graduating group of 187 students from this course revealed that 62 per cent of them continued to engage in risky behaviour. Credible messengers? I doubt it very much. The big mistake we can make is to equate knowledge or education with motivation. It is very difficult in many cases to personalise the information to make people really believe that HIV infection could happen to them.

The major issues and controversies

The AIDS epidemic has allowed many societies to see their weaknesses and strengths in the clearest of lights. Prejudice and ignorance, always bad bedfellows, have led to attitudes and decisions that have increased suffering and hindered the implementation of policies that would minimise the spread of the disease. On the other hand, many individuals and organisations have worked furiously, compassionately and intelligently to meet the challenge. As a result we have many controversies to deal with, but many new facts to help with this task.

HIV antibody test

Seeking the 'fingerprints' of the HIV virus in an individual by screening his or her blood for antibodies to the virus remains our best tool for following the flow of the epidemic, planning for future health services and helping, through early diagnosis, an infected individual. Despite all these worthwhile uses of antibody testing, screening programs remain controversial.

The test itself is no longer controversial: its strengths and weaknesses have been clearly defined. Eighty per cent of individuals infected with the HIV virus declare this to be the case by producing circulating antibodies to the virus in their blood two to three weeks after infection. Almost 100 per cent do so by three months after infection. A report from Finland of two individuals who did not develop antibodies for fifteen months after infection is of interest, but such an event is so rare that it is not significant in the general context of testing and diagnosis. In any case, the Finnish data have been challenged by a number of scientists who feel that the problems they reported lay with the testing methods used rather than the patients' antibody system.

Antibody testing does have to deal with one obvious and unavoidable weakness: if someone has a negative antibody test, all that can be said is that, if that individual could not have been infected with the virus in the three months prior to the test, he or she is not infected with HIV. If they could have met the virus in that time period, they will need a second test after three months in which there has been no possible exposure. Then, and only then, can the all-clear signal be sounded. In the majority of studies any delay in sero-conversion is not a problem.

The handling of the results, not the performance of the tests, continues to produce controversy. HIV antibody screening is not just another test. A positive result tells an individual that he or she has a life-threatening infection. It may also abolish any quality their life may have because of the discrimination that may follow. Time and time again I have seen individuals who, having shared the burden of knowing they are infected with HIV with a friend (a problem shared is a problem halved), immediately lose that friend.

Some families withdraw and even throw an HIV-infected member out into the street. Schools reject HIV-infected children. Not long ago a court in Florida, having reviewed the scientific evidence, ordered a school to educate three infected children on the school premises. The teachers and parents obeyed the order by buying, from their own money, a caravan and placing it in the far corner of the schoolyard, confining the three children to the caravan during school hours and calling for volunteers to teach these little 'lepers'.

A patient for whom I am now caring lives on a property thirty kilometres outside a largish country town. On a routine check-up from his doctor, blood tests were ordered. Apart from the usual full blood count and cholesterol levels that the doctor checked each year for his patients, he decided to order an HIV antibody test for this forty-year-old man. Recently, he had received information from the Red Cross reminding him that patients who had had blood transfusions between 1978 and 1985 should be tested to see if they were infected with HIV. This particular man had been in a car accident and required a blood transfusion just before testing became available. As the doctor thought it was extremely unlikely that the test would be positive, he didn't say anything to the patient but simply scribbled his request for HIV antibodies to be measured on the pathology form. A week later, on a Friday afternoon, the wife of the man, whom we shall call Tom, received a telephone call from the doctor. 'Mary,' said the doctor, 'I've just got Tom's blood tests back and I know you're not going to believe this but he's got AIDS. Can I speak to him, please.' Now as it so happened, Tom was out on the property and not contactable at that moment but Mary turned to Eleanor, who was visiting her at the time, and exclaimed in surprised anguish, 'On my god, Eleanor, Tom's got AIDS!' She then continued to talk to the doctor, who said that on Monday morning it might be a good idea if she and Tom came in to discuss what it was all about.

You can imagine the trauma in that family that night as Mary told Tom the bad news, while being totally unable to answer the innumerable questions that flashed through his mind. The next morning when the couple went into town to do some shopping in the supermarket, they were greeted by the manager of the store, who told them that he had heard of Tom's problem and would really prefer it if they did not use his supermarket, for the news was out and surely this would disturb many of his customers.

Tom did not have adequate life insurance nor did he have adequate sickness benefits lined up and, as a result of his being tested without being counselled about the significance of having a positive test, he ended up losing his property. He now lives unhappily in a small apartment in another town that he and his wife were forced to move to, despite the fact that they had grown up and worked for their entire lives in the now discriminating community.

The message here is clear. Both pre- and post-test counselling are absolutely essential with HIV testing. The consequences for individuals can be quite devastating and it is imperative that every effort be made to keep the results confidential. To tell someone that they are HIV positive over the telephone (or worse still, tell a relative) and not give people the chance for some immediate personal counselling is downright cruel.

Discrimination against HIV positive people continues all around the world. Robert, a 38-year-old gay accountant, worked in an inner city building which also housed the office of his dentist. Requiring some dental work, he asked me if he should inform his dentist of his infection with HIV. I told him he should, and emphasised to him that dentists had the same dedication to respecting the confidentiality of information revealed by their patients as did doctors. It transpired that when Robert told his dentist that he was HIV positive, the good man thanked him and went about his business. But the dental nurse, who was assisting with the procedure, enjoyed at lunchtime on the same day one of those well-known 'Now don't you tell another soul, Susie' conversations with one of her friends in the building. 'Can you believe that Robert from such and such an accounting firm on the seventh floor has got AIDS? You'd never know it to look at him, would you?' Apparently, numerous such 'Don't you tell another soul' conversations occurred that afternoon and the next morning when Robert arrived at work, his desk was in the hallway. Colleagues wanted to have nothing to do with him and six weeks afterwards, despite interventions from myself and some of my team, Robert jumped to his death from the top of that very building.

A brown flat cancer cell being attacked by T cells. Two elongated
T cells show blebbing and are dying; two others are alive and well, while
the cancer cell is almost dead.

Top: A mast cell coated with IgE antibody has exploded after an antigen recognised by the IgE has landed on the surface of the cell. Tiny granules full of powerful chemicals like histamine are inside these granules. Twenty four per cent of us suffer 'allergies' when an excessive release of these chemicals affect blood vessels and the bronchial tree.

Below: The invasion of a T cell by HIV is illustrated in the bottom pictures. Moving from left to right the HIV can be seen binding to the CD4 molecule then being swallowed by the T cell. The top pictures, again moving from left to right, show new AIDS virus budding out from the dying T cell.

AIDS viruses escaping from a dying T cell and ready to move into new T cells and produce more damage to the immune system.

Top: A diagrammatic representation of the human immunodeficiency virus (HIV). The central core of the virus contains the genetic information that the virus needs to reproduce itself. The highly complex egg-shaped projections covering the surface of the virus allow it to attack CD4 lymphocytes in a unique fashion.

Below left: The retina of a patient with AIDS: the retina is usually pink and blood vessels can be seen running over its surface. The white patches represent infection with cytomegalovirus.

Below right: The eye of the same patient a week later, showing how rapidly the infection can spread when T cells are unavailable for defence.

Top: Normally the immune system is readily able to destroy fungi that enter the body. For patients with AIDS however, invasion of the mouth and oesophagus with Candida albicans is a common and painful event. *Below:* Patients with AIDS are more susceptible to developing a number of cancers. A particular problem is Kaposi's sarcoma, a cancer in which there is a malignant proliferation of the blood vessels in the skin.

The human immunodeficiency virus started
to infect humans in Africa. For years
before the AIDS epidemic was recognised
for what it is, a debilitating and fatal
illness affecting young black men and
women was referred to as 'slim disease'
because it was so often associated with
enormous weight loss.

AIDS is sweeping through India, which will have more people infected
with the virus than any other country by 1995. Two of the children in
this picture were infected with HIV before they were even born.

Top: HIV could also be known as the 'poverty virus'. Many women in this village have been found to be infected with the virus as a result of sex with their husbands, who had themselves been infected by prostitutes.
Below: In the redlight district of Bombay, 150,000 prostitutes work every night. Some studies show that already more than 60% of them are infected with the AIDS virus.

Top: This highly allergic individual has undergone scratch testing with numerous antigens to find out what he should avoid. The white weals on his back represent positive responses to antigen scratched into his skin.
Below: The weals develop after mast cells covered with IgE antibody bind in allergen and explode to release histamine-like chemicals that affect blood vessels.

If an individual is considering being tested in such a climate, he obviously weighs carefully the pros and cons of the exercise. If the test is negative he may be mightily relieved but, if it is positive, can the information help him as an individual? If he is to risk discrimination he will not be interested in our desire to gather statistics on the speed at which the disease is spreading. If misguided governments have, as is unfortunately the case in a number of countries, introduced penalties with which to punish those people infected with the HIV virus who have sex with anyone without telling them of their infection, then voluntary screening for the HIV antibody seems even less appealing. A jealous lover could accuse one of all kinds of indiscretions. If, as is also the case in many places, laws have been passed which allow health officials to demand from doctors the names and addresses of individuals tested if they feel they need that information, individuals who contemplate being tested are further troubled.

Early diagnosis of HIV infection is helpful for a given patient. His battle with the HIV virus can be assisted and complications treated. But for the community, even more than for the individual, testing is essential and it is therefore necessary for all countries to work diligently to remove impediments to voluntary screening programs.

Why such widespread discrimination continues is worth examining, indeed researching. Given the irrefutable evidence that you can catch the HIV from another only if his or her blood or sexual secretions enter your body, why is there so much fear that leads to rejection? Prejudice against homosexual men is part of the problem. At a meeting of mortuary attendants who had refused to assist with autopsies on patients who had died from AIDS, I was asked, 'Why should we put ourselves a risk by cutting up a dead poofter?' No amount of explaining the facts, including the obvious one that not all AIDS victims are gay, had any effect on these men.

Recently, a patient of mine in the terminal phases of his struggle with AIDS decided he would like one final weekend in his attractive apartment by the sea. A heterosexual and single man of fifty years, he had been infected by sexual intercourse with a prostitute. All his life he had been involved with the surf lifesaving movement and was a champion swimmer and instructor. His club was his life. One of his young protégés, who had been asked to get some food into the apartment for this last weekend at home, called me to ask if Bill was well enough to enjoy a surprise. Twenty of the lads from the surf lifesaving association wanted to be there when he arrived home to pay their respects, show their appreciation of his help in years gone by and sadly to say goodbye. It was well known that Bill was dying. Bill had not hidden this fact from his friends, but had chosen to tell them that he was dying from cancer.

I thought the surprise party was a wonderful idea. An ambulance was ordered to take Bill home on a Saturday after-noon for the weekend.

On Sunday morning while on a ward round of my patients in the AIDS unit, I passed Bill's room. To my surprise, he was in his bed sobbing quietly. Enquiries soon revealed how the surprise party had gone sadly astray.

The ambulance men who picked up Bill from our AIDS unit, despite the protestations of the patient and staff, wore space suits. They were covered from head to feet and wore thick yellow kitchen gloves. Bill was amazed but did not know what was waiting for him at his home and therefore resigned himself to their stupidity and his embarrassment. When the gathering awaiting Bill saw him being carried into his apartment by these weirdly dressed ambulance men, surprise gave way to consternation. The true cause of Bill's illness was revealed to his friends and to his gaping neighbours.

There was no party. All but one of our well-meaning but igno-rant young men vanished and a distraught Bill, who had not wanted his friends to know of his AIDS, let alone feel their rejection, came back to hospital to die in misery two days later.

I was furious with the ambulance officers, who had not followed the guidelines laid down and accepted by their organisation for the transfer of AIDS patients. When I confronted the ambulance officers involved, one of them defended his actions with a defiant 'you guys don't know as much as you think you know'.

This was a telling phrase, typical of a new attitude among many to medical science and the doctors who practise it. We constantly see intelligent people, who could not have escaped information on the lack of infectivity of AIDS from social intercourse, acting unintelligently: magistrates who refuse to have HIV-infected indi-viduals in their court rooms, policemen who demand danger money for arresting an HIV-infected prostitute, airline personnel who won't have such people in their planes, etc.

The changing attitudes of many to orthodox science and doctors may be attributed, no doubt, to many different factors. With a break-through behind us that saw vaccines and antibiotics developed to wipe out so much of the suffering of humanity, we find ourselves in a period when the tough problems remain tough and yield their secrets reluctantly. We need breakthroughs in cancer, heart disease and even ageing to win back many who expected the flow of medical miracles to continue.

Physicians must assume some of the blame. Too many of them, in these difficult economic times, practise turnstile medicine, dis-pensing good drugs for poor reasons as they fail to give patients sufficient time to explore exactly what is and what is not wrong with them. Sadly, there are many of us teachers of medicine who feel that the standard of medical practice in the Western world is falling despite more practical knowledge being available than ever before.

In fact, the rapidity with which sound, useful and complex knowledge about the HIV virus and its ravages has accumulated is a triumph of modern medicine. We have much to learn about the HIV virus, of course, but there will be no retreating from the well established modes of transmission. Only when HIV-infected fluids enter one's body is one at risk. The only fluids which contain sufficient amounts of virus to produce infection are sexual secretions (male and female), blood (and some blood products) and breast milk. Saliva, tears and urine are not infectious unless they contain blood.

Who should be tested?

Testing is desirable in the following cases:

- Anyone who is worried for any reason. Often a test is needed to dispel unwarranted fear that will not evaporate, even with expert counselling.

  A modern phenomenon that I suppose was unavoidable is AIDS phobia. Often people want to be tested who really have no reason at all to believe they could have been infected. Pre-test counselling will usually allow those people who have nothing to fear from HIV to realise that fact and go away happy, without having a test. But if someone insists on having a test, it is preferable to let them find out their results and be counselled once again. The majority of people who are negative will breathe a sigh of relief and that will be that, but there are increasing numbers of individuals who cannot accept a negative result. They want the test done again and again and again. They have developed a totally irrational fear of HIV for some psychological reason.

  Recently, a doctor came to see me and told me that he was terrified that he was infected with HIV. Had he had an AIDS test, I asked. Yes, several, he replied. All negative but he still was worried about the possibility. At this point in the interview, the extremely alarmed man took out $500 from an envelope in his pocket and put it on my desk and begged me to do the test for him one more time in my laboratory. His own doctors had refused further testing. Clearly, the man was psychologically disturbed. When I questioned him further it turned out that a few months earlier, after a few drinks, he had done something he had never done before: he had picked up a street prostitute.

She took him to her room and, as he undressed, she nibbled at his left nipple. With the shock of that kiss, he told me, he came to his senses, quickly put his clothes on again and left and nothing more happened. He was convinced, however, that that nibble had been enough to infect him with HIV. It took months of psychiatric treatment to cure this man of his phobia.

- All gay men who have been sexually active in the last 15 years.
- All hemophiliacs who have received factor VIII.
- Everyone who had a transfusion of blood or blood products (plasma, platelets, etc.) between 1978 and May 1985, when antibody testing of all blood donors was introduced. Some countries still do not test blood donors and in such countries the risk of acquiring HIV from a transfusion remains.
- Individuals who have had sex with a prostitute, particularly in Africa or in Asia.
- All male and female prostitutes.
- All intravenous drug users who have ever shared a needle or syringe.
- All sexual partners of intravenous drug users.
- All children born to HIV-infected mothers.
- All donors for sperm banks.
- All donors of organs for transplantation.
- All blood donors.
- All prisoners.
- All members of the armed forces.
- All diplomatic personnel sent to countries where AIDS is a major problem and the blood supply is not screened.

In many societies where HIV infection is a major problem, women planning pregnancy should be tested, as should immigrants moving from those countries to any others. Couples in an evolving relationship will much more commonly seek reassurance from each other that their previous sexual experiences have not exposed them to HIV. This will be necessary before sexual intimacy can safely take its place within that relationship. Unromantic? Yes. Necessary? In many places, definitely. The advice will hold for many more cities and countries in the not too distant future, unless we halt the spread of this disease.

I feel that I must emphasise once again that, because of continuing discrimination problems, no one should have the HIV antibody test without the advantage of prior counselling about the consequences of a positive result. Similarly, immediate counselling must be available to those whose tests turn out to be positive. Pretest counselling should include a discussion of the discrimination that abounds, the necessity of keeping the news of a positive result to a very limited number of people, the inability of HIV positive individuals to get life assurance, the fact that being HIV positive is not synonymous with having AIDS, etc.

Antigen testing

One technical problem associated with antibody testing, namely the window period, will be solved by antigen tests. None of the discrimination problems will disappear, however. By antigen testing is meant the detection of the virus itself, rather than antibody to the virus. Antigen testing is rapidly improving as more and more sensitive techniques are forwarded that allow us to search a patient's blood for minute amounts of the proteins that make up both the coat and the core of the virus. These proteins can be detected within twenty-four hours of infection but the amount present in the blood then decreases for a considerable time, indeed until AIDS is developing, before returning in full force. Techniques for antigen testing have to be very sensitive to ensure that false negative results are not reported.

Antigen testing will be invaluable in helping us diagnose HIV infections in the newborn babies of infected mothers. All these infants have antibodies against HIV in their blood but it may be antibody produced by the mother, not by the baby. Only when all the maternal antibody disappears and is replaced by the baby's own gammaglobulin (about the age of one) can a diagnosis of HIV infection be made by antibody screening. Sufficiently sensitive antigen testing will solve that problem. Antigen testing will also eliminate the vulnerability that troubles blood banks. Theoretically, donors who have been infected within three months of giving blood could nevertheless have a negative antibody test. While in practice this is not a problem, the advantages of the antigen tests are obvious. Unfortunately, the expense will deprive the Third World of this advance for many years.

Heterosexual AIDS

There is a frightening complacency among many heterosexual individuals about the potential of the AIDS epidemic to affect them. Why is it so difficult to get an appropriate tone into the debate about the risk of HIV transmission by heterosexual activity? On the one hand, we have insufficiently informed individuals declaring authoritatively that heterosexuals having vaginal intercourse have nothing to fear from the HIV virus. They claim that calling for a modification of sexual behavior among heterosexuals can come only from moralists or homosexuals who wish to have the heterosexual community sexually shackled like themselves. At the other extreme, we have statements from individuals who see AIDS as a punishment for sin and who predict that soon the heterosexual community will be afflicted by a massive plague that will sweep away the sexually promiscuous.

As is so often the case in hotly debated issues, the truth is very much in the middle. Here are the facts. You can decide for yourself.

Women having anal sex, in which HIV-infected seminal fluid or even the secretions that emerge from the penis prior to ejaculation enter their rectum, face the same risk experienced by a gay male in a similar situation. While it is entirely possible that one such episode could lead to a fatal infection, statistical analysis of the available data tells us that one's chance of becoming infected after ten to fifty such episodes with an infected male is about 48 per cent. Is physical trauma necessary? I don't think so, but there is no doubt that bleeding or the tearing of mucous membranes would increase the risk, as would any anal or rectal sore. Many men and women who regularly engage in anal sex are able to dilate their anal sphincter readily and not be traumatised by an erect penis. Recent studies in the United States show that 10 per cent of women regularly engage in anal sex for pleasure; 25 per cent do so occasionally. On these figures, more women in that country have anal sex than do men.

What are the risks for a woman who has only vaginal intercourse with an infected man? Some variables have to be considered here.

The infectiousness of a man's sexual secretions increases with time; they become even more dangerous as his T cell count begins to fall. As the years of the epidemic pass, we have seen a big increase in the number of infected wives married to hemophiliacs or to men themselves infected by a blood transfusion. Thus it is important for women to realise that some infected men are far more dangerous than others. One African man who visited Europe and had only vaginal sex with sixteen European women infected nine of them.

As is the case with anal sex, vaginal sex can result in infection after only one episode. I care for a number of patients who have had this experience. However, statistics tell us that repeated exposure is usually necessary. To try to quantify the risk, a review of the world's literature together with my own experience would suggest that a woman who has vaginal intercourse with an infected man between ten and fifty times has a 17 to 33 per cent chance (mean 26 per cent chance) of being infected.

A recent report on a wire service told women all around the world the good news from one study. Sixty-six per cent of the wives or regular lovers of HIV-infected men who had in fact been living with these men for a year or more were not themselves infected with HIV at the end of that period. The virus was not so bad after all!

Surely such a report should have contained a completely different emphasis. What a tragedy it is that 34 per cent of the lovers of HIV-infected men have themselves become infected with the deadly virus. The English have a pithy advertisement on billboards in which an elegant young woman looks you in the eye and says, 'I like sex, but I am not prepared to die for it'.

The other variable that must be re-emphasised is the genital health of women. While the infection of women during artificial insemination tells us that neither trauma nor an obvious break of the vaginal lining is necessary for infection, strong data indicate that women with genital ulcers, cervical erosions, a previous history of gynecological surgery or sexually transmitted diseases are significantly more vulnerable. Genital problems are very frequently found in underdeveloped countries and they are anything but uncommon in Western society. Without regular inspection of the genital tract many women could be unaware of the existence of some of these problems, for symptoms may be minimal.

What about oral sex? If a woman allows male (or female) sexual secretions to enter her mouth or swallow such secretions, can she be infected? Here the data are circumstantial. We know that HIV can infect babies fed infected breast milk. We know that infected blood, taken inadvertently into the mouth of health professionals, has resulted in their infection, and we have one case report where a lesbian was infected by taking infected secretions from her female lover into her mouth. The risk from oral sex we believe is minimal but not insignificant; it is, after all, a deadly virus of which we speak.

Infection of heterosexual men

A man having anal sex with an infected woman faces the same risks that he would experience if his partner were an infected male. His chances of being infected from vaginal intercourse alone can be looked at statistically. With ten to fifty episodes of vaginal intercourse with an HIV-infected woman, he faces a 12 to 15 per cent chance of becoming infected. Again, a number of variable factors greatly change the risk for a given individual. Abrasions, cuts or ulcers on the penis increase the risk considerably; it should be emphasised that macroscopic (as opposed to microscopic) breaks in the skin of the penis are not necessary for infection. It is quite possible that the sexual secretions of a woman could contain so much virus that some HIV could enter the body through the urethra (the opening in the penis).

In less developed countries men are at greater risk of infection during vaginal intercourse. This is thought to be related to the fact that many women in such countries experience poor genital health as a result of the inadequate treatment of sexually transmitted diseases, malnutrition and unskilled obstetric care. Not long ago, 16 healthy English engineers spent 6 months in Africa on a construction job for their company. Fifteen of them returned to Britain infected with HIV contracted by vaginal sex with African prostitutes. In Haiti, 55 per cent of male partners of HIV-infected women have themselves become infected.

The cervical and vaginal secretions of HIV-infected women contain virus and virus-infected T cells episodically. Virus can be recovered from vaginal secretions at a time it cannot be recovered from blood. Vaginal virus is not related to the menstrual cycle and does not represent a spillover from blood. A woman, however, may be more infectious and more vulnerable to infection during her period.

HIV will never spread through the heterosexual community in the West at the speed with which it devastated the gay community. Reassuring articles are written because of this, often quoting the fact that in the United States only 3 to 6 per cent of the known cases of HIV infection have occurred in heterosexual men and women whose only risk factor was sex with a carrier. But imagine that you picked up the paper one morning to find a headline: 'Ninety thousand heterosexual Americans infected with deadly virus spread by sexual intercourse'. That is the reality in the US and the Center for Disease Control tells us that the doubling rate for new heterosexual cases is ten months. Three per cent does not sound much but it certainly represents a lot of suffering. Indeed, new infections are occurring more rapidly in heterosexual women than in any other group.

Surely we need to make every effort to stop this virus from spreading through the heterosexual community. Unless sexual behaviour is modified, it will spread relatively slowly but inexorably into this community—and we should in no way be complacent about the matter. Studies in various Western societies have revealed very similar data. Thirty to thirty-five per cent of young people in the fifteen to twenty-seven age bracket regularly engage in activities that will facilitate the spread of the disease.

Condoms

The promotion of condoms as a useful weapon in the fight against AIDS has been controversial everywhere. The scientific facts are clear. The HIV cannot pass through an intact condom. Provided a condom is used throughout the entire act of intercourse, does not break, and none of its contents are allowed to spill during withdrawal of the penis from the vagina or anus, the risk of HIV transmission in either direction is minimal. The problem is that years of experience in the use of condoms for contraceptive purposes tells us that a 5 to 10 per cent problem rate is to be expected. Tearing of the condom accounts for only 1 per cent of the problem and this risk is highest with anal intercourse. The major problem has been, and remains, user error.

There is a lot of resistance to the use of condoms, mainly by men, and unless the sheathing of the erect penis is done as part of sexual foreplay there is often nothing to put a condom on. It takes practice. Women in most Western societies will have to insist on condoms and indeed carry them in their purse, given the attitudes of males towards this precaution. Numerous studies have shown that men will wear condoms if asked to do so, but are much less likely to suggest their use than are women. There is reasonable scientific evidence to suggest that condoms containing the spermicide antiviral agent nonoxynol 9 provide somewhat better protection than condoms without this agent.

The real controversy is confronted when health authorities try to promote the use of condoms. Some claim that such promotion will increase sexual activity among the young; there is no evidence for this. Others object to discussion of the subject on television and would never accept the type of demonstrations shown in Scandinavia and the United Kingdom, in which a model of an erect penis was employed to illustrate the correct technique for using condoms.

Societies can be hypocritical in this regard. Some time ago I was waiting in a television studio to discuss the abandoning of effective television advertising of condoms on the grounds of public disquiet. In the studio where I was waiting I saw on the monitor, in glorious color, a movie about a man living in a Mediterranean villa with two women he loved and who also loved him. As the three of them frolicked by his beautiful pool in the altogether, the phones in the television studio were quite silent. The television interviewer and I looked at each other and laughed as the irony struck us both simultaneously.

The churches are struggling with the theology of condom usage as an anti-AIDS measure. If one uses a condom to protect oneself from the AIDS virus and at the same time this prevents conception, can a married hemophiliac still have intercourse with his wife? The Catholic Church, for example, has decided that what is important is the theology of 'first intent'. It is certainly lawful to use a condom in such a situation if the first intention is to prevent the spread of infection rather than ensure contraception. Would a young teenage girl who has no intention of having intercourse with anyone be placed in the path of sin if she carried some condoms in her purse?

Numerous studies reported at the International AIDS Conference in Amsterdam in 1992 highlighted the fact that educating young people about the use of condoms and the carrying of condoms if anything decreased sexual activity, and certainly did not increase the frequency of casual sexual contacts. While many of us are not troubled by such questions, they are important for thousands or indeed millions who look for guidance on this matter to church authorities.

Sex and AIDS education in schools

Many societies are having difficulty accepting the advice from most health authorities that children from the age of twelve years up need to be told about AIDS in language appropriate for their age but nevertheless explicit. School systems are not used to being called upon to assist in health emergencies. While many school systems in Europe and the United States responded rapidly, most have not and survey after survey tells us that children are still confused. In the western suburbs of Sydney, recently, an investigator seeking answers to an alarming increase in IV (intravenous) amphetamine use among teenagers asked them, among other things, if they were not concerned about developing AIDS with all the needle sharing going on. 'Hell, no,' was the answer. 'We're not gay.'

Aids and IV drug use

Most people who use IV drugs and share needles are not addicts but recreational users. The two groups have an equal risk of being infected with HIV. In many parts of the United States the sharing of needles has become the major method for HIV transmission. New Jersey is the best (worst?) example. On Manhattan island, 275 000 IV drug users are infected and health authorities have already decided to ignore them as they put all their energies into preventing new cases.

What can be done with the IV drug-using population? Some can be educated and change, according to a recent report from San Francisco. Some can be taught to rinse their syringes and needles with household bleach before passing the equipment on to the next user. Some can be diverted from their IV use by accelerated acceptance into a well-run methadone program in which an oral preparation is substituted for the IV drug. Perhaps the best but most controversial step is issuing free needles and syringes to drug users on an exchange basis. In Amsterdam, where a pilot program was conducted, 80 per cent of the needles and syringes were returned to the distributors. For many, however, the thought that we are giving sterile syringes and needles to people whom we desperately want to stop using drugs is distressing. Recently, in advocating acceptance of such a program to a group of clergymen who certainly looked doubtful, I was helped by an archbishop who jumped up and gently rebuked me for suggesting this philosophy and who emphasised the difference between 'the end justifies the means' and 'the lesser of two evils'. He told us a story about St Thomas Aquinas and his efforts to establish brothels, not because he was in favour of prostitution, but because he could not stand to see the robberies and murders associated with uncontrolled street prostitution. The archbishop won the day for me, I believe. All authorities agree that in Western society IV drug users are largely responsible for introducing HIV into the heterosexual community.

Retrovir (AZT)

In recent years a most exciting advance in the therapy of HIV infection has produced an ethical dilemma for governments and society. The British pharmaceutical giant Burroughs Wellcome developed a drug that markedly reduces the rate at which the AIDS virus can multiply. The drug is a DNA chain terminator. Its chemical name is Azidothymidine (abbreviated almost universally as AZT); its tradename is Retrovir. As the virus instructs T cells to cement together the building blocks that will construct a new AIDS virus, the drug binds to one of the blocks, preventing the next piece of the virus being correctly aligned. Given to patients in the early stages of Group IV disease, that is, patients losing their battle with the virus but who have not yet developed AIDS, the drug can improve health and add between one and two years of quality life to 60 per cent of patients. It doesn't cure and it is less useful to patients with AIDS than to those with a less serious complication of HIV infection. Most patients with AIDS are young and our approach is based on the hope that a major curative breakthrough is around the corner. Retrovir is valuable for keeping patients as well as possible for as long as possible.

It is a very significant advance; the problem is one of expense. The drug costs about $US5000 per year per patient and it doesn't cure them. Many cannot afford the drug as they have lost their jobs and are heavily burdened with medical bills. In the United States only the wealthy and those helped by family or friends can afford it. In countries with a national health scheme governments are balking at the bill, especially as scientific evidence accumulates suggesting that we should give AZT in combination with other anti-retroviral drugs to people in Group II; that is, infected, infectious, but well patients. It may help them fight their HIV infection and we already know that it reduces their risk of infecting a sexual partner. In a number of countries governments have said, 'No more'. A quota system has been introduced and after the quota has been supplied, no more government money will be available for the drug.

This has sparked a debate which must catch fire and spread. It is up to all of us in society to decide how many of the technical advances that are now or soon will be available to prolong an individual's life we can or will afford. From AZT to artificial hearts, the debate must lead to a societal discussion about the priorities we place on an individual's life. Certainly those of us who have to look into the eyes of a patient infected with the AIDS virus, and tell them that they are a week too late for getting help from AZT, feel that no Western society has spent enough on this drug at this time. We all realise, however, there must be a limit. That limit cannot be set by doctors. For forty cents per week per patient we could eliminate malaria, but we won't spend the money. Issues such as AIDS may force us to come to grips with decisions about affording what is possible but very expensive. Can a city build a new opera house while thousands of young people cannot be given a life-preserving drug? I suspect so.

The blood supply

Because most individuals infected with HIV remain well for years, many infected people donated or sold blood to the Red Cross or commercial blood banks prior to May of 1985. Donated blood is more often than not split between two recipients: the red cells may be given to one patient and the plasma to another. Thousands of patients around the world were infected in this manner, when 100 per cent of people given an infected blood transfusion were themselves infected.

Vicious rumours circulated on a number of continents that gay men, infected with HIV, deliberately gave blood to blood banks to ensure that the heterosexual community also became infected. There is no evidence to support such a claim anywhere in the world.

In May of 1985 most Western blood banks began the labor-intensive and expensive but obviously essential job of screening all donated blood for the presence of antibody to HIV. Well before this time they had introduced measures to deter individuals belonging to high risk groups from donating blood. Written information was given to prospective donors explaining explicitly just who should not give. Combining antibody testing with the completion of a detailed questionnaire, blood banks have virtually abolished the risk of contracting HIV from blood or a blood product. When antigen testing is available, the tiny risk that some pathological personality infected within a few weeks of donation will be able to lie his or her way through a questionnaire and escape detection by antibody screening will disappear. A number of problems remain, however.

In many countries hundreds, indeed thousands, of people infected by contaminated blood are unaware of their infection. This is bad news for them and of course means that their sexual partners are at risk. Many countries that can afford the gesture are asking patients who received blood or blood products during their country's vulnerable period (1978–1985 in the US) to have an HIV antibody test. It is difficult to conduct such a look-back program without causing panic and rekindling fear about the blood supply today. In Sydney 275 000 people needed to be screened in the attempt to find 400 infected recipients.

A further problem of considerable significance for travellers needs discussing. Many countries are not screening blood donors. Most cannot afford it (Africa, the Philippines, Indonesia and others) while some are remarkably tardy in introducing these measures. By the time you read this one hopes that the situation will have changed, but travellers should know if a country that they plan to visit has a safe blood supply. This information is available from most airlines.

The lack of universal testing sees many diplomatic services demanding that all their personnel be HIV-tested before being despatched to foreign posts. In this way they are able to rely on each other as a source of blood should this be necessary. Such reasoning lies behind the decision of many countries to test all personnel in the armed forces. In the latter case the realisation that HIV infection of the brain can alter the appropriateness of decision making before the major complications of HIV infection are manifest has added impetus to the screening program.

The AIDS epidemic has been the establishment of a number of private blood banks that will store your own blood for you in case you ever need small amounts close to home. This is a reasonable idea, though expensive. Of course such banks will not be able to help you if major trauma demands immediate transfusion or if your problems develop far from home. For this reason, it is important for all to realise that the blood supplied by banks that question their donors and screen their blood can now be considered safe.

Mosquitoes

Many find difficulty in believing that mosquitoes don't spread HIV. They *don't*, and we now know why they can't. Careful scientific analysis of mosquitoes deliberately allowed to feed on HIV-infected blood has taught us that there is not sufficient blood left on the biting parts of the mosquito, after a feed, to have enough infected T cells to pass on HIV to the mosquito's next victim. In addition, the virus passing into the mosquito's stomach cannot multiply and infect the mosquito. In fact, the virus is killed. Without replication the virus cannot be concentrated in the mosquito's salivary glands, a necessary step for the transmission of organisms when one is being bitten.

Mosquitoes don't inject us with blood; they wish to feed on the blood of someone they are biting. In order to facilitate this they inject saliva into the tissue being pierced, for their saliva contains an anti-coagulant that will stop blood clotting during their subsequent feeding. What could be more frustrating for a hungry mosquito than to have the blood that it is sucking up its thin straw-like mouth parts clot? HIV does not get into the saliva of mosquitoes. The diseases that mosquitoes do spread involve parasites or viruses that have adapted their lifestyle to enable them to survive, and in some cases thrive, inside the mosquito. We are indeed fortunate that in its modelling, HIV neglected the adaptation steps needed to use mosquitoes.

Professor Duesburg's claim that AIDS is not caused by HIV

Virologist Peter Duesburg of the University of California at Berkley has repeatedly claimed that scientists who believe that AIDS is caused by HIV, or any virus for that matter, are misled. What's more, doctors, far from helping patients with the drug AZT, are in fact hastening their deaths.

Now these two extraordinary claims, both definitely wrong, are much loved by the media, who have delighted in the controversy created. Here is the brave Professor Duesburg challenging the collective wisdom of thousands of scientists, who because of their study of the subject are convinced that HIV causes AIDS. Duesburg has stated publicly that he would not be the slightest bit worried were he to be injected with a pure strain of HIV, so certain is he that this virus is in fact harmless. He argues that the decadent lifestyle led by many, featuring especially and most dangerously the use of drugs coupled with anal intercourse, leads to an inexorable de-terioration in T cell function, and that this in turn produces AIDS.

He started his questioning of the established theory because of a reasonable enough concern. Scientists could only find HIV in relatively few T cells at any stage of the infection with this virus. 'If only 1 in 1000 T cells are infected, how could the virus be responsible for the death of all the others?' he asked. 'HIV cannot be the cause of such a profound immunodeficiency.' The facts have been described earlier but are worth repeating.

At first we thought that 1 in 10 000 to 1 in 1000 CD4 cells were infected and producing virus and, as viruses kill cells when they multiply, some other mechanisms must come into play to account for the death of so many apparently non-infected cells. Today, however, using more sensitive techniques, we know that in fact about 1 in 20 CD4 cells are actually infected with HIV and producing new viral particles. Earlier in the chapter we discussed the other virus-induced mechanisms that contribute to the destruction of our immune system. With the discovery of so many other mechanisms by which HIV is capable of killing T cells, and the new evidence that in fact many more cells are infected with the virus than was previously thought, Professor Duesburg's concerns should have ceased. They haven't.

The one unifying feature of all the cases of AIDS in the world, whether we are talking about children or adults, homosexual or heterosexual individuals, injecting drug users, men with hemophilia, etc., is the presence in the body of HIV. Recent studies have looked at large cohorts of gay men, whose lifestyle has featured over a number of years the use of inhaled and injected drugs and experience with numerous sexual partners. Cohorts from cities as far apart as Toronto and Sydney have been carefully studied to find out who had suppressed immune systems. Quite clearly, the answer was 'only those infected with HIV'.

Lifestyle could not of course explain the following. A nineteen-year-old cadet warder at one of our major prisons, fit and healthy, in fact a champion soccer player, was on duty in the prison yard one afternoon when a prisoner who had been working out in the gymnasium requested that a gate be unlocked so that he could move from one restricted area to another. Our cadet warder did as was requested but as he turned to lock the gate once more he felt a sharp jab in his left buttock. 'Have some AIDS, you bastard,' the prisoner yelled at the young man and walked away. Panicking, the young guard went to the First Aid station where a nurse examined his buttock and found a mark consistent with a needle-stick injury. There was also a small amount of blood noted on his underpants.

The police were summoned and on searching the area around the gate found an empty but blood-stained syringe. There was enough blood left inside for an antibody test to be performed and, tragically, it was found that this blood contained HIV. Young Rodney sero-converted five weeks later, while the prisoner, who soon after the incident developed AIDS, died five months later. Rodney's T cells have already fallen significantly.

Numerous other clinical facts would not sustain Duesburg's argument, including the development of AIDS in people who were transfused with blood containing HIV. Indeed, he should have re-tired from the debate when pure cultures of the simian immuno-deficiency virus, SIV (the monkey variant of HIV which causes AIDS in Macaques), was found to produce AIDS in healthy monkeys injected with the material. In the monkey model, also, an apparently low number of T cells are actually carrying virus at any given time. What we have seen, however, is a persistent counterattack from Duesburg that features increasingly less convincing arguments, and an ever more stubborn display of intellectual arrogance.

Urged on by the medical press and a TV station in Britain, the Duesburg ideas continue to cause problems, however. Editorial opinions in India, swallowing the Duesburg line, queried the usefulness of testing people for HIV in that huge country destined to have the worst AIDS epidemic of any nation.

That any number of co-factors might alter the natural history of HIV infection is certainly possible, indeed likely. We already know that a double dose of retroviruses, for example infection with HIV and HTLV1, may hasten the onset of AIDS as does a co-infection with hepatitis B and certain herpes infections. The epidemic that is sweeping the world, however, is caused by HIV; there is no doubt at all about this fact.

As far as the drug AZT is concerned, there is an abundance of evidence that it can provide as much as two and a half years of additional quality life to people infected with HIV. On the low doses used today (average 500mg/day), fewer than 15 per cent of patients experience significant side-effects. The total number of white blood cells does fall somewhat in patients on the drug, but not seriously so, and CD4 counts actually increase, although unfortunately only transiently. AZT and the other drugs that we now have available cannot cure and cannot even hold back the progress of the disease indefinitely, but such drugs are important nonetheless. There is much momentum in AIDS research and, if you consider that together with the fact that the majority of people infected with HIV are young, then our philosophy must be to keep as many people as possible as well as possible for as long as possible, as we await a definitive therapy.

The Duesburg phenomenon illustrates the fine line that exists between constructive criticism, with the issuing of appropriate challenges, and destructive stubbornness. Our Californian professor is lucky that no one has taken him at his word and demanded that he receive in public an injection of HIV.

A new virus?

Is there a new AIDS-producing virus that is not related to HIV? Such a possibility was hinted at during the Amsterdam AIDS Conference in July 1992.

At the Conference much was said that was very newsworthy, for example, the plight of women infected with HIV in India, the tremendous increase in drug-resistant tuberculosis around the world, and of course the fact that the AIDS epidemic continues to spread rapidly around the world. Such stories however attracted little if any publicity. What received most attention, and undue attention at that, was the discovery of about twenty cases of T cell suppression that a collection of immunologists (a 'clone' of immunologists?) could report where no evidence of HIV infection could be demonstrated.

CD4 and sometimes CD8 cells were known to slowly decline in this handful of patients and some had developed an AIDS-like illness, not surprisingly. The consequences of losing one's T cells will be the same, no matter what the cause. In fact we have known for more than twenty years that Acquired Immune Deficiency States develop in both the B and T cell system. There is no evidence whatsoever of transmission of these defects from one person to another by sexual or any other form of contact. Such unusual cases, important and all as they are for the individuals affected, do not in any way suggest that a new virus has learnt the tricks of HIV and will now sweep around the world making blood supplies unsafe, etc. In fact I am caring for such a case at the moment and the details have been passed on to the American Center for Disease Control, which will collect and analyse all these cases to be sure that there are no similarities that suggest an infectious cause. Specimens will be looked at to see if any viral proteins (fingerprints) are present in the blood of these cases.

I suspect that, with the publicity received and the call for cases to be reported to the CDC, a few hundred will be documented from the six billion sets of T cells on the planet and that genetic rather than viral factors will be involved in the generation of this form of immunodeficiency. It is of course not impossible that a new virus could one day appear and cause an AIDS-like illness, so while there is no scientific reason for any alarm to be generated because of the report of these cases, there is no room for complacency either and thus the situation will be watched carefully.

My case is a fairly typical one. Harold, fifty-two, was sent to me because he had disseminated and painful shingles. Shingles is caused by the chicken pox virus, which is referred to as *herpes zoster* when it causes shingles and *varicella* when it causes chicken pox (the connections were made after the names had been generated). Once infected with the chicken pox virus (most children are, of course), the virus is there forever. It retreats to a hiding place under the protective sheaths that are wrapped around nerves, and there lies dormant by inserting its DNA into that of the local nerve cells. While our T cells are competent it is usually forced to stay dormant. Factors released by T cells and not yet well understood block any attempt the virus makes to multiply. If one lets down one's T cell guard, however, the virus bursts out into the skin over these nerves and causes painful blisters. Our T cells fight it off unless we are so immunosuppressed that we offer no resistance, in which case the condition can even be fatal.

Often shingles flare up in people who are stressed or generally unwell, and there is a higher incidence in people with cancer. Sometimes it happens for no obvious reason at all. Rarely we run into the problem faced by Harold. This man is an easy-going dynamo. The contradiction in terms is produced when one marries a most pleasant disposition to unbridled energy. Harold has numerous businesses and is doing well. He is happily married.

Harold had had three attacks of shingles in eighteen months prior to our first meeting. Otherwise, he had been well. In giving his history, he did tell me about an attack of syphilis which he contracted during some rest and recreation leave while in Vietnam as a soldier thirty years earlier. That problem had been treated and never reoccurred. That was the end of his flirtation with commercial sex.

Since then he had been well until his shingles developed. When I examined him there was nothing else to find, but the laboratory reported that his CD4 count was 180 per microlitre. His T cells did not respond well to challenges in the test tube. On Acyclovir, the most effective antiviral agent we have to fight herpes infections, his shingles subsided and have not returned—he takes medication daily. His T cell count has fallen no further. His wife and children are well, and an exhaustive search for HIV has failed to find any suggestion that the virus is present. No other infectious agent can be detected.

I have seen two other similar cases over the past twenty-five years. The other cases did not feature even one episode of a sexually transmitted disease. The man and woman in question remain moderately ill but did not progress to a stage where they had no T cells, as happens all too often with patients infected with HIV.

In discussing the transmission of HIV, what is safe sex?

All sexual activity is free of the risk of contracting HIV if the sexual partners involved are free of infection. Recently, I was giving a lecture to the public in the Town Hall in Kuala Lumpur, Malaysia. Little formal education about HIV had been available. One young girl, obviously puzzled, asked me after the lecture why sex suddenly became safe when one married. 'What is it about marriage,' she asked, 'that changes biology?' It's the HIV status of your partner that is important, not whether you are married or not.

Actually, someone in a long-term relationship, where both parties have been faithful to each other and are HIV negative, has no chance of being infected by sexual activity. For them, sex is absolutely safe. But, in this less than perfect world, relationships are often less than perfect and infidelity is extremely common. That a faithful partner may be unaware of infidelity, even for a number of years, is also a fact and therein lies the dilemma.

Ken is a structural engineer and his company required him to spend six months as a consultant in Zimbabwe on a lucrative project. He left his wife, six-year-old daughter and five-year-old son at home and travelled to Africa. When he returned, his wife was later to tell me, she asked him jocularly, 'Now Ken, you were faithful to me while you were away, weren't you; you didn't play around darling, did you?' He reassured her and they resumed their normal sexual activity. Ken had lied to her, however.

Two months later, he could not pretend that there was not a small discharge from his penis and, annoyed, he went to see his doctor. While in Zimbabwe he had used the local prostitutes a few times, as had most of the other men he was working with, and as a result he had contracted gonorrhea. A course of antibiotics had been prescribed and all seemed well but now, however, the damn thing had re-occurred. His doctor, after listening to the story, sent some fluid off for analysis and was soon able to confirm that, indeed, Ken had a chronic infection with gonorrhea. He then added, 'You'd better have an HIV test as well, Ken, you know that HIV is common in African prostitutes, even though you'd be unlucky to be infected.' Ken was unlucky. When his test came back with a positive result, he was to tell me a few weeks later, he went into a state of shock. HIV is something you read about in the newspapers. It doesn't happen to Mr Average, thought Ken. Ken's doctor of course told him that he would have to tell all to his wife, who would also need a test for HIV and gonorrhea. While the doctor was talking, Ken slumped further and further into the chair, was silent for a few seconds, and then told his doctor that not only his wife would need testing. Ken had resumed an affair on his return home with a flight attendant he had met a few years earlier. She also would have to be tested.

Both women were positive, and thus infected, and his wife in fact screamed at Ken and punched him after learning the result. To be betrayed and to be infected with a deadly virus was shattering. To realise that in all likelihood their young children would be orphaned filled her with a black despair.

Infidelity in marriage or a stable de facto relationship is not just a problem for heterosexual couples, and of course women can do the betraying. But women are far more easily infected with HIV than are men and many more men than women use commercial sex workers, though more women than ever before are indulging.

A woman faces an additional HIV hazard if her man is bisexual. This is a particularly dangerous situation in many Western countries where large numbers of homosexual men and gay prostitutes are carriers of HIV. Because of the difficulties associated with keeping a long-term gay relationship from a wife, bisexual men often engage in extremely careless casual sexual behaviour, often retreating to 'beats' where they may have sex with someone equally anxious that the activity be handled discreetly. Many bisexual men in fact don't consider themselves to be gay at all, even if they find that their real sexual preference is for men, and they are often not reached by HIV warnings in the gay press.

Are there signs that a woman can look for that may suggest to her that her husband is bisexual? After many years of seeing bisexual couples caught in the AIDS trap, I do not believe there is any stereotype or indeed any reliable or consistent behavioural signs that might alert a woman, even if she dared to allow herself to contemplate such a thing. In this difficult age, it would be wrong to suggest to all women that every husband should be suspected of infidelity or of occasionally or regularly having casual sex with men. To do so would see many marriages and partnerships placed under inappropriate strain. However, 5–10 per cent of men who are married have sex with men so the problem is enormous. Clearly, women are best protected if the whole of society is educated about the dangers that everyone faces as a consequence of careless casual sexual behaviour. Personalising such messages, however, is a difficult matter.

While safe sex is sex with a faithful partner where neither partner is infected, and this of course is now a medical as well as a moral imperative, what is *safer* sex?

Two hundred million of us will experience a new sexually transmitted disease this year. Hundreds of millions already are infected with such diseases. In record numbers, young women are developing cancerous changes at the entrance to their uterus because of infection with certain strains of the human papilloma virus (HPV). Many, as you read this, are weeping because they have been told that they cannot have a baby, so badly scarred are their Fallopian tubes as a result of infection with chlamydia. Clearly, the war against AIDS is in fact a war against all sexually transmitted diseases. If any such infections are increasing in a specific population, then so are the chances for the spread of HIV in that population.

For those whose sexual activity might place them at risk of HIV infection, how can this risk be minimised? One is in danger every time sexual secretions from someone whom you can't be certain is not infected with HIV enter one's body. Saliva is not a sexual secretion. You cannot get infected with HIV by kissing. Last year, Italian scientists (who else!) published the results of a kissing experiment. Volunteers were recruited, probably with little difficulty, and asked to kiss passionately nonstop for 2, 4, 6, 8 and 10 minutes. Saliva was then collected to see if any bleeding had occurred, for any danger when kissing would be associated with the presence of blood in the mouth. A few red blood cells (but no frank blood) were found in the mouth of the 10-minutes kissers, but not enough damage was done to produce any risk of HIV transmission. However, to be on the conservative side, keep your kisses under 10 minutes and all will be well!

What about oral sex? Women need to understand that when a man becomes sexually aroused, even before he has a fully erect penis, a small amount of fluid can often be discharged from the urethra, the opening of which is at the tip of the penis. This fluid, in an HIV-infected man, is dangerous. Thus safer sex practices require that a male or female lover does not continue oral stimulation of a penis once sexual arousal is occurring. Certainly, to have a man ejaculate semen into the mouth could be dangerous. Oral stimulation of the penis is safe if it is covered by a condom, provided that the stimulation is gentle and teeth are kept out of the way. Flavoured condoms are available for the purpose. Condoms should sheath the penis from the moment it is sufficiently erect to accept a condom.

Safer sex requires a cautious approach to oral stimulation of a woman's clitoris, labia and vagina. It is inevitable that her sexual secretions will enter the mouth of the lover doing the kissing, and there have even been reports of lesbian couples being infected in this way. The female sexual secretions may well contain infected T cells if she is HIV positive and the risk of oral sex may be greater just before and during menstruation.

The danger of the other common oral sexual practice, namely kissing a lover's anus, which often involves a little penetration of this orifice with the tongue, may be dangerous but for obvious reasons it is hard to study. No one engages *only* in this form of sexual activity. When we advise homosexual men on safer sex, we recommend against anal kissing. The actual risk of contracting HIV in this way is unknown but can't be negligible. Although admittedly the evidence is nothing more than circumstantial, it nonetheless suggests that oral/anal contact may be associated with infection with an as yet unidentified agent that is responsible for Kaposi's sarcoma.

Now let me emphasise at this point that the risk associated with any form of oral sex is certainly much lower than that associated with vaginal or anal intercourse. Scared of HIV infection, many in recent years have limited their sexual encounters to oral intercourse; some individuals who have had no other form of sexual intercourse have still been infected with HIV. Whether it is necessary to have an ulcer or some other subtle lesion in the mouth is not clear, but since we are talking about a virus that will almost certainly kill one if it enters one's body the risk is certainly not worth the pleasure involved.

In this discussion most of the activity we have described involves lust not love, and to die for lust is really stupid. Real lovers, however, who get caught in the AIDS trap where one partner is infected often find a terrible strain developing which inhibits sexual intimacy; we will return to that matter shortly.

If we turn our attention to vaginal intercourse, the rules for safer sex are similar but even more imperative. A condom must be covering the penis before a woman allows any vaginal penetration to occur. Some couples only use a condom when the man becomes so excited that ejaculation is imminent but that is far too dangerous an activity as control is hard to guarantee, and in any case a woman is then not protected from the pre-ejaculation secretions described above. Care of course must be taken to hold the condom in place as the penis is withdrawn from the vagina.

Condoms used must be of first-rate quality or sex is anything but safer. Many cheap brands available in Asia, for example, are consistently found to be defective. They must also be the right size for the appendage involved. If they are too loose they will fall off, spilling sexual fluid, and that of course is the end of any safety.

A good friend of mine, a Professor of Public Health in Thailand, told me how his university was forced to become involved in research to find out the size of the average erect Thai penis. Imported condoms were often too big and manufacturers needed accurate data. He approached a group of female prostitutes and asked for help. He would give them 50 cents for every erect penis they measured in terms of length and diameter. One can only imagine the reaction of clients when, as things were really getting interesting, the girls reached for a tape measure! Well, the girls got the data but when my friend told them they could stop because he had all the information he needed, they offered to do the job for 10 cents, so much did they enjoy being scientists!

What about anal sex? Well of course the same rules apply and the gender of the recipient partner has nothing to do with the risk. Special strength condoms are available for anal intercourse and should be used, as ruptures are much more common during anal rather than vaginal intercourse.

Traumatising the anus in any way will of course add to the risks involved, for infection will become easier and it is possible that bleeding will occur.

The above precautions should, in my opinion, be adhered to by all people engaging in sexual activity with someone whom they are not certain is uninfected with HIV. What about sexual relationships involving people who *are* infected with HIV? Over the years, I have had hundreds of conversations with HIV-infected individuals about this matter. Clearly, whether one is talking about a heterosexual or homosexual couple, providing both partners are fully aware of the risks involved the degree of safety they employ in their sexual activities must remain a matter of personal choice. However, because of the deadly nature of the virus, because of the psychological consequences associated with infecting someone that one loves, because I have seen so often a breakdown in a relationship following the infection of a partner even though that partner may have been fully aware of the risks involved, I tell all my HIV-infected patients that I feel it is better for them to avoid all sexual activity that could possibly lead to another infection. This of course includes anal or vaginal intercourse even if a condom is used. Many follow that advice; many couples choose not to. It is an extremely difficult matter and particularly so for heterosexual couples who are anxious to have children. The wisdom of creating a new life when one parent is infected with a virus which may cause their premature death is debatable but, again, a very personal matter, and all the physician can do is counsel and help ensure that any discussion of the matter is an informed one. Much research is being done in an attempt to safely separate sperm cells from seminal fluid in a way that would guarantee that they are not contaminated by T cells or virus. In this way, artificial insemination of a non-infected woman may be possible without putting her at risk.

Clearly, when love is involved rather than merely lust it is sexual intimacy, that is, the sharing of activities of a sexual nature that one would share with no one else, that assumes the greater importance. In this situation, penetrative sex becomes much less an end in itself. Touching, kissing, mutual masturbation (HIV cannot pass through intact skin) and many other forms of safe sexual intimacy can be explored, and there is no doubt that physicians and trained counsellors should help HIV-infected individuals discuss sexual intimacy.

AIDS and health care workers

It has been distressing to see over the last ten years that discrimination, which can add immeasurably to the suffering of those infected with HIV, has involved health care workers in many countries. Usually, ignorance is involved and sometimes prejudice compounds the problem. Recently I was involved in the following court case.

A young homosexual actor playing a major role in a hit musical became ill after a performance one evening. He called his local doctor, who came to his house, examined him and said he had appendicitis and must go to the emergency room at a nearby major teaching hospital. This he did, and was promptly seen by a young intern who agreed that he did indeed have appendicitis. She called the surgical registrar, who ordered a theatre to be prepared and called in from home one of the hospital's leading surgeons to perform the operation. So far, all was efficiency and routine. As the surgeon was preparing to take the patient to theatre, having examined him and agreed with the diagnosis, the intern remarked that in taking a history she had discovered that the man in question was gay. He had not, she told the surgeon, had an HIV antibody test, was in a stable relationship and did not think there was any likelihood that he was infected. The surgeon, however, became very worried on hearing this news and after reflecting on the matter told the patient that perhaps he didn't have appendicitis after all. Perhaps he had a complication of HIV infection which could mimic appendicitis.

The surgeon rang a local infectious diseases hospital and asked them if they would take the patient. They refused. The surgeon then sent the man by ambulance to another major teaching hospital in the city that had a large AIDS unit. The poor man was reviewed in that hospital, told he had appendicitis, not an AIDS-related illness, and was sent back to the original hospital. The surgeon decided to watch him overnight and the next morning, in disgust, his local general practitioner removed him to a smaller private hospital. Before a second surgeon could operate, his appendix ruptured. The man spent six weeks in hospital in a serious condition.

The court ruled that discrimination had occurred and the episode cost the doctor (or rather his insurer) $400 000.

In another case in which I was involved as a witness, a young man went to see his doctor because of a small (1cm x 1cm) lump in his left breast. His general practitioner thought that any lump should be checked out by a surgeon. At the time of consultation the surgeon explained to the young man that breast cancer did occur in men, that indeed there are some 900 such cases reported each year in the United States, and that the lump should be removed. He arranged for this tiny procedure to be done on a day-only basis at a local hospital. In a manner similar to the previous story, as he was preparing to remove the lump under local anaesthetic, the intern helping him informed him that the man was gay and had not had an HIV antibody test. The surgeon refused to do the operation and, when the hospital authorities heard about the case, the man was summarily dismissed from the institute.

The ignorance that led to discrimination in both of these cases is disturbing. As is true in the rest of the community, AIDS has brought out the best and the worst in medical practitioners. Older physicians who constantly risked their personal health to care for people during the polio epidemics of the 50s find it very hard to understand the reluctance of people with 'Dr' in front of their names to help HIV-infected individuals.

There is no room for complacency among health professionals when caring for HIV-infected individuals or when handling blood which could possibly be infected. By using 'universal precautions'— that is, always presuming that blood could be infected and taking appropriate precautions—the risk of being infected as part of one's occupational activities is minimal indeed. With twelve million people infected and an epidemic that is ten years old in the Western world and much older than that in the developing world, there are only

35 known cases of individuals who have been infected while caring for people with HIV. Most of these are nurses and laboratory technicians who were tragically involved in accidents because they did not use appropriate precautions. Even if one has a needle-stick injury while caring for someone with AIDS, the chance that one will be infected is about 1 in 400. Thus while there is no room for complacency there is no room for panic, and no one should get a medal for looking after HIV-infected individuals.

It makes no sense whatsoever to test all patients coming into hospital, even those who require surgery, for in emergency situations there is no time to do the test. And, in any case, the window period, which means that antibody tests may provide a false negative result during the first three months of infection, demands that universal precautions be practised at all times. Duty of care in such a situation is clear cut. There is very little, if any, advantage to health professionals in knowing the HIV status of individuals they are caring for (unless they are caring for the HIV problem itself), and there is every likelihood that careless use in an institute of the knowledge that an individual is HIV positive may lead to discrimination.

Sport and HIV

The Magic Johnson affair has brought to the world's attention the problems that can develop if our knowledge of HIV is not used appropriately when deciding on the risks involved in playing contact sport with someone infected with HIV. The risks in most situations are so minimal that it is totally inappropriate to ban an HIV-infected athlete from playing basketball, football or any other contact sport. The only exception should involve boxing, in areas where there is a high prevalence of HIV. Clearly, it is possible to have blood on a glove that could be pounding into a wound and in such situations (although it has never occurred to our knowledge) there is a slight risk of infection. In general, providing all wounds are treated for their own sake as soon as they occur, there is no risk involved in playing sport with someone who is HIV positive. The chance that someone who is infected with HIV would have an injury and begin bleeding and have their blood splash into an open wound on another player who was not bleeding (obviously, if two people are bleeding blood is coming out, not going in) is extraordinarily remote, and the fact is that ten years into the epidemic we know of no such occurrence.

There are many other aspects of the AIDS epidemic that we simply cannot discuss here. Problems in prisons, the roles of non-government organisations, school policies, euthanasia, the legalisation of drugs, the availability of research programs to those infected, travel restrictions placed upon those infected with HIV and the unfortunate attempts of some communities to introduce quarantining of those who are infected all deserve our attention. Hopefully, armed with the information contained in this chapter, you will be able to argue sensibly on all of these points.

HIV is indeed presenting us with many serious challenges. Future historians will be able to tell much about us (if HIV doesn't win) in their documentation of whether we were intelligent enough to eradicate a virus that could be beaten without a drug or a vaccine by simply modifying dangerous behaviour. As we accept that challenge, let us double our efforts to find a cure. At least ten people have died of AIDS while you were reading this chapter, and 250 more have been infected with the virus.

PART IV

WHERE ARE THE GENERALS?

8

Understanding allergies

IN 1905, Austrian scientist Clemens von Pirquet was involved in the research work that gave the world the term 'allergy' and pushed back the frontiers of the infant science of immunology. His work culminated in a huge manuscript which he published in an American medical journal in 1911. Sandwiched between an article on the hazards to women's health if they wore corsets too tightly and one on the hazards of cross-infection in poorly ventilated trains was his eighty-five-page account entitled 'Allergy'.

To understand the significance of Von Pirquet's work, we need to spend a little time setting the scientific scene. It was known by the turn of the century that immunological protection (i.e. the reason why one does not get the same infection twice) was related to the appearance of chemicals in the blood of a person who has recovered from an initial infection. These chemicals were called 'antibodies'. There was no knowledge of the thymus gland's role in any of this, no knowledge of T cells; the concept of cells specifically attacking tissue invaders was forty years away.

Among infectious diseases in Europe none was more devastating than tuberculosis (TB), a killer with no respect for age. From the organisms that caused this disease Von Pirquet had isolated and extracted a protein that was very useful: tuberculin. It was harmless, as it was not infectious, but when injected into the skin of people one of two things would happen. Either no reaction would be noted or, slowly over forty-eight hours, a red itchy lump would appear at the injection site: a tuberculosis reaction. This latter was

223

very important, for it meant that the bacteria that caused TB had been or were still in the body, and the immune system had responded or was responding. Patients with suspected TB but negative skin tests would have another cause for their problem.

Today, we can envisage the protein extract from the bacteria being recognised by T cells in the skin, and the alarm being sounded. Defence mechanisms are rushed in to do battle and, if one has had previous experience with these organisms, one's defences are so efficient that at the end of forty-eight hours a massive attack is under way and clearly visible. All Von Pirquet knew for certain was that a positive reaction meant that at some time the patient had come in contact with the organisms that caused tuberculosis.

In his experiments designed to learn more about this reaction, Von Pirquet used guinea pigs and another protein that was easier to come by—albumen, the protein in the white of the ordinary egg. If his theory about the tuberculosis reaction was correct, then an injection of albumen into the skin of guinea pigs that had not been immunised (sensitised) with albumen would produce no reaction. However, after injecting egg albumen into his laboratory animals and waiting for a week or so, a skin test with albumen would produce in about forty-eight hours a reaction similar to that which he had noted when injecting tuberculin into patients with TB.

What Von Pirquet found, however, was not what he expected. When he injected the egg material into the skin of the guinea pig, he noted an *immediate* reaction. Within minutes, sometimes within seconds, a red reaction occurred at the injection site. Clearly, this was quite different from the reaction that took forty-eight hours to develop with his TB extract.

Further research showed that this immediate reaction was no predictor of immunity and, in fact, could be dangerous. Sometimes, when Von Pirquet and other scientists interested in the same phenomena injected certain proteins such as egg albumen into the skin of immunised animals, not only would they show an immediate reaction but they might also become acutely ill. Some of the animals would start to wheeze, gasp for breath and then die before the alarmed eyes of the scientists.

In his 1911 paper, Von Pirquet summarised all his work on the subject and formulated the following concept. Clearly, immunising an animal (even the human one) altered the energy level of the immune system's response to the material. A vigorous response characterised the sensitised individual. This altered state of immunological energy he called 'allergy', a word he compiled from two Greek words: *allos* meaning altered and *ergeai* meaning energy. Von Pirquet subdivided allergy into two forms, useful and useless. An immediate reaction to whatever you had been sensitised to was a

Clemens von Pirquet, a Prussian aristocrat who became a brilliant scientist and introduced the concept of allergy into immunology.

useless, perhaps even dangerous, form of allergy. On the other hand, the delayed reaction was very useful.

Since 1911, the strict definition of the term 'allergy' as described by the coiner of the word has been modified. In most quarters, the word 'allergy' has become restricted to that useless but potentially dangerous form of immunity known more correctly as immediate hypersensitivity. Tuberculosis-type reactions are known as delayed hypersensitivity.

The fascinating story of Von Pirquet contains many other episodes of original discovery ranging from his observations on the medically beneficial effects of sunlight to important new knowledge about nutrition.

Von Pirquet had a reputation for not suffering fools gladly (he was a terrifyingly autocratic figure in his hospital) and had a wife whom everyone thought was all wrong for him. She was not his mental or social equal. She was fat, lazy, unreasonably demanding and spoilt. Somehow, however, she had him where she wanted him; she often called him at his hospital and, despite a pressing conference or urgent experiment, he ran home to do her bidding. It was the strangest of relationships.

At the height of his fame, while still very productive, Von Pirquet

went home from work one evening, made some efficient arrangements for his planned absence from the hospital and had a pleasant
dinner with his wife featuring a good bottle of wine. He and his
wife then moved out of this world via a couple of cyanide capsules.
The world was so imperfect and so resistant to change that he and
his wife had had enough.

And so we come to our examination of this important subject
of 'allergy', an area of immunology that is shared by the best and
worst scientists in our field, by some well meaning but misguided
non-medical healers and those opportunistic charlatans who can
make fortunes from the suffering of others.

Today, we understand that too much energy in our immune
system, the useless allergy of Von Pirquet, results from a lack of
appropriate regulation of our immunological forces. The 'thermostat' is set incorrectly, and thus there is too much heat in the system. We have the intellectual luxury unavailable to Von Pirquet of
approaching the subject in terms of B and T cells. We know that an
excessive, undisciplined response can occur in both systems. I should
point out that such an approach to the reality of allergy is indeed
very new. For a long time it was thought that allergic reactions
producing discomfort and disease were restricted to the B cell
system. Certainly, it's B cells that produce the antibody responsible
for immediate hypersensitivity.

The unpleasant effects induced by immediate hypersensitivity
reactions are suffered by 17 to 24 per cent of humans. Whether this
reaction is triggered by pollen in our nose or airways, crayfish in
our intestinal tract or a dose of penicillin in our buttocks, the
mechanisms are identical to those noted by Von Pirquet when injecting egg protein into his guinea pigs. We must begin by describing
the mechanisms responsible.

For a long time we have known that the cause was circulating
around in the body and was therefore likely to be an antibody. We
owe that discovery to Drs Prausnitz and Kustner, members of that
inquisitive German school of investigation that dominated medicine
during the first years of this century.

These two scientists illustrated again what Louis Pasteur meant
when he said that luck favors the prepared mind. Prausnitz and
Kustner went out to dinner together one night. Kustner ordered
fish, enjoyed it very much and then had a violent reaction to the
meal. He developed itchy hives on his skin and wheezing as his
bronchial tree suddenly spasmed and produced an acute attack of
asthma. Clearly, Kustner had developed an 'allergy' to fish. This is
a useless sort of immune response but obviously clinically important; people do die during allergic reactions of this type.

The two friends discussed the incident after Kustner had recovered and decided that one of their pet theories was ready for testing. If certain antibodies in the blood were responsible for allergic reactions to such things as fish, tomatoes, nuts and chocolates, etc., could one expect that an injection of serum obtained from an allergic individual into the body of one who is not allergic to a particular substance (e.g. fish) would alter the state of immunological energy within the recipient, who would consequently acquire passively the allergic state of the donor?

Kustner's blood was taken, and the serum (the blood minus the cells contained in the blood) was injected under the skin on Prausnitz's arm. With that accomplished without ill effect, Kustner proceeded to the big test. What would happen if a little fish extract was injected into the skin where the serum had been placed?

A violent local allergic reaction occurred immediately. The scientists, in an unconventional but convincing manner, demonstrated that this allergic reaction was caused by something that circulated within the blood, presumably an antibody. That antibody we now call IgE: E for 'emergency' if you like.

Now, as was emphasised in the description of the immune system, there is nothing abnormal about manufacturing and secreting IgE. How *much* one makes is the important point here.

When you scratch your hand while pruning the roses and some bacteria get into the wound, a local battle must be fought if the defence system is to sterilise the wound and to allow healing to occur. Cells and antibodies needed for the job must be delivered to the infected scratch site via the blood flowing through the nearest blood vessel. It would clearly be an advantage if one could increase the blood supply adjacent to the scratch site. If tiny blood vessels in the skin around the scratch would only dilate, more blood could flow into the wound area.

After dilation the pores in the blood vessels, through which cells must escape if they are to enter the tissues, would be significantly enlarged. Blood vessels have circular, muscular coats wrapped around them. When the muscles contract less blood flows through the vessel; when the muscles relax, the opposite it true. The body can thus take more or less blood to a specific area as conditions warrant. Certain chemicals make the blood vessels relax, while others cause them to open up or dilate. Of the many chemicals that can be involved in such a reaction, the best known is histamine. To allow us to control blood flow in this way, Nature has designed a series of little chemical mines, i.e. cells full of different sorts of chemicals that can be exploded in the tissues when needed. Such cells are called mast cells and they are liberally scattered throughout our tissues.

To release these chemicals, IgE is needed. The mast cells, which are full of chemicals such as histamine, have an outer membrane that can bind IgE. To allow this to happen, mast cells (and very similar cells that we find in the bloodstream called basophils) have specific parking spots arranged on their surface for IgE. The tail of this antibody, i.e. the opposite end of the molecule to the one that binds antigen, has a three-dimensional structure that can bind to a receptor for this molecule on the surface of the cells we have discussed. In this way, these cells become 'armed' with thousands of IgE molecules peppering their surface with the antigen binding sites projecting out into the environment around the cell. All that is needed is for an antigen to bind to two of these molecules simultaneously, i.e. to bridge two IgE molecules, and the mast cell is activated, indeed explodes into action. In Figure 17 immediate hypersensitivity and delayed hypersensitivity are compared and contrasted. It all seems so simple now; how confusing it must have been for Von Pirquet.

By producing IgE very early in an immune response, Nature has supplied us with a 'gatekeeper' for blood vessels. By harnessing the chemicals in mast cells we can deliberately dilate blood vessels in areas under attack and unleash from the blood-stream the immunological soldiers that will win the day for us. Thus IgE, with its ability to release histamine-like chemicals, is not useless—far from it. This form of *controlled* immediate hypersensitivity is an essential element of the human defence system.

The chemicals released from mast cells are meant to act *locally* and certainly not meant to have effects far removed from the site of the initiating events. But, as with so many things in life, there can be too much of a good thing. Too much IgE means that too many mast cells will explode; too much histamine will be released and the local effect will be exaggerated. The chemicals from the mast cells will find their way to other parts of the body.

As a group, the chemicals in mast cells tend to open blood vessels by causing the muscles surrounding them to relax, but the same chemicals have the *opposite* effect on muscles surrounding the airways—that is, the pipes that transport the air we inhale down into the lungs wherein oxygen is delivered to the blood.

The muscles of the airways go into spasm and breathing becomes difficult during a generalised allergic reaction, while at the same time the blood vessels may dilate excessively. During an allergic reaction, affected blood vessels in the skin will allow too much fluid to escape into the tissues, which consequently become stretched and then irritated by the chemicals therein. This accumulation of irritating fluid causes a swelling known popularly as a 'hive'—an itchy red swelling which is technically known as urticaria.

Figure 17. The difference between immediate and delayed hypersensitivity

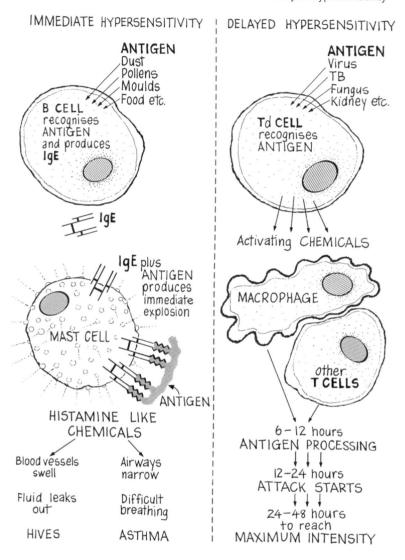

IMMEDIATE HYPERSENSITIVITY

ANTIGEN
Dust
Pollens
Moulds
Food etc.

B CELL
recognises
ANTIGEN
and produces
IgE

IgE

IgE plus
ANTIGEN
produces
immediate
explosion

MAST CELL

ANTIGEN

HISTAMINE LIKE
CHEMICALS

Blood vessels   Airways
swell   narrow

Fluid leaks   Difficult
out   breathing

HIVES   ASTHMA

DELAYED HYPERSENSITIVITY

ANTIGEN
Virus
TB
Fungus
Kidney etc.

Td CELL
recognises
ANTIGEN

Activating CHEMICALS

MACROPHAGE

other
T CELLS

6-12 hours
ANTIGEN PROCESSING

12-24 hours
ATTACK STARTS

24-48 hours
to reach
MAXIMUM INTENSITY

So you can see that Von Pirquet, in the light of current knowledge, would have to modify his concept of useless allergy. It is only useless and harmful if overdone; properly controlled, it is a great system.

Even the uselessness of excessive IgE reactions is being challenged. Scientists have long pondered the unusual fact that up to a quarter of the world's population suffer from allergic reactions of one sort or another. Nature does not usually make such chronic and large mistakes. Over the eons, populations with inferior biological responses tend to disappear. Could immediate hypersensitivity therefore be an example of a biological tradeoff? Could Nature have found that potent IgE-mediated reactions protect us from something far worse than the discomfort of hay fever, asthma and hives?

There are a series of biological precedents for this form of accommodation. Here is one example. In certain parts of the world where malaria is a big problem, an enzyme deficiency is common. This deficiency produces a mild form of anemia that inconveniences the populace but also protects its victims from getting malaria, a far worse problem than the anemia.

More than twenty studies in the literature claim that individuals who suffer from allergies experience less cancer than do others. This certainly would be a nice example of a biological tradeoff if it were true; unfortunately, many other studies in the literature deny the association. Nevertheless, some advantage to being 'atopic', the medical term used to describe the tendency to have too much IgE, may yet be revealed.

By carefully taking a history, a doctor may determine that hay fever symptoms are restricted to those six weeks of the year when ragweed pollen is predominant in the air. Patients may report that their itchy eyes, wheezing, stuffed-up nose etc. are really bothersome only during the summer or when they are at work. They are not allergic to summer work, but may well be allergic to the fungus that grows on the filters of the office air conditioner. Such organisms may be blown around the room with that nice refreshing cool air that they crave.

Someone may only have to get into the car of a cat fancier to have an attack of wheezing. Even if the cat is not *in* the car, as long as it has been there and left behind some dander, those tiny and therefore easily air-dispersed flakes of cat skin can cause much trouble for the person allergic to this material.

Historical detective work is all-important in getting to the basis of an allergy problem. Year-round allergies mean year-round exposure to the one or more things you react to. One of the most common causes of this problem is house dust or, more specifically, something contained in house dust.

Someone who is proud of the cleanliness of his or her home may notice that, if the bed is made when the sun is shining through the window at the correct angle, millions of little particles are dispersed into the air. The same thing occurs every time anyone crosses a carpet or plonks into a well upholstered couch. Such house dust frequently contains fecal particles from an uninvited but common visitor to the home: the house dust mite.

In the average North American mattress one can expect to find hundreds of little tick-like creatures called mites. Several studies suggest that even more of the animals may be found in the mattresses of Europe. These little mites thrive on the privacy to be found inside your mattress and the warmth (sometimes heat) of the body or bodies lying on top.

The mites themselves do little harm, but relatively speaking they do produce many fecal particles. These would be harmless if it were not for the peculiarly fastidious nature of the mite. Unlike most other species, the mite wraps its feces in a gluey liquid material; that is, it bundles it up for disposal, so to speak. For those with the right (or wrong) genes, the coating around the feces is highly immunogenic and many become overly sensitised to the material. Problems develop when they breathe the coated particles into their airways, where they can trigger off reactions mediated by IgE.

To make absolutely certain that you know how, for example, ragweed or similar plant pollens found all over the planet could cause a blocked nose or indeed make a nose run like a tap, let us meet a sufferer. John, at thirty-six years of age, has suffered from seasonal rhinitis (inflammation inside the nose) for many years. For six weeks a year his nose is pretty well blocked.

We use our nose to discern flavor. The taste buds of our tongues are in reality useless to us in the subtle business of distinguishing a gourmet sauce from the everyday variety. Our tongue can distinguish the difference between sweetness, sourness and bitterness, etc., but it cannot subdifferentiate flavors. With your nose completely blocked, an apple or an onion tastes the same. Wonderful nerves in our nose *recognise*, in a very 'immunological' way, distinctive odors on which we depend for pleasure when eating and for alarm signalling in other situations. Individual nerve fibres ending in the nose have little projections extruding into the cavity of the nostril. Just as lymphocytes can recognise only one antigen, so also any one nerve cell can recognise only one odor. When a particular nerve recognises its 'odor' it sends an electric message to the brain and we 'taste' or 'smell' the odor that will consequently be conjured up in our brains. This wonderful distinguishing capacity is denied when the nose is blocked.

The nose is also used to add water to the air we inhale. Nature meant us to breathe through the nose. The rich blood supply to the nose (which may make it bleed easily) and the mucous glands of the nose that contain so much moisture mean that we can rapidly warm and humidify the air we inhale. The hairs inside the nose trap a great deal of airborne debris that should not enter the lungs. All in all, the nose is a most complicated, sophisticated and essential organ; hence its removal from action is considerably more than a nuisance.

When ragweed pollen enters John's nose, some of it is absorbed through the vascular membrane of that organ. This can happen to all of us. The antigen is soon recognised by B cells but unfortunately for John they are programmed to make an excessive amount of IgE to this antigen. Subsequent inhalation of ragweed pollen into John's nose will set up a situation where the pollen, on being absorbed through the membrane of the nose, meets a great deal of already formed IgE antibody. The IgE that is present on second and later exposures to ragweed is sitting on top of mast cells, as we have already described. Chemicals from mast cells are released once the ragweed interacts with the IgE. These chemicals will cause the copious blood vessels of the nose to swell or dilate. As they swell, the pores in the membrane will open up and much fluid will escape from the blood vessels into the surrounding tissues. This will force the delicate membranes of the nose to swell and an occlusion of the nostrils will follow. It is possible for the mucosa of the nose to swell so much that, having become heavy with water, the membranes will actually prolapse, forming what we call a nasal polyp. Such is the nature of allergic rhinitis. Sometimes, the excessive fluid literally drips from the nose.

John has trouble with ragweed because he makes too much IgE to an antigen of this particular pollen. His wife does not. She may well have some IgE against ragweed in her bloodstream and indeed even in her nose, but not enough to produce the excessive reaction that causes symptoms.

In determining which symptoms described by a patient are caused by an immediate hypersensitivity reaction, physicians must rely on their detective skills and their knowledge of the types of disturbance the various chemicals involved may cause. They can be helped considerably by using Von Pirquet's skin-testing trick providing they know the pitfalls. Many doctors who practise 'allergy', I must warn you, do not.

If you scratch into the skin a trace amount of something you suspect a patient may be allergic to, an immediate reaction will confirm your suspicions while a negative one throws doubt on the matter. We like to use scratch tests (as opposed to injections into the skin) for two reasons. The injection of even small amounts of antigen into the skin of a subject who is extremely sensitised can provoke such a violent reaction that death may actually occur. Secondly, we are looking for extremes of sensitivity when we skin-test a patient. As explained earlier a reaction is, in itself, not an abnormality. It is the extremes of the reaction that we seek. Normal people will not produce an immediately visible reaction to trace amounts of the material being investigated.

I can well remember as a young intern itching to do a little surgery on my own. On rare occasions the intern, who is of course the lowest form of life on a medical team, will be allowed to suture a wound or perform some very minor surgical procedure. At the end of one very long operating day a surgeon turned to me and told me my big moment had arrived. The last patient on the list had a small wart-like polyp on his back which I could remove all on my own. All I had to do was to inject a little anesthetic around the area, cut out the lump and then put one or two stitches in place to stop the bleeding. Not exactly a heart transplant but I took it.

With only a pair of admiring nurses left to watch my skill I began to inject the local anesthetic. I could not have injected more than a few drops of fluid before the patient collapsed on the table and rapidly started to wheeze horribly and turn a deathly shade of pale. The patient had had an immediate hypersensitivity reaction to the local anesthetic. It took two days in the intensive care unit with all sorts of sophisticated machinery and drugs to get this patient back to normal. I have had a very healthy respect for immediate hypersensitivity from that point on.

Very sensitive blood tests may now measure IgE antibodies to a whole array of antigens (or allergens, as they are often called in this context). The assays use radioactive isotopes, which can be chemically attached to IgE antibodies and are very sensitive indeed, though not very easy to interpret.

Some time ago I saw a pale and wasted IBM executive who had been referred to me for his terrible problem with allergies. The poor man had developed chronic hives six months earlier and since then had been almost unremittingly miserable because of the itching and swelling that constantly worried his eyes, hands and feet. His local doctor had referred him to an allergist who had ordered a myriad of IgE blood tests looking for antibodies to more than seventy different food substances as well as drugs, grasses, pollens, etc. Three thousand two hundred dollars later, the IBM executive was told the bad news. He had IgE antibodies to almost every food line for which tests had been done.

He immediately protested that he had never been allergic to anything in his life before and certainly could not relate his hives to eating. The allergist, however, assured him that all that was now changed. An exclusion diet was devised for the poor man which allowed him to eat only rice, lettuce and some lamb. Everything he liked was banned.

Valiantly he struggled on, attempting to observe the diet for many months. During this time he lost weight, which he did not need to do, as well as his urticaria (hives). The doctor was gratified; the patient was not, because he felt that the cure was worse than the disease. A rebellious spirit arose within him and he sought a second opinion.

In talking to this man I learned that the doctor whom he had first consulted had relied on the blood tests exclusively rather than the story of the reactions which, as it turns out, contained important clues. I also learned that no attempt had been made to eliminate one food group at a time. After I questioned him closely, I was not convinced he needed to be on such a strict diet.

At the time his urticaria had developed he had been under great strain at work and I suspected that his problem might not be allergic at all. Not all urticaria, that is the abnormal dilation of blood vessels in the skin, is caused by IgE-related mechanisms. Slowly we returned this man to a normal diet and his urticaria did not return.

The moral in all this is that drastic treatment based on the exclusive use of these very sensitive blood tests is a mistake. The tests that pick up IgE antibody to various things are valuable in confirming suspicions based on history and skin testing and they supply us with a valuable research tool, but they are not themselves diagnostic.

In searching for an allergist, check with the local college of physicians for ways of identifying individuals who have successfully completed training in immunology. In the United States, look for a doctor who is a diplomate of the allergy/immunology board, a sub-specialty group sanctioned by the American Medical Association to examine and then proclaim an individual's successful completion of training in this area.

I believe it is particularly important to avoid those doctors who practise ear, nose and throat surgery but who throw in 'allergy' as an extra. Unfortunately, there is an ever-increasing number of such individuals in North America and elsewhere. Although there are some exceptions, most doctors who are basically ENT surgeons are less than adequate when it comes to handling allergic diseases. Time and time again I have had patients referred to me who have been completely mismanaged by these individuals.

For many ENT surgeons, allergy is a lucrative sideline. Be particularly wary of the doctor who tells you how lucky you are that he actually has in his office a machine that will do the blood tests described above. These tests, which are unlikely to be interpreted correctly by the untrained observer, may cost you a fortune.

One of the major problems in the allergy business is only slowly being solved. Relatively few substances that cause allergic reactions have actually been purified.

Imagine you have an allergic reaction every time you eat tomatoes. In loose unscientific terminology, you might say you are allergic to 'tomatoes'. What you actually mean, of course, is that you respond to something in the complex makeup of a tomato. This may not even be present in the undigested tomato; it may turn up in your body only after your metabolism has got to work in breaking down the chemicals present when you first swallowed the tomato. For this reason, allergy tests that use crude extracts of a particular food tend to be very unreliable.

Recently a team of excellent immunologists from San Antonio, Texas, examined scientifically all the available tests to diagnose food allergy, including those already described. They concluded that the only way to diagnose food allergy was by careful history taking, followed by the removal from the diet of food or groups of food about which one had become suspicious. If the patient improved, this could be followed by a challenge, with a suspicious item or items being reintroduced into the diet. Done carefully under controlled conditions, this is a safe procedure that may prevent someone from being unnecessarily deprived of some of life's great pleasures. What all this boils down to is that patients with suspected food allergies need careful assessment and management by experienced physicians who understand the mechanisms involved and the limitations of our present knowledge.

It is possible and indeed likely that in rare cases a patient, after eating something specific, may develop severe symptoms via a mechanism that has nothing to do with allergy. Food is nothing more than a currently acceptable bunching of chemicals with nutritional or appetite-satisfying properties. Some individuals' metabolism (body chemistry) may be different from that of most people and their reaction to the ingestion of, say, apple juice may be very different from yours and mine.

Sometimes the ingestion of a particular substance by such people may lead to the release of some of the chemicals that IgE can also release. In this case, however, the release is not activated through an immunological mechanism.

A few years ago I was involved as an 'expert witness' in a tragic case which was the subject of litigation. A medical mistake resulted in the death of a mother and of a medical career.

Susan was a 33-year-old mother of three. She was generally well but was being investigated for abnormally painful periods associated with severe headaches. Before the full-time demands of motherhood, Susan had been a nurse and she suspected that a growth in her uterus had something to do with the problem. One month, while her problem was still under investigation, her period began and by 11 a.m. on the morning of its second day she was so uncomfortable that she took herself and her three young children to the emergency room at her local hospital. Here she was seen immediately by the nurse, who filled out a brief medical history chart.

To the routine question 'Are you allergic to anything?' Susan replied, 'Yes, I am allergic to aspirin.' At fifteen, she had been given aspirin for an attack of flu-like symptoms and developed a rash and wheezing. A doctor had told her she must not take aspirin again. She was eventually seen by the doctor, who listened to her story, examined her and came to his conclusion: this patient, he reasoned, was being investigated by a competent gynecologist; his job was to relieve her present discomfort, nothing more.

As is not uncommon in busy emergency rooms, he had four or five other patients in various cubicles simultaneously and he flitted from one to the other in attempts to be efficient. The nurses' notes for each patient were on his desk, paperwork to be completed in a quiet moment.

The young doctor in question was training to be a specialist in internal medicine and was supporting himself and a young wife and child by helping out in the emergency room. He was knowledgeable, but inexperienced. He prescribed a relaxant–analgesic preparation for Susan and at 2.16 p.m. his patient was discharged from the emergency room at the hospital. The preparation he prescribed contained, among other things, significant amounts of aspirin. At 2.35 p.m. Susan had her prescription filled by a pharmacist. By 3.15 she had taken the first tablet and, after leaving the children with her next door neighbor, had sunk gratefully onto her bed to await relief.

At approximately 4.30 p.m., the young doctor at the hospital was catching up with his paperwork. As he filled in Susan's forms he recalled the case and noticed, underlined, the nurse's warning: 'Patient allergic to aspirin'. After his initial shock at realising his mistake and the possible consequences of what he had done, he reassured himself that probably no real harm would come to the patient. He clearly must call, however, and tell her not to take any more of the tablets.

No one answered the telephone at Susan's house. Even though he thought it most likely that the unanswered telephone meant that she was out, some uneasy premonition made him call at her address after he finished his roster at 5.30 p.m. Susan was dead and had been so since approximately 4 p.m. A post-mortem examination revealed that the cause of her death was consistent with acute bronchospasm; following the ingestion of the aspirin, she had suffocated.

Reasonably, under the circumstances, Susan's husband sued the hospital and the doctor and a considerable amount of money was awarded to the family, but it could have been of little consolation.

I tell you this story about the aspirin because there is no evidence that in that particular type of reaction IgE antibody is involved at all. When Susan said she was allergic to aspirin, she was not being scientifically accurate. After ingestion into our bodies, a number of chemicals alter various biological pathways on which we rely. In some patients, as we saw earlier, these alterations lead to the release of those very same chemicals that affect our blood vessels and airways in an allergic reaction; however, they cause the damage directly, rather than relying on antibody.

Aspirin affects some pathways in the brain, enabling us to relieve pain, but it is also very useful as an anti-inflammatory agent. Whenever you have painful red and hot swellings in your body, for example in the case of arthritis, aspirin is often useful. This drug is able to produce these anti-inflammatory effects by blocking the metabolic pathways that lead to the development of those chemicals that actually produce the inflammation.

The trouble with a number of drugs is that they do not know when to stop. In other words, blocking one metabolic pathway that, for example, may make your joints feel better if you have arthritis may simultaneously unblock a second pathway or perhaps even stimulate a second pathway that produces harmful effects. The significance of these potentially harmful effects may be clinically important in only a few individuals. This is what can happen when aspirin is ingested. A small number of people are so sensitive to the drug that while it produces the normal aspirin effects in them, it also leads to the accumulation in the body of chemicals involved in allergic-type reactions. These chemicals can make blood vessels dilate and airways constrict. Immunology does not come into the story at all.

The same mechanism can occur with a number of food preservatives and dyes. For example, the food preservative tartrazine and the red and yellow dyes we find in so many of our foods today can cause these problems for an individual who is particularly sensitive to these compounds.

Because of their knowledge of such situations, physicians and scientists must keep an open mind on the possibility that some bizarre symptomatology which we occasionally have described to us by patients is in fact biochemically induced by that individual's particular metabolic sensitivity to some ingested substance.

Abdominal discomfort, mood changes, fatigue, etc. may be attributed to food 'allergies'. In reality, such reactions might involve chemical sensitivities and such claims are notoriously difficult to study scientifically. It is thus vitally important that physicians be extremely objective about such a situation. While it is necessary to acknowledge that such problems exist, albeit rarely, one must be extremely careful not to explain away genuine psychological problems by postulating such mechanisms.

This problem is becoming increasingly serious in a number of Western countries, particularly North America. A number of misguided or unscrupulous individuals are making a considerable amount of money from seriously psychiatrically disturbed patients by telling them that their problems are related to allergic reactions to things in the environment. In other words, they are supplying an organic reason for the bizarre symptomatology of a number of patients who would much rather believe this than face the fact that they are mentally disturbed. Thus, while not denying that some people may have very unusual biochemical pathways within their bodies that may make them extremely sensitive to environmental factors that cause most of us no problem at all, such a situation is, in my experience, very rare indeed.

The following case illustrates the extremes to which unscientific thinking can go, and the financial and medical hazards that can follow.

Rebecca is twenty-nine years old and lives in New York City. Intelligent, attractive and well educated, she has not worked for a number of years, ostensibly because she cannot find a job. She is a trained social worker who has researched the problems of paroled prisoners and their integration back into society. Rebecca's childhood was not happy; though, unfortunately, not really extraordinary. She had an inadequate mother, a drunken bully of a father and a brother on drugs; all these things caused her much distress. Since the age of fifteen, she has suffered from seasonal allergic rhinitis and depression.

In 1980, Rebecca developed a most unusual medical problem: an allergy to Avery Fisher Hall in New York City. As a music lover, this was a real problem for her: many of the city's major concerts are held in this hall.

To be accurate, Rebecca's allergy was to the *foyer* of Avery Fisher Hall: she could not make it into the hall proper. Within seconds of walking through the door of the foyer, she became weak, dizzy and breathless and sank to the floor unconscious. When she visited two or three apartments belonging to friends, the same thing happened. In discussing this matter with her undoubtedly very concerned friends, she was eventually advised to seek the advice of a 'clinical ecologist' practising in New York City. This she did and was told she must enter a clinic for prolonged testing. She went to a southern state for two weeks of investigation at a clinic designed specifically to study such problems.

I met Rebecca a few months later in my outpatients' clinic at Yale University. When I entered the examination room with my nurse and greeted the patient routinely, there was no answer, and indeed no movement of any sort from Rebecca. The nurse and I approached her and spoke to her again and, with an obvious effort, she slowly moved her hand, extended her finger and pointed to the pocket of her jacket. The nurse removed from her pocket a note and a small bottle containing a clear fluid and dropper. The note was brief but informative: in case of catatonia, place three drops of histamine under the tongue.

Catatonia involves rigid immobilisation of muscles. Rebecca slowly opened her mouth and it was obvious what she expected us to do. We dutifully placed three drops of the fluid from the bottle marked histamine under her tongue and a miracle occurred. Within two seconds she relaxed, smiled and said hello.

After that most unusual start to her interview, a full history was taken. Rebecca had come to see me because she was still not well after her trip to the southern clinic but at least she now knew that her problem was due to T cell dysfunction; could I help?

It turned out that she had been admitted twice to the clinical ecology unit in the southern state. On the first visit they told her after $4800 worth of tests that she had total allergy syndrome. Rebecca was allergic to everything.

She had been discharged with thirty-two bottles, from which she was to inject tiny amounts of matter into herself.

Rebecca came home, got worse, not better, developing these strange attacks of stiffness, and returned to the clinic for further help. After one week, one of the clinic specialists told her that she had the most severe form of this problem. They explained that her really severe case of total allergy syndrome was caused by a lack of normal T cells. She discharged herself, apparently with great difficulty, returned to New York and saw me.

On that first visit, she emptied the contents of her brown bag on to my desk. The thirty-two bottles of injectable extracts appeared, all hand labelled and made at the clinic. There were also vitamins and amino acid preparations, including one made from the testicles of a New Zealand bull!

Rebecca was clearly a psychiatrically disturbed young woman and I am pleased to tell you that with help from a psychiatrist at a major university in New York City, she is employed and almost symptom free at this writing.

As you can probably guess, there is no such thing as 'total allergy syndrome' or '20th century allergy syndrome'. A careful study published recently in America strengthened my opinion that the majority of people who claim to be allergic to our century's environment are either psychologically disturbed or charlatans. The former can be helped with appropriate psychotherapy but have often been led by unscientific individuals into a delusional state.

Recently, I took part in a television show looking at the phenomenon of '20th century allergy syndrome'. Two case studies were reported.

In one, a woman, twenty-five years old and six months pregnant, was shown imprisoned in her environmentally safe cell. The TV cameras and reporters were not allowed into her room so the scenes were shot through the window, with the woman shouting replies to questions in order to make herself heard. The room was stripped of carpet and was unbelievably spartan. This woman was convinced that to come out into the outside world would cause intolerable symptoms: headaches, panic attacks, pain in all her joints, abdominal cramps, and no doubt a miscarriage of her baby. She was allergic to everything.

After my comments on the show, her relatives tried but failed to persuade her to seek orthodox medical assistance. Psychiatric help might well have cured her of her fears before the birth of her baby. Later reports suggested that after the birth, a 'faith healer' managed to supply the necessary psychological help.

The second case concerned a man who lived on an island with five children all gaining sickness and isolation benefits from the government because of their allergies. They could not mix with the real world.

A film clip showed the man standing in the street outside a general store on the island, yelling to Tom inside to please make up a parcel of this and that which he needed. The man explained to the TV team that he could not enter the store. The man and a child who was with him wore spacesuit-like protectors. Later the TV reporter became suspicious, for Tom the store manager had asked what all this was about. Jack, he commented, had always come into the store before! The TV crew then surreptitiously approached Jack's isolated home and found him, de-spacesuited, spraying paint on to the side of his house! Social Security officers were alerted.

How often does one find an uncritical media presenting these dramatic stories to an unsuspecting public, as if they were discussing scientifically established conditions?

At this point, I think I should say a few words about the disease asthma. There is much confusion on this important subject; between 4 and 8 per cent of the population are made miserable at some time because of this problem.

The word asthma is derived from two Greek words meaning 'difficult breathing'; and if you have ever seen a patient suffering from an attack of asthma, you will surely agree that this is a very conservative name for a horrible condition. Asthma is one of the major health problems in the world today, causing a great deal of suffering to many people, both children and adults, and costing billions of dollars in lost productivity. Particularly disturbing is the fact that in many countries the death rate from asthma, after decreasing for a number of years, is rising again.

We have already noted the fact that blood vessels are surrounded by a circular coat of muscle that can contract and therefore narrow the diameter or relax and increase the diameter of the vessel. The same is true of the bronchial tree. Air breathed in through the nose or mouth must travel to the lungs by means of a network of pipes that together make up the bronchial tree. The first part of this branching system is called the trachea, and you can feel this by putting your hand on your neck just above the little notch you have at the bottom of your throat. Here you can feel the hard rings of cartilage which make the trachea the big patent pipe that it is. As the bronchial tree branches and takes the air downwards into the lungs, the cartilage that supports the major airways disappears and the diameter of the lumen is controlled by muscles arranged in exactly the same way as they are around blood vessels.

When an individual suffers from episodic attacks wherein there is spasming (narrowing) of the small airways, the condition known as asthma (reversible airways obstruction) occurs.

While the mechanics and physiology of breathing are very complicated, we can easily present the basic facts. When taking a breath we inhale into our lungs air containing about 20 per cent oxygen. The lungs extract the oxygen and deliver it to the red blood cells. These whisk the oxygen around the body, delivering it to muscles and tissues that could not survive more than a few minutes without this precious commodity. It is obviously necessary to breathe out before we can breathe in again, but Nature does not waste the expiratory part of the breathing cycle. When we breathe out we expel the gas carbon dioxide from our lungs and our bodies. Carbon dioxide is a by-product of many metabolic processes in the body and it must be regularly cleared from our system. If it is not, it forms an acid in the bloodstream which is extremely dangerous.

When you take a deep breath you expand your chest, and the pressure inside your lungs decreases so that there is a natural tendency for your airways to open up. This is a fine arrangement because that is exactly the time when you want the maximum amount of air to go down into your lungs. As you breathe out, the reverse happens; the pressure in your airways increases and it is normal for the bronchial tree to narrow during expiration.

Patients who suffer from asthma have airways that are too narrow so that not only do they have trouble in getting enough air into their lungs, they may find it impossible to get the carbon dioxide out. As they try to exhale, their airways narrow, but to such a point that frequently no air movement is possible and air that is devoid of oxygen and therefore useless is trapped in their lungs. The brain, sensing that it is not getting enough oxygen to enrich the circulating blood, sends all sorts of panic signals to the lungs and chest. Patients begin to fight for more air and in their struggles often become exhausted.

The important question, of course, is why do some people have airways that spasm? Why do the muscles surrounding the bronchial tree of asthma victims try to suffocate them? In order to understand the answers to these questions, one must appreciate the fact that Nature loves to control most things in the body using a tug-of-war system. Right now, your heart is beating at a certain rate that represents the net result of two sets of simultaneously active but opposing nervous stimuli. One set of nerves is trying to speed up your heart while the other is trying to slow it down; the balance between these two opposing tug-of-war teams determines your heart rate.

Exactly the same is true of the muscles controlling the diameter of your airways. In any given moment, signals are passing down nerves to release chemicals that instruct the muscle cells of the airways to relax. Simultaneously, however, messages are coming from other nerves that tell the very same cells to contract. The tone of the muscle, which is the net influence of the two opposing forces, determines just how open or closed your airways will be at any given moment.

Asthma is caused by a defect in the control of the muscle cells of the airways. These muscles possess little receptors on their membranes which can interact with or interpret the chemical messages released by the nerves that want the muscle to relax. These are known as beta receptors. Quite distinct receptors accept messages telling the muscle cells to contract. When a tug-of-war team is evenly balanced, one side will win handsomely when an extra person is placed on that side. Exactly the same result will occur if one person is dropped from the opposition. In either case the result will be a movement in the same direction. With this analogy in mind you can imagine that asthma might be due to increased sensitivity to the signals that cause the muscles to constrict, or equally to a loss of sensitivity to the chemicals that tell muscles to relax. In most cases, the latter situation seems to be responsible for the asthmatic's problems. The muscle cells are not particularly responsive to signals trying to activate the beta receptors. Whether such receptors are damaged in patients with asthma or simply present but in insufficient numbers to do the job properly is currently a matter for some debate. The result, however, is quite clear. Even normal stimulation from those chemicals that cause muscles to constrict will not be opposed by the normal counterbalancing forces that stop constriction. The net result will be airways which are significantly narrowed. It is important to have these mechanisms discussed because asthma is widely held to be an allergic disease, i.e. that it is caused by mechanisms involving IgE antibody. The truth is that asthma is a disorder of the airways; and allergic reactions around those airways, because they release chemicals which cause muscles in the airways to constrict, can trigger off an attack of asthma. The basic defect must be present before an allergic reaction can produce bronchospasm.

A patient with asthma is like a man walking along the edge of a dangerously high cliff. While he is walking along the edge of the cliff and has not tumbled over, he is perfectly safe. The closer he is to the edge of the cliff, however, the closer he is to danger. If he is teetering on the edge of the cliff, one good push and tragedy could develop. In other words, even when a patient with asthma appears to be perfectly well his airways will be narrower than yours or mine. He no longer has any reserve capacity as he cannot function normally with any further narrowing of his airways. Under such circumstances an allergic reaction will precipitate an asthma attack— push him over the cliff.

With the vulnerability caused by these imbalances in the airways, an asthmatic patient may have an attack precipitated by emotion, pollution in the air, exercise, sudden exposure to cold air, infection, certain drugs and allergic reactions. Modern therapy is designed to identify triggering factors that can bring on an attack of asthma and if possible remove them from the patient's environment. This is combined with treatment of the underlying condition. In this day and age this, basically, involves attempts to make the beta receptor more sensitive to the chemicals that normally activate it, while administering drugs to the airways that stimulate the receptor. The disease is such a significant problem that I feel I must add a few notes for those of you who are victims of asthma to help you determine whether or not you are getting the best therapy currently available.

You are in good hands if your doctor has been at pains to explain the mechanisms I have just described so that you can feel comfortable that you understand what the disease is all about; if he emphasises that modern treatment concentrates on delivering the necessary drugs via the airways rather than through injected or swallowed medication; if, in putting you on inhaled medication, he has thoroughly checked more than once to make sure the technique you are using to inhale the medicine is correct; if he gives you a peak expiratory flow meter that you keep at home and use so you can determine for yourself what progress you are making with your disease. These little gadgets measure how narrow or wide your airways are, and tell you such things as whether or not you are responding to the medicine you have been asked to inhale. A fall in the reading on the meter suggests you are heading for a severe attack of asthma, an observation that allows you to alert your doctor. Your doctor should also have ensured that blood levels have been taken frequently to determine the right dose of theophylline which you need to give you maximum therapeutic response (theophylline is a drug which has the ability to dilate the bronchial tree). And, realising that your problem may be brought on by exercise or cold air, he should have explained to you that you can prevent these attacks by using an inhaled stimulant of the beta receptor before beginning exercise or venturing into the cold air. He should have told you that only in the most unusual circumstances are desensitisation attempts (shots) warranted for the patient with asthma.

The mention of desensitisation needs further explanation. Desensitisation is a technique that has been used for many years by allergists in an attempt to reduce IgE-mediated sensitivity. The technique, which is practised on millions of people every week of every year, involves repeated injections of tiny doses of the allergen thought to be causing a patient's symptoms, over a long period of time.

Why should this technique be useful? Until recently the most popular theory as to how desensitisation might work involved the production, after the 'shots', of IgG antibody to the allergen in question. When natural exposure to the allergen occurred there would be, sitting there waiting for it, another antibody in the body which could compete for the allergen with the IgE sitting on top of mast cells. If there is enough IgG in your circulation to pounce on the allergen as soon as it enters your body it may be able to bind it all up, so that little is around to trigger the IgE on the mast cells in the tissues.

This was quite a logical theory and, in fact, there may be some truth in the suggestion, but it is certainly not the complete answer. Very recent studies strongly suggest that, on occasions, immuno-regulatory T cells that can control IgE production to a specific allergen may be stimulated by the desensitising injections. This may allow the patient to regain control of his IgE production. You may remember that, in our discussion of the organisation of defence, we examined the T cell control of antibody production. The thermostat determining how much IgE you will or will not produce is set by the genetic apparatus in T cells.

Unfortunately, it is very difficult to ensure that desensitisation of any patient will result in success. The technique may produce serious results as we are dealing with a very powerful system. If too much allergen is given, an allergic reaction of dangerous proportions can be triggered right in the doctor's office. Nevertheless, in skilled hands, the risks associated with it are quite acceptable and the cost–benefit ratio needs to be closely examined until we can more scientifically formulate the right dose for an individual. This will become much easier as more purified allergens become available. You will find that most clinical immunologists working in a university centre are very conservative in their approach to desensitisation, and tend to put an enormous amount of emphasis on finding the allergen that is causing the trouble and then helping the patient to avoid it. If this is not possible then reliance is placed on the use of pharmacological approaches that will block the consequences of IgE-mediated reactions.

At this writing I can say confidently that we are good at desensitising people to things like ragweed and now cat dander, and that beneficial effects can be expected when the allergens causing the problems for a specific patient are clearly identifiable and few in number. If your skin lights up like Times Square on New Year's Eve when you are skin tested, it is extremely unlikely that desensitisation will be able to control your problems. You have simply developed allergies to too many different things.

There certainly are indications for attempting to desensitise people with allergic problems and a classic situation involves sensitivity to bee and wasp venom. A number of deaths occur each year from massive allergic reaction following a bee sting. People can become extremely sensitive to the venom of these insects. But the interesting fact is that more people die of their fear of being stung than the reality of being stung. Statistics show that people who know they are allergic to bee and wasp venom frequently become terrified when they find themselves in a moving car accompanied by a bee or wasp, and are likely to have an accident.

Initial attempts at desensitising people to bee and wasp venom relied on a crude extract from the insects. The bodies of a particular type of bee or wasp suspected of causing the problem were literally crushed, and the fluid squeezed from the hapless creatures was diluted appropriately and injected into the patient. Results were not very encouraging. However, far purer venom extracts are now available from various bees and wasps and it is possible to skin test patients to find out which particular variety of insect is a problem for them. Results of desensitisation using venom are very encouraging.

In general, desensitisation has a much better track record in controlling symptoms referrable to the nose and eyes rather than the chest. You are more likely to benefit from desensitisation therapy if allergic rhinitis is your problem, rather than asthma.

Diagnosing genuine allergic reactions to food is also a very difficult business. If at the first bite of food cooked in peanut oil your tongue and pharynx swell, there is not much doubt about the diagnosis. But it is not easy when the reactions to food are delayed, as they frequently are; and the further the time of reaction from the time of ingestion the more difficult is the historical reconstruction of the possible precipitating events.

Many 'allergists' claim to be able to diagnose your food allergy with pinpoint precision. As in the case of the IBM executive discussed earlier, they may tell you that you are allergic to many things which, in reality, cause you no trouble at all. The tests they use represent some of the worst examples of empiricism in modern medical practice. They vary from 'cytotoxic testing', wherein some of your blood cells are taken and exposed to food extracts only to die if you are allergic to the food, through to challenges where you eat a food and have your nose swabbed at hourly intervals. The appearance of certain cells in the nose, some would suggest, indicates that you are allergic to that food. All such tests are useless and you should avoid any doctor or paramedical person who has any faith in this approach.

If your allergist has explained all these facts to you, you are probably in good hands. If he has asked you to vacuum up some of the dust on your floor so that you may bring it to his office and have him prepare an extract to use for desensitisation purposes, you are in trouble. If he makes such an extract and asks you to put it under your tongue, you are dealing with a physician who has drifted far away from the mainstream of modern immunological thought. If he has told you that all those colds you get, especially those sore throats you had last winter, may be due to allergies to bacterial products and he is therefore desensitising you with 'bacterial vaccines', run a mile to your nearest board of certified allergists and get some informed help. All these approaches are distressingly common in many countries of the world.

One further aspect of allergic disease must be discussed which concerns that wonderful immunomodulator known as breast milk. Nature is faced with a dilemma in protecting the intestinal tract and the upper airways of the newborn baby from bacterial infection. The baby's immune system must mature over the first few months of life, learning first how to make IgM then IgG before it can make IgA, that antibody which protects our delicate mucous membranes. In order to make sure that IgA is available to the intestinal tract of the baby, mothers are meant to breastfeed their infants. Nature has made specific arrangements to ensure that adequate amounts of IgA antibodies that can protect the baby's intestinal tract are in breast milk.

In recent years it has become clear that there is an association between a natural inability to produce IgA and allergies to a number of things, particularly to certain foods. Recent research has revealed that much of the sensitisation to such things as gluten, soy and milk proteins, which have caused so many people so much trouble, occurs during the first year of life. Apart from the ability of IgA to protect us from viral and bacterial infections, these molecules may also have an important role to play in protecting us from developing allergies. Abundant quantities of IgA in the intestinal tract can certainly minimise the absorption across the mucous membranes of gluten, soy and milk proteins and probably many other things as well.

In the absence of IgA, these proteins, which we normally do not absorb in an allergenic form, stimulate IgE production and the allergic cascade commences.

Researchers in Scandinavia have shown that babies born to parents both of whom have 'allergies' have a very high chance of developing severe allergic symptoms before the age of one. That risk, however, is very significantly reduced if babies are breastfed for the first year of life. Apparently, keeping IgA available to the infant's intestinal tract during that first year blocks the absorption of material that can sensitise the child. As we mentioned earlier, a number of milk banks have been established in Scandinavia and elsewhere so that breast milk is available for 'therapeutic purposes'.

Let us conclude on a positive note. Those of you who find immediate hypersensitivity reactions to be producing symptoms that interfere with the quality of your lives should be heartened to know that competent clinical immunologists are available to help with most problems in this area.

T cell allergies

In a sense, what we have been describing could be thought of as T cell allergy, as IgE production is controlled by T cells. But the question we are now going to examine is this: are there situations where T cells and perhaps macrophages under their control secrete excessive, undisciplined amounts of cytokines and as a result produce disease? The answer is 'yes', and I am proposing that to separate the two forms of allergy we use the 'B' and the 'T' to come up with a new terminology that will enable us to talk of ballergy and tallergy. If you will accept that distinction, then what we are about to discuss could appropriately be called tallergic reactions. Here is an example of what I mean.

Stewart was in the best of moods and the best of health. He and his girlfriend Helen were happily in love and, after a party, they found themselves alone in Helen's room. They very much wanted to make love, but Helen was hesitant. It was the second day of a heavy period and she was not certain whether he would enjoy sex under these circumstances. However, Stewart brushed her doubts aside. Helen undressed, removed her bloodsoaked tampon and they made love.

The following evening Stewart was most unwell, with fever and a headache. By midnight he was desperately ill and a worried roommate had rushed him to the emergency room in the hospital, where I was called in to see him.

This strapping young footballer was delirious with a high fever and an abnormally low blood pressure. A red rash covered most of his body and around the edge of the rash the skin was already drying and flaking. The inside of his mouth had red, angry-looking spots on the delicate mucous membranes and he started to vomit uncontrollably. Blood tests revealed that his liver was being damaged and that the particular blood cells needed to help clot his blood were in dangerously low supply.

It was not possible to get a history from Stewart and so, although he was obviously suffering from the effects of a serious infection, we were at a loss to know what organism was causing the problem. We commenced empiric treatment and a battery of diagnostic tests.

When a very concerned Helen arrived in the emergency room, a bright young intern who had been reading some recent literature asked whether she was well, was having a period and had had sex with Stewart recently. When she answered 'yes' to all these questions, we sought her co-operation and cultured some of the menstrual blood in her vagina, in which we were able to identify 'golden staph', *staphylococcus aureus*.

Stewart was suffering from a then newly recognised disease now known as the 'toxic shock' syndrome. Bacteria had passed, perhaps because of a skin abrasion, through his penis into his body, and something was now happening that seemed likely to kill him. Stewart's illness might well have saved Helen from a similar battle, as it is possible that she could have developed the same syndrome within forty-eight hours. Fortunately, antibiotics were administered in time to protect her.

Warnings about the necessity of being cautious with the use of tampons and the need to change them frequently if they are used are so widespread and commonplace that the occurrence of this problem has become significantly less common in the last couple of years. Certainly, toxic shock syndrome represents an example of how bacteria can change rapidly to give themselves a better chance of survival. Despite the availability of the best in modern medicine, we nearly lost Stewart. A less fit young man could easily have succumbed.

What has toxic shock syndrome got to do with tallergy? Certain strains of *staphylococcus aureus* which grow rapidly in blood, especially if that blood is kept warm and moist on a tampon that has been left inside the body for more than a few hours, can produce proteins that provoke an excessive release of T cell cytokines and these, in such large amounts, produce toxic symptoms.

We discussed earlier the fact that all T cells have receptors on their surface which are composed of two chains, usually (90 per cent of the time) designated as α and β. A small number of T cells have slight variations within their receptors, which are thus called γ and δ instead of α and β. If we use our hand and arm analogy to think of a T cell receptor then imagine there emerging from the cellular soup, to project into the environment around the cell, an arm with a hand so cupped that only one thing will have a best fit into this lock. The arrangements you can make with the hand are almost infinite, and will of course be different on different T cells, but the arm is the same, or very nearly the same, on all T cells. When antigens bind to T cell receptors, the membrane of the cell is distorted and activation signals that follow start the immunological band playing.

Now if certain organisms produced a substance that would bind to and distort the arm of the T cell receptor on very many T cells, then chaos would occur for all those cells would be activated. Normally when an antigen is recognised by due processing, as described earlier, only about 1 in 100 000 T cells will be activated.

Proteins that can activate large numbers of T cells simultaneously are called 'superantigens' and they are very dangerous. At least three families of bacteria can produce them, including certain staphylococci. Nature has attempted, through genetic manipulation, to program out that segment of the β chain of the T cell receptor to which these superantigens usually like to bind, and for this reason most of us are not susceptible to the development of any dangerous toxic shock syndrome. Such reactions only occur if the arm of the T cell receptor has a particular shape that allows the toxin to bind. Toxic reactions that follow represent an extreme form of T cell allergy.

T cell allergies are increasingly being recognised as the mechanism by which many disturbances are produced. The problems that could be discussed under such a heading vary from the contact sensitivity that makes some women develop a painful sore on their back where the nickel in their bra strap rubs the skin, to more serious matters associated perhaps with cancers occurring in CD4 cells, eczema, diseases such as sarcoidosis and even, as we will explore later in great detail, the mysterious chronic fatigue syndrome.

Fortunately, we can all be confident that major advances in immunology and pharmacology over the next few years will greatly improve the management of such 'useless allergies', so clearly described but not understood by Von Pirquet at the beginning of this century.

9

The painful subject of autoimmunity

THE man in question had brutally attacked his wife after a domestic argument.

A psychiatrist was discussing this case with his fourth-year medical students, who had been present when he had examined the man. The students, who had seen photos of the wife's condition immediately after the assault, were not sympathetic to the man's protestation of remorse and promises of change. They wanted him locked away for years, and trotted forth newspaper accounts they could recall where men such as this one, when dealt with leniently by the courts, went on to do worse damage to their victims, perhaps even killing some of them.

The psychiatrist tried to bring a more professional, dispassionate perspective to the case. The man was clearly not psychotic; he could distinguish reality from fantasy. Nowhere in his testing did he reveal disturbances of thought patterns that would suggest that his personality was hovering on that dangerous tightrope that separates the merely neurotic from the frankly psychotic. Although the man was not particularly intelligent he knew right from wrong and had himself and his aggressive tendencies under control at most times.

All his episodes of violence had followed the consumption of a significant amount of alcohol at a time of family financial crisis.

'There are thousands of men and women like that one out in the real world,' the psychiatrist pointed out to the students. 'They don't have strong personalities but with help many such men can gain better control of themselves, especially if they are carefully watched

by an emotionally indifferent, author itarian and potentially puni-
tive third party. Probation, supervised help for his drinking problems and family counselling might save this man. Oh sure, the
failure rate is high, but what are the alternatives? Lock him away
for many years in case he does not reform? As a society, we must
generate universally acceptable constraints that reinforce the need
for self-control.'

The above case and discussion are purely hypothetical, although
one knows that they are only too likely to mimic real-life situations.
But the analogy between the incidents related above and the
deviations of an immune system that is attacking self will, I hope,
become obvious. When we talk of auto-immunity we are discussing
a situation in which less than perfect genetic starting material,
combined with environmental stress, can lead to a breakdown in
self-control that can produce disease.

Among the four to six hundred billion lymphocytes that secure
your body are some that are potentially 'sociopathic'; in this sense,
I suppose you could say 'organopathic'. Just as with human personality, there are numerous genetic permutations and combinations
that affect the performance of lymphocytes.

We know that each and every lymphocyte is capable of recognising
only one antigen, using its membrane receptor for the task. This
receptor has a three-dimensional spatial configuration that allows it
to act as a lock into which only one key can fit properly. The potential problem with all this lymphocyte individualism is that Nature
has generated cells that can recognise 'us' as well as foreignness.
Just as many cells may recognise your own kidney cells as can
recognise a herpes virus.

At one stage in the evolution of immunological knowledge it was
thought, or rather presumed, that under normal circumstances
Nature would have instituted a system for eliminating cells with
'attack potential' for self. This 'clonal abortion' (killing of a family
of autoreactive cells) would presumably occur as the cells were
formed. As a result of this smart move, we would then have no
chance of developing an autoimmune disease in which an organ
could be viciously attacked and damaged by an 'organopathic' cell.

When it became obvious that such tissue attacks did occur, the
theory was modified. It seemed that some of us were unfortunate
enough to lack the ability to induce clonal abortion and so these
potential 'time bombs' survived in our bodies.

None of us, it turns out, aborts all those T cells that can recognise
self tissues. We humans must accept the fact that millions of cells
in our body would attack us mercilessly if they followed their basic
inclinations. For our survival, therefore, they need to know that this
is not the right thing for them to do, so they may exert a measure

of self-control over their auto-aggressive natures. They need to be aware that big brother is watching them and urging passivity. It is the same situation that faces our wife basher; self-control and third-party regulatory pressures offer the best chance of avoiding dangerous escapes from acceptable behavior.

Lymphocytes can only recognise, for example, a specific section of our nervous system because they have been given the receptor to do so by genetic selection. A wife basher has less of an excuse for attacking her than does our auto-aggressive lymphocyte for attacking the nervous system. Nevertheless, these cells are breaking carefully laid down rules if they do attack us. Let us examine the controls that the immunological society places upon them.

Our immune system has to deal with a compromised situation since the system is not yet perfected, just as human society has to deal with the far from Utopian makeup of human interactions. We discussed in Chapter 2 the attempt nature makes in the thymus gland to kill cells that are capable of recognising and attacking or inducing an attack on our own tissues. If such a system were perfect then autoimmune diseases could not occur. Clonal abortion, as such a mechanism is called, is hard to study in humans but it is obviously very important if imperfect in the mouse as we imagine that the biology in humans is similar.

CD4 cells with receptors for our own tissue components do escape from the thymus and fail-safe mechanisms must therefore be brought to bear to protect us from autoimmune diseases.

All day every day, T cells from this inducer family look at our own tissues, recognise them and decide not to attack. This crucial and of course correct decision means that those other T and B cells that can recognise our own tissues do not get the 'go ahead' signals they need to attack. All remains peaceful and our organs go about their business unassailed.

Why do T cells that recognise us, using a perfectly legitimate and specific membrane receptor, not attack 'self' while others, appearing to take part in exactly the same sort of interaction but with 'foreignness', launch into battle? There are, as you would probably imagine, numerous reasons for this restraint as it would be very dangerous to have all our self-control eggs in the one basket.

Generally speaking, our T cells 'tolerate' the presence of self. This tolerance can be divided into two types, passive and active. Passive tolerance is 'self-contained'. Imagine a stray dog has adopted your family. You do not really want a dog but the kids want to keep it. You debate the issue, shrug your shoulders, smile at the kids and the dog moves closer to the fire. That is passive tolerance. On the other hand you may dearly wish to reject the mangy dog and would do so if a superior authority did not intervene. 'Henry,' says mother firmly, 'the children will be broken-hearted if you do not let them keep that dog; don't you even think of getting rid of it.' That is active tolerance. The dog immediately curls up in your favorite chair.

In immunological terms, many T inducer cells that can recognise our own tissues and escape destruction in the thymus are *passively* tolerant (clonal anergy). During fetal life when immature, indeed simplistic, cells are grouping themselves to form our early tissues and organs, T cells are genetically instructed to look at those developing structures. If they recognise them during the critical phase of fetal development they are instructed by genetic messages from within their nucleus to be tolerant. Before eighteen weeks of fetal life, cells are instructed that *anything they recognise* is 'self' and therefore it must be left alone. During fetal life the only thing around to look at should be 'us', and therefore this instruction should ensure that tolerance develops only to self. Since many of those T cells present at, say, ten weeks of fetal life will still be working sixty years later, the educational message given to the youngsters can control autoimmune tendencies for most of life.

Simultaneously and, some feel, more importantly, immuno-regulatory T cells that are active during fetal life are taught to recognise self and then secrete specific chemicals that will actively prevent a T inducer cell from coming off the appropriate tracks should it ever be so inclined. This is very much *active* tolerance. (Figure 18.)

Tolerance can be infectious. Apparently new T cells that are derived from the thymus a little later in life receive signals from both the passively tolerant and the actively tolerant cells. We mentioned earlier that in humans T cell production is at its height before birth and in the first few years of post-uterine life. We have no reason to believe that T cell production in any stage of life will be associated with complete elimination of cells that can recognise our own proteins. Thus while tolerance induction may be at its most efficient in fetal life, it must continue after birth. Undoubtedly other mechanisms besides infectious tolerance play a part in regulating these cells produced after birth. We still have much to learn about this whole question of non-reactivity to self tissues.

We do not worry too much about B cells in this system; they live no more than a few weeks. We could speculate that it would be a waste of biological energy to teach them tolerance as their life is too short and they cannot do anything without T cell help anyway, however it is interesting that B cells can be made tolerant, at least in the mouse.

As you can imagine, just how well all of this works and its ability to function throughout life depends on the quality of the genetic

Figure 18. Acceptance of SELF (biological tolerance)

program setting it up in the first place. The quality of this informat-ion varies from individual to individual, as with everything hu-man. Some people have superb control of the potentially lethal time bombs inside them; others have a tenuous hold on auto-aggression.

We are beginning to learn how to recognise these latter folk and that is an important development in preventative medicine. Weaker than normal genetic control of potential auto-reactivity leaves us walking through life on a biological tightrope, rather than down the middle of a broad pedestrian esplanade. People on a tightrope can fall off spontaneously, but can also easily be pushed off their centre of balance. Much of human disease results from an inter-action between 'second-class' genetic information and environmental circumstances.

Let me explain by giving an example. Diabetes is one of the most common and most serious diseases to afflict people. In its more severe forms, which tragically most frequently affect the young (sometimes even babies), the pancreas, the gland that secretes the hormone insulin, is the victim of auto-aggression.

The pancreas has two important functions. It produces chemicals that help us digest our food. These chemicals are squirted into our duodenum when we eat. We can live without them, but we cannot live without the literally vital production from specific beta cells within the gland: the hormone insulin.

Insulin is vital for many metabolic processes in our body, the most obvious of which is the pumping of sugar into our cells. Without insulin the sugar dams up in our blood, where it is useless and can have dangerous effects on the brain and other tissues. But much more is involved than that. Without insulin our bodies age prematurely; a forty-year-old diabetic looks like a 65-year-old non-diabetic. When diabetes occurs in childhood, life expectancy can be reduced by as much as twenty-seven years. Children frequently develop premature hardening of the arteries, leading to heart attacks, blindness and severe kidney disease. Cataracts tend to form in the eyes and all the sugar in the blood and urine make the patient more susceptible to infection; bacteria love sugar. Even with the most careful attention by the patient and doctor to the injection of insulin and general health matters, the diabetic must face many problems.

Slowly, over a period of months or more often years, patients with diabetes have their beta cells destroyed by their own T cells, a drastic example of autoimmunity. No pain is associated with the destruction and by the time the patient comes to the doctor with the first symptoms 80 per cent of the beta cells have already been destroyed. Even while we are working hard to develop means of transplanting the pancreas we are very interested in an even more attractive solution to the problem. We are attempting to perfect ways of detecting individuals experiencing an autoimmune attack on the pancreas before serious permanent damage has been done. Having done this we must try and get those cells back on the straight and narrow path that is non-reactivity to self. Call off the attack on the pancreas, and diabetes will not develop.

Picking up potential diabetics in a phase where they are still well is possible because of our ability to seek genetic markers that make us suspicious that self-control may not be all we might desire.

You will recall that we humans all have biological trademarks that we display on the surface of our cells. They proudly proclaim 'me', that almost unique individual. These proteins are well displayed on white blood cells so we refer to the system as the HLA system—*h*uman *l*eucocyte (white blood cell) *a*ntigen system. In an earlier chapter, we discussed the fact that these cell markers are what make transplants so difficult.

The eight major and many more minor self antigens were not put there by Nature to make transplantation difficult; they are there to help our immune system distinguish between self and foreignness. Remember, we will not attack anything unless it is presented to T and B cells in association with these molecules.

With the transplantation era came the development of technology for tissue-typing people for their eight major HLA antigens. Using this information, perfect matches could be sought for transplantation purposes.

With many profiles being generated among both candidates for transplantation and potential donors, an astute Frenchman made an astounding observation: some of these HLA profiles seemed to turn up repeatedly in people with certain diseases. Sometimes only one of the eight major antigens seem to be associated with the disease (or sometimes unusual resistance to a disease); in other cases a constellation of HLA antigens seemed to be linked in some unknown way to a specific illness.

With the work that has gone on since those pioneering observations, we can report that we now know of more than one hundred diseases that seem to be associated in one way or another with an HLA profile. Such genetic profiles can supply you with better predictive information than you will ever get from reading your horoscope.

Now the big question raised by those observations was: why should the presence of something on every cell in your body (remember we use leucocytes for testing only for convenience) have anything to do with your getting a disease in one organ, such as psoriasis which affects the skin, arthritis which affects the joints, cancer, diabetes, etc.?

For a while it was suggested that certain HLA antigens might act as receptors for certain viruses but in humans no evidence for this hypothesis has been found. Certain HLA antigens might produce disease *per se* when expressed on certain cells (they can cause a form of diabetes in mice for example), but in humans this remains no more than a reasonable hypothesis. What seems likely to be most important in the association of HLA antigens and human autoimmune disease is a matter perhaps best described as 'genetic company keeping'.

If you were here in a long dark alley off 11th Avenue in New York and into the opposite end of the alley comes one kid who looks like a member of a tough neighborhood gang, you would not be surprised to find four seconds later that ten or twelve more members of the gang come swinging into the lane. The first kid may be harmless but he tends to keep company with a gang that is anything but harmless. You do not need to see the whole gang to know trouble could be on the way; just a glimpse of the first kid and you move right on. He keeps bad company.

Some HLA genes tend to mix in immunologically disreputable company. These HLA genes, which produce the antigens we detect by our tissue typing, are harmless, but their presence indicates that on the sixth chromosome lurks a group of bad immunoregulatory genes that tend to allow disease processes such as autoimmunity to occur.

Now, of course, the kid from the gang could be followed into the alley on some occasions by a Salvation Army band. *He* is not the villain. Seeing a certain HLA antigen does not mean a definite propensity for a certain disease, it just increases the likelihood.

This association is much stronger, however, with certain profiles. One such profile consists of cells displaying D locus genes known as 3 and 4. This is a bad combination, increasing the risk that disease-causing genes for many problems are present, including multiple sclerosis, rheumatoid arthritis and diabetes. About 30 per cent of people in the world are unaffected by the presence of DR3 and DR4, however.

The reason that certain HLA genes and genes coding regulatory performance stick together through many generations needs explaining. Chromosomes do split and link up again during cell division, but it is a random process (same old theme, mix up the genes). Imagine you have a piece of wood that is 3 metres long and you are going to cut it into two pieces with your eyes closed. If you paint two spots on the wood, one blue and the other red and the spots are 2 metres apart, the chances are that when you wildly swing your axe to cut the wood in half, the red spot will be on one piece and the blue on another. Repeat the process, however, with the red and blue spot 10 centimetres from each other and the chances that both will remain on the one piece of wood after it has been severed are very high. Immunoregulatory genes that look after such things as non-reaction to self are very close (in the geographical sense) to genes that code for HLA antigens. Hence, if you see a red spot the chances are that a blue spot is nearby.

A boy with diabetes who also displays the DR3 DR4 combination will very likely have a brother who also carries DR3 DR4 antigens on his cells and who may also be vulnerable to diabetes. With that suspicion, can we diagnose his disease early, well before most of his pancreas' beta cells have been destroyed?

Glucagon is a hormone that stimulates the release of insulin from the pancreas into the bloodstream. A healthy pancreas will respond immediately to an injection of the hormone with the release of a specific amount of insulin. This normal response can be quantified, hence an abnormally low output of insulin would suggest that the pancreas is in trouble, though a long way as yet from clinical diabetes. If you follow the siblings of diabetic children or even their parents for ten years, those who have the same HLA profile as the family member with diabetes have an almost 100 per cent chance of developing the disease. Hence our interest in early diagnosis.

One of the better known autoimmune diseases is 'multiple sclerosis'. Sclerosis means scarring, and indeed the pathology of this disorder results in multiple scars occurring randomly throughout the brain. A scar tells us that nervous tissue has been destroyed by an inflammatory process and the scars, or plaques as they are sometimes called, are the monuments to an auto-aggressive attack that can cause so much disability.

Betty was only twenty-four years old when her first symptoms appeared. One Saturday afternoon Betty, a keen and very good tennis player, was about to serve when she noticed that as she tossed the ball high into the air, the object she was about to assault looked somewhat blurred. Nothing dramatic but as she continued to play a mild pain developed behind her right eye, and when she looked at the strings of her racquet and closed each eye in turn her right eye was not only painful but not seeing clearly. That night the blurring of vision was noticeable although not significantly worse, but the pain was bad enough to keep her awake well into the early hours of the morning. It was relieved somewhat by the ingestion of a few aspirin tablets. On the Monday she made an appointment to see her doctor, but when she arrived on Tuesday afternoon to be examined in his office she felt a little embarrassed about troubling him at all, for all the symptoms had completely resolved. Her doctor examined her thoroughly nonetheless, and declared that all was intact. Peering into her right eye with his ophthalmoscope, he looked at the huge optic nerve that races visual images into the brain for interpretation and noted no pathology.

Three months later, however, Betty was sitting at her desk at work when she noticed a funny feeling in her legs. It wasn't so much a pain but rather a decrease in sensation, or a mild numbness, similar to what one might get if one's legs are crossed for too long. Betty thought that perhaps if she moved around the office for a few minutes the symptoms might disappear, but walking and standing did not help. Indeed, this time her symptoms did not go away quickly and the lack of feeling in her legs became pronounced and troublesome.

This time, her doctor was able to demonstrate an abnormality and sent Betty to a neurologist, who admitted her to hospital for a day so that she might have a lumbar puncture. A needle was placed between the vertebrae in her lower back so that some of the cerebrospinal fluid that circulates around and through the brain could be extracted and analysed. In that fluid, T cells and abnormal antibodies were detected and a week later the neurologist told Betty that she had multiple sclerosis. Two months later, to Betty's relief, the sensation in her legs returned as mysteriously as it had disappeared, but in less than three months her legs were weak rather than numb and she could not play tennis or even walk normally. Nor would she ever again.

Out paths were not to cross for a further fifteen years, by which time Betty was confined to a wheelchair, required help with dressing, washing and eating, had such slurred speech that she was difficult to understand and because of a loss of bladder control, lived with a catheter in place: all this physical disability in a woman who intellectually was completely normal. Remarkably, it was the emotion of frustration rather than depression that troubled her most.

Multiple sclerosis, as is true of so many diseases, seems to be associated with a combination of genetic and geographical coincidences. In general, the frequency of the disease in a given population increases steadily the further one moves away from the equator. In temperate northern and southern climates, the incidence of the disease is about 60 per 100 000. Females are slightly more likely to develop the disease and the onset of symptoms occurs most commonly between the ages of 20 and 30 years. One's chance of developing the disease is slightly greater if a relative has been affected.

Just as the wires carrying electrons along a cable must be protected by a sheath, so must many of our nerves. Instead of rubber or plastic, however, the body wraps nerves up in a specialised tissue known as myelin, and proteins within myelin are the targets for the autoaggressive cells of the immune system that, after attacking, produce the disease multiple sclerosis. An illness very similar to multiple sclerosis can be generated in laboratory animals by injecting them with protein obtained from myelin, together with an adjuvant, i.e. a substance that facilitates the introduction of the protein to the cells of the immune system.

Why do T and B cells from the immune system turn against self and attack myelin? Why do they attack and then stop, allowing, for some years, healing to occur? Why do they so often return again in a more vicious mood to destroy once and for all nervous tissue, leaving a scar and a useless nerve behind? We don't really know the answers to these questions. We do know that there is a significant association between multiple sclerosis and certain genes associated with the production of our antigen-presenting proteins. The simplest explanation would involve a viral infection of the myelin itself giving the immune system some sort of excuse for attacking innocent tissue but, despite many an exhaustive search, no infectious agent has been found.

There is no satisfactory treatment for the condition, although

steroids help with acute attacks early in the disease and suppressing the immune system to a degree that leaves the patient still able
to make a reasonable response to infection may be useful.

Why was Betty seeing me? My unit was interested in applying to
multiple sclerosis a new technique with the potential to reorganise
the immune system, helping it to get its house in order and return
to a life of attack against foreignness not self. The technique in
question is known as Total Lymphoid Irradiation (TLI). Numerous
experiments in animals and preliminary studies in humans have
demonstrated that low-dose irradiation applied to all the lymph
glands of the body, using the same equipment that we use to treat
patients with cancer, may so affect T cells that they return to a more
fetal life state where they can learn once again what is self, thus
becoming tolerant to tissues that they were inclined to attack. Sadly,
we did not help Betty with this approach; perhaps it was too late
in her case or perhaps we still do not understand enough about the
technique to maximise its potential. Experiments are continuing,
however, for multiple sclerosis is one of the most serious of autoimmune diseases.

To recapitulate, some of us inherit a set of genes that do not
establish the normal control mechanisms that stop attacks on self
with the precision of another (obviously preferable) set of genes
inherited by other individuals. As a result, some of us walk through
life on a biological tightrope. But what things tend to disturb our
precarious balance?

For the person with less than perfect immunoregulation the known
environmental hazards are stress, drugs and infections, especially
viral infections. The defect may be spontaneous or it may be triggered by some mechanisms currently unknown to us.

Psychological stress, especially when coping mechanisms cannot
be generated, can quite drastically disturb immunological function.

What about the ability of drugs to disturb immune control? All
biological reactions can be translated into biochemical events in
which soluble molecules move around the micro-environment ar-
ranging various sophisticated reactions. When you swallow that
capsule, grimace at that injection or watch some therapeutic marvel
dripping into your veins, you face a calculated risk associated with
adding potent chemicals to a delicately balanced system.

Many drugs are wonderfully effective and safe for most of the
population, yet they cause a lot of problems for people who live on
an immunological tightrope. Antibiotics, drugs for controlling blood
pressure, chemicals that make you pass a lot of urine, agents that
control the rhythm of your heart, etc.—in fact more than one
hundred commonly used drugs—can trigger off an autoimmune
reaction in the susceptible individual.

What about infections? Viruses are the main culprits here, and we have yet to learn a great deal about how they damage self-control mechanisms. We know that viruses can disturb the best of immune systems (e.g. in the case of AIDS) but less spectacular derangements occur with herpes viruses such as the one that causes mononucleosis, and there are a number of other viruses that we think may be involved with specific diseases.

A nasty little virus called Coxsackie is a strong candidate for diabetes. There are at least two non-mutually exclusive possibilities here. A virus could decide that the beta cells of the pancreas would make the ideal home. Once ensconced, the virus may or may not damage its chosen residence. If viruses did damage the beta cells, their appearance could be so distorted that they may look 'foreign'; that is, have membrane profiles different from those displayed on normal cells. In such circumstances immune cells may swoop on what they now perceive to be foreignness and may cause more harm than good by destroying not only the virus but the beta cells as well. The weaker our immunological self-control, the more likely we are to attack altered self. The alternative explanation involves viruses disturbing T cells directly, with the result that they behave inappropriately and attack self. Probably both these things happen simultaneously on many occasions.

With that background information, let us look at some of the autoimmune diseases themselves.

I should point out that these diseases are essentially those of women. For most of the conditions we will discuss, doctors see ten women with the problem for every male. It is true that men are worse affected than women, but fewer get these diseases. Why? The female immunologists of my acquaintance claim that men with such imperfections do not even make it out of the uterus to put up a fight. There may be a measure of truth in that but sex hormones do play an important role in setting up the regulation of the immune system.

Although we talk of 'this' and 'that' system within the body as if they were independent if nicely integrated modules, in the real living body integration is so complete and the interdependence so profound that in reality there is just a functioning total system. We do not understand how, but an excess of male sex hormones (testosterones) over female sex hormones (particularly estrogens) tends to play a role in perfecting immunoregulation. Little female mice get an autoimmune disease seldom seen in their male litter mates. Giving girls testosterone from birth prevents them from developing the disease. (Of course, it also stops them from being girls.)

The diseases we call autoimmune fall into two big clusters. In one group of diseases specific organs tend to be targeted. Diabetes is obviously an example of that. In the other group, the problems are largely caused by immunological damage to blood vessels. Tissues relying on blood from the damaged vessels are themselves damaged.

The first group tends to occur in women and often there is a history of this sort of disease among other females in the family. The victims have HLA profiles that suggest that their disease is caused by an immunogenetic deficiency that allows an autoimmune attack to occur. For reasons that are quite unknown, such cases frequently occur in women who have premature greying of the hair and often have small spots of depigmentation in their skin called vitiligo. Here are a few case reports to show you the range of these target-orientated attacks.

One day I was observing a woman screaming at a child of about four, obviously overreacting to the fact that the child's ice-cream had obeyed the laws of physics and a temperature of 40°C and had rapidly slid down the child to find the floor. As I looked at the woman I realised her hands were trembling seriously, she was in a lather of perspiration and she had very protruding eyes that looked as if they wanted to pop right out of her head. As I walked closer the diagnosis was clinched. A telltale swelling in the neck told all. She had an enlarged and overactive thyroid gland that was pouring forth the hormone thyroxine that drives so many of the body's metabolic processes. Too much and we tremble, we lose emotional control and we develop diarrhoea, changes in our hair and nails, disturbances of periods, severe weight loss, a racing heart and many other symptoms.

Unhesitatingly, but I hope politely, I asked the woman if she knew she had a serious problem with her thyroid gland. For a moment I thought I might have a serious problem, so horrible was the stare she gave me; but she calmed down and told me that she had not sought medical help for her problem. I arranged for her to visit my professor the following week and, indeed, she benefited significantly from the urgent treatment she was given.

What I did not realise at the time was that, in that unfortunate thyroid of hers, T and B cells had congregated and were literally destroying the gland. Some of the antibodies she was producing, directed against the cells of her thyroid gland, actually stimulated them to release more and more hormone. The thyroid is a favorite target for autoimmunity when T cell regulation goes astray.

One of my favorite patients has diabetes and another autoimmune disease. At the age of twenty-nine, she was referred by her doctor because of increasingly frequent episodes of muscular weakness. She runs a plant nursery and has the soft, caring personality one so often finds in people who work with trees, flowers and plants.

Ellen was a strong girl, although not big, and was used to lifting plants around her nursery and unloading bags of fertiliser and the like. For the few months before she consulted me she had noticed that walking up a flight of stairs made her legs feel extremely weak. She could unload the first two bags of fertiliser from a delivery truck but then strangely each subsequent bag got heavier and heavier until she could not move her arms at all. After some rest, she would recover. She also complained that she was having trouble with her eyes. When reading for any length of time she would develop double vision.

On asking her to open and close her hands repeatedly one could quickly see how soon she tired and we immediately suspected that she suffered from myasthenia (muscle weakness) gravis (severe). Our investigations supported the diagnosis and we rushed her into hospital and had our best surgeons open her chest to remove her thymus gland. Remove her thymus gland? The soul of her immune system? Yes, I know it sounds shocking, but let me explain.

Myasthenia gravis is perhaps the most fascinating of all the autoimmune diseases (and can be one of the most serious). To understand it you have to know how nerves tell muscles to move. Please tell your left hand to form a fist right now. From the time your mind said 'okay' to my request and the time your hand formed a fist was but a fraction of a second. From your cerebral cortex a message sped at incredible speed down the nerves in your spinal column to move out to and then down the nerves in your arms to your hand.

When the electrical message carried by your nerves got to the muscle, however, a change occurred. Between the end of the nerve and the trigger point on the muscle, which must be activated for it to move, there is a gap. Across that space the message from the nerve telling your hand to move will be carried, not in the form of electricity, but in the form of a chemical. It is like a breathless runner arriving at the edge of a river bank and begging a man to row him across to the opposite side so that he can deliver a message to a person waiting there. The chemical reaction is almost as quick as the electrical one, however. The chemical races across the gap and binds to the trigger point on the muscle, which is stimulated by this chemical. The substance in question for most muscles is called acetylcholine (ACH) and the trigger point in question on our muscle is called, reasonably enough, the receptor for ACH.

Myasthenia occurs when we make an immunological attack on that receptor, which becomes covered in antibodies. The result is that it is very difficult for the ACH to get its message through.

We all get tired muscles if we work them continuously but after just a few contractions people with myasthenia gravis cannot supply sufficient amounts of acetylcholine to break through the antibody barrier and stimulate the muscles. Should the receptors that are being blocked be on muscles involved in making the chest wall move, patients could die without the help of mechanical respirators. Why remove the thymus? Thousands of years ago, the thymus had two jobs: the production of T cells, of course, but also the production of a hormone we no longer appear to need that actually facilitated neuromuscular transmission. To produce the hormone, the thymus had in its tissues a few isolated muscle cells with receptors for acetylcholine. These odd muscle cells are still to be found in the human thymus.

In patients with myasthenia gravis, within their thymus gland T cells suddenly attack those muscle cells as if they were foreign and it appears that the specific antigen that irritates them is the receptor for the neurotransmitter. It would not matter so much if the attack stayed in the thymus gland which, as we noted before, is not a very important organ in adult life; but the T and B cells which we can see congregating in the thymus in this disease leave this organ and go out to the peripheral muscles and attack important receptors. The dissemination of these auto-aggressive cells from the thymus can be minimised by surgically removing the thymus. We try to do this as early as possible in the disease.

Other diseases that fall into the same mechanistic category—that is, a deliberate immunological attack on a specific tissue—include pernicious anemia, where an antibody is formed that blocks the ability of an intestinal hormonal-like agent known as 'intrinsic factor' to absorb vitamin B12. This vitamin is essential for the production of red blood cells and the health of our nervous system. In other diseases the ovaries, the testes, the parathyroid glands that control calcium metabolism, our red blood cells and our platelets can all be attacked and seriously damaged.

There is a second large cluster of diseases, however, where an immune system's deranged behaviour causes damage in another way. The prototype of such diseases is systemic lupus erythematosus, understandably abbreviated by doctors and patients alike to SLE. Thousands of people suffer from this disease which has, as its basis, damage to blood vessels.

Mrs L was a thirty-five-year-old mother of two healthy children when she returned from a two-week holiday in Jamaica feeling decidedly unwell with painful joints, a moderate fever, a feeling of overwhelming doom and a strange rash on her face. She thought at first that she had been suffering from sunburn but soon realised that this was different. From one cheek to the other a red scaly rash had appeared which narrowed to bridge her nose in butterfly-like fashion. Her family doctor recognised the characteristic rash of SLE and she was sent to us for investigation. We controlled her disease but could not cure her; she remains only moderately well.

What had happened to Mrs L? A T cell malfunction had developed because of failure of one of the mechanisms that protects us from autoimmunity. In some people it appears that ultraviolet light can be a trigger that disturbs less than perfect immunoregulatory cells. Mrs L began to make antibodies to her own tissues. In the case of SLE the target seems harmless enough. Every day we constantly regenerate lost cells, that part of us which died yesterday, and the debris is usually cleared from our system by an inhouse garbage collecting organisation featuring scavenger cells that can literally eat tissue debris. The system is mainly focused in the liver and spleen.

Poor Mrs L's lymphocytes were making antibodies to the naked nuclei of cells that had died and were being removed. These antinuclear antibodies were being produced in great quantities. As the garbage system was trying to remove the nuclear material, the antibodies bound themselves to these proteins, forming big complexes that the scavenger cells found hard to deal with. As a result some complexes were not cleared rapidly enough from blood vessels. The complexes were then becoming trapped in certain sites in Mrs L's body, usually tiny blood vessels, and the immune response that followed featured a lot of damage to the blood vessels that were unfortunate enough to be clogged with these complexes. The blood vessels became inflamed, lost their patency and a number of tissues suffered.

SLE primarily affects skin, joints, the central nervous system and the kidneys. The last are particularly vulnerable. Why people suddenly start making antibodies to self debris is not clear, but genetic and environmental factors (in this case sunlight) are very important. Many diseases feature this kind of pathology rather than the organ-orientated approach seen with, for example, thyroid disease. Rheumatoid arthritis is another classical example.

With ageing there is a natural tendency for self-control to diminish so that autoimmune diseases and phenomena may appear late in life when the integrity of our very definitely finite T cell system starts to wane. Fortunately there is a lot we can do for many of these problems, but we cannot cure them. This subject then is a distressing one, providing yet another example of how the development of ever more sophisticated weaponry for defence leaves the defenders in great danger if the forces they control turn inwards. Wasn't it poor Guillotin who lost his head at the knife of his most famous invention?

10

The chronic fatigue syndrome: an immunological mystery disease

FOR immunology, and indeed most medical disciplines, the truism 'the more you know, the more you realise how much you don't know' is undoubtedly accurate. That is not to say that it is perceived as such by the majority of physicians. If anything, the story that follows would suggest the opposite. The case histories I'll relate illustrate how patients with unusual symptoms that currently defy explanation are too easily considered to be hypochondriacs, victims of a neurosis.

Carol is twenty-eight and introduced herself to me as a 'debilitated airline stewardess'. She had led a normal life until the age of twenty-four, when happiness and a bright future turned to despair in a matter of months.

Carol flew international routes for a well-known airline and had been doing so since she was nineteen. She was pretty, popular and an excellent athlete. Sure, she would get tired after eight hours with 400 people in a jumbo jet, but she recovered quickly and enjoyed her stopovers. She had a multi tude of interests which she was able to accommodate despite her hectic jetting around the globe.

Her problems started on a flight to London. She remembers leaving New York in perfect health but was feeling decidedly unwell three hours into the flight. At this point she had a headache, a sore throat and some muscle aches. She was able to work but she remembers thinking to herself, 'I am in for a bad dose of the flu'.

By the time she arrived in London all her symptoms were worse and she was sure she had a temperature. She went to her hotel and by 7 a.m. was in bed, hoping that six hours of sleep would see the virus spent and her good health returned to her.

She fell into a deep sleep and woke at 5 p.m. considerably worse. Her nightdress was soaked from perspiration and she was experiencing a shaking chill. Never could she recall having a throat as sore as the one she awoke to; never had she felt so wretched. Realising that she was unusually sick she called for the hotel doctor, who came promptly, examined her carefully and confirmed that indeed she had a high temperature. He told her that almost certainly she was suffering from glandular fever, alternatively referred to as infectious mononucleosis. He informed her that the very severe pharyngitis she was experiencing was typical of this particular viral infection. Aspirin and antibiotics were prescribed; the first for the fever and pain, the second to ward off any secondary bacterial complications. Blood tests were ordered for the following day to confirm his diagnosis. In the meantime she was to drink a lot of fluid and rest completely. Carol had no choice but to follow the latter advice for, as she recalled, she felt utterly exhausted.

After four days in her hotel bed she felt considerably improved. Though she still felt weak the sore throat and fever had all but gone. She arranged to fly home (as a passenger; she was not well enough to work) and remembers being somewhat uneasy when her English physician told her as she departed that all her blood tests had been negative—that is, he had been unable to confirm a diagnosis of glandular fever. Despite this, he remained confident that 'mono' was the cause of her problems and that in six weeks she would be her old self again.

We have discussed the common problem known as infectious mononucleosis already. This disease is caused by a virus from the herpes family that invades almost 100 per cent of us at some time in our lives, usually before the age of twenty-five. For reasons that are not altogether clear, infections in childhood, especially before the age of six, rarely result in any significant symptoms. When one is infected with the virus it can be found in saliva and therefore can be spread as a droplet infection and move easily into bodies that come close to those that are infected. A cough or a sneeze can discharge thousands of viral particles into the air around us. It is particularly well transmitted by kissing; hence it is frequently, if somewhat romantically, described at the 'kissing disease'.

The particular virus involved is called the Epstein–Barr virus (EBV) after its discoverers. It is unique in that, in addition to invading our throats and liver cells, it also takes up residence in our B cells. Once it invades these antibody-producing cells the only way to get rid of it is to kill the infected B cells. In a prolonged struggle, our T cells do manage to kill most EBV-containing B cells; but in a few the virus becomes dormant, not signalling to any passing T cell that they are hiding in a particular B cell, and thus a flare-up of the disease at a later date is possible although unusual. As most B cells live in our lymph glands the battle between the EB virus and our T cells is fought out in these glands, which become swollen and tender—hence the alternative name of 'glandular fever'.

For a period that varies from one individual to another, the immune system is disturbed by an infection with the 'mono' virus and inappropriate immunological reactions can take place. For example, patients often develop allergies for the first time and experience autoimmune disorders during that phase of the illness which occurs before the T cells manage to kill the virus. A number of patients may remain ill for months as they battle the virus. They have a long drawn out, i.e. continuous, infection. Other patients infected with an equal dose of the same virus don't even know that they have met up with such a challenge, so efficiently does their immune system handle the invasion. The range of scenarios observed following an infection by the EB virus is determined by the variety of genetic programs available to direct, more or less efficiently, the immunological attack against the virus. The potency of the virus is constant, the host response is variable. The 'mono' we have been discussing is not what troubled Carol, but as EBV will become a central player in our mystery disease the preceding explanation was necessary.

On returning to New York Carol saw her own doctor, who felt that her English physician was most likely correct and ordered her to bed for two further weeks of complete rest. A good patient, she did as she was told and got her reward. After two weeks she felt 95 per cent better and was ready to return to work. Further blood tests had not shown the presence of antibody to the EB virus so the diagnosis of infectious mononucleosis seemed unsustainable. Her physician told her that her problem, now almost resolved, must have been caused by something similar to the EB virus.

At her doctor's insistence, Carol took another ten days' rest before she returned to work, ready to get on with her life. Shortly thereafter, however, our mysterious disease struck in full force.

Two months into her normal routine, Carol would have said she was still struggling slightly to regain full health, being about 85 per cent of her former energetic self. Then, on one easily remembered morning, she awoke only to find that overnight her body had departed and a new one had been slipped into her bed.

Her new body was that of a very old woman, she thought. It protested that it did not want to move; it was exhausted. More than that, it ached from head to toe. She could feel each muscle protesting even as she lay immobile in the bed. Many of the muscles felt tender to her touch. With the maximum amount of willpower she dragged her new self to the bathroom, then collapsed back on her bed, utterly exhausted from this effort. She had been tired before but never had she felt anything approaching this sensation. Her head was pounding and she recalls how confused she was. Certainly she could not work in this condition and this was worrisome as she had an uneasy feeling that she was meant to work that day. Try as she might, however, she could not bring her mind to focus on her timetable. As she tried to analyse her working movements over the past week she felt herself incapable of the mental agility required. Carol called her airline, found that she was indeed due to fly to Frankfurt, apologised, said she was sick and withdrew her services, much to the chagrin of the rostering clerk.

When her doctor arrived she told him how she felt and promptly burst into a bout of uncontrollable crying. She remembers the sobbing that accompanied an overwhelming feeling of depression. The doctor, the same caring physician she had consulted earlier on her return from England, admitted that he was confused. He could find nothing abnormal on examination of his patient and told Carol so. 'You might be coming down with another virus, Carol, or this could be a flare-up of your "mono"; that can happen, you know. In any case stay in bed, rest and I am sure it will either declare itself or pass off quickly and you can get back to work.' Carol has not returned to work and it is now four years since the start of her problem.

What followed for Carol can only be imagined in the context of a nightmare. This new body of hers was out to torture her. She had days when some of her exhaustion lifted, but if she tried to do even the simplest task for herself she would experience three days of such extreme fatigue that she could not force herself to walk across a room.

Carol returned to her parents' home, where sympathy was forthcoming. As the months rolled by, however, sympathy gave way to puzzlement and frustration set in for patient and family alike. Her own physician performed a battery of tests and nothing abnormal turned up in any of the high-technology screening programs called upon to analyse her blood.

As the agony continued, some major symptoms were most consistent: headaches that were not typical of either tension or migraine blighted her every morning, and the mental confusion and emotional lability that descended on her 'like a veil being placed over my mind' continued and even worsened. This once energetic and resourceful young woman was but a shadow of her former self. In addition to these two constant symptoms, her extreme fatigue and muscle aches continued.

She noted other things about herself. Sometimes eating made her fatigue worse and her daily nightmare did not leave her in sleep. She was attacked almost nightly by horrifying meaningless nightmares, most notable for the vivid colours featured.

Of course, she was referred to a consultant physician for help. The first to see her considered that her increased fatigue after eating was due to low blood sugar levels, a not uncommon diagnosis but in fact an extremely rare problem associated with an overenthusiastic release of insulin after sugar is ingested. The usual dietary manipulations that help patients with this problem did not, however, help Carol. After that, many physicians tackled her problem, all remaining puzzled and unhelpful in the face of her constellation of symptoms. The third consultant, in what was to be, would you believe, a series of sixteen, looked at his totally unrewarding test results, looked at Carol and told her calmly and confidently that she was suffering from a psychological rather than an organic problem. She was troubled by a severe neurosis; urgent psychiatric help was essential.

She dutifully accepted the advice and consulted a psychiatrist, an older man with a down-to-earth disposition. After a number hours of discussion and examination he told an anxious patient and her desperate parents that he could find nothing untoward in her personality that wasn't entirely explained by the frustration of her situation. As this did not seem to be of much help to Carol, it was decided that a second and younger psychiatrist should be consulted. This was done and he came to exactly the opposite opinion. This man seized on the fact that, just before Carol's well-remembered trip to London when she first became ill, she had terminated a romance; this, he declared, was the undoubted cause of her problem.

When Carol pointed out that it was she who had called off the affair and that indeed she had been relieved to be out of an unsatisfactory situation, her explanation fell on Freudian ears that saw a plethora of subconscious reasons for her psychosomatic disorder. Urged on by her parents, Carol entered into therapy with this man. After six months, however, both patient and doctor were frustrated by the lack of progress and agreed to part company.

Unfortunately, her psychotherapy failed Carol in two ways. Not only did it not help her but indeed it harmed her. Her employer, friends and even her family were instantly convinced that psychotherapy meant that hers was a real psychiatric disease. Bizarre symptoms in the face of normal blood tests are so easily dismissed as neurosis.

After two years of all this Carol was spiritually alone, severely depressed, weak, confused and apathetic. Her once vital smile and twinkling eyes had been replaced by a despondent, lifeless stare. Some of the doctors she consulted along her painful journey were humble enough to discuss their ignorance and the possibility that this was a strange but definite disease. What were they to make of a patient whose muscles looked normal (even under the microscope), were not wasted (as occurs in patients with polio), responded normally to electric stimulation, yet would not allow her to walk around the block without extracting a penalty of three days' absolute rest in bed?

Carol was certainly not the first patient I had seen with this problem; far from it. At the time I first saw her I had seen many such cases, and now, because this problem has become a major research interest, I have studied more than 1700 individuals, the quality of whose lives has been much compromised by chronic fatigue syndrome. I remember well, however, the first case I ever saw—fifteen years before I met Carol. I was consulted by an airline pilot (a coincidence, I know: I am not suggesting that flying is in any way linked to this problem). He could no longer fly his jumbo jet, not only because he was too weak but because he could no longer make the swift and accurate decisions needed for his profession. He told me a tale similar in many ways to that told by Carol, but his problem was less severe. His troubles had started with a well-documented attack of glandular fever. He developed quite readily detectable antibodies to the Epstein–Barr virus during his flu-like illness.

Now as many of you will know from recent publicity all around the world, the fatigue syndrome we are discussing is far from rare. Depending on the part of the world in which you live it is variously referred to as the Iceland syndrome, Royal Free disease, epidemic neuromyasthenia, chronic EBV syndrome, myalgic encephalomyelitis (ME), post-infection fatigue syndrome or the term that we will use throughout this chapter, chronic fatigue syndrome (CFS). I prefer the last title as it doesn't pretend that we know more than we do. To put our knowledge about CFS into historical perspective let us look at how this disease, whatever one may call it, first came to medical attention.

In London in 1955 trouble was brewing (incubating might be a better word) at one of that city's great teaching hospitals, the Royal Free. Ancient, admirable and academic, this hospital had much to be proud of. One of the finest liver units in the world had been established there and the attending physicians read like a *Who's Who* of British medicine. On 13 July two of the staff, one a doctor, one a nurse, reported to the appropriate hospital clinic with a puzzling and similar condition. They were admitted to the hospital for investigation. Over the next two weeks seventy more of the staff came down with the same illness and were also admitted. While all the staff were greatly concerned at these developments panic was absent for, after all, this was a hospital whose staff had been dealing with the dangerous polio epidemic for years. As hospital officials could not be certain what was happening to their staff it seemed prudent to close the hospital; in any case, staff were now in short supply. On 25 July this great hospital closed its doors and did not open them until October. During that time 292 members of the staff were seen with similar symptoms and 255 were admitted. Obviously an epidemic of something was occurring, but what?

The patients all had similar symptoms, though the severity and mixture of symptoms varied. Headaches, emotional liability, extreme tiredness, pain in the back and neck and often one limb, dizziness, troublesome blurring of vision and swollen lymph glands were all common. Most worrying were clear signs that the major nerves running inside the head were not functioning normally. Twenty per cent had paralysis of the muscles of their face, many had difficulty swallowing, muscle spasms, double vision and sensory disturbances.

Most of the staff recovered fairly quickly but the major persistent problem, noted time and time again, was extreme muscle fatigue. No infectious agent was found that could explain the epidemic but it was presumed that some new agent, probably a virus, had swept through the hospital and that this virus had a specific predilection for muscle and the nervous system. For some of the staff of the Royal Free Hospital the disease did not disappear rapidly but persisted for many weeks, months or, for a small number, indefinitely. With no causative agent found it was quite understandable that the problem was called, for want of anything more scientific, 'Royal Free disease'.

What the physicians struggling with the problem at the Royal Free Hospital did not know was that in February of that year an outbreak of a very similar disease had occurred in three areas in northwest London. To the Royal Free symptoms were added a very rapid pulse rate and vivid technicolor nightmares. Apart from these additional symptoms the problems described by these patients were identical to those given by the staff of the Royal Free Hospital.

With the publication in 1957 of the Royal Free story in the medical literature, reports started to come in from all around the world describing similar outbreaks. For example in February 1955, at the time northwest London was experiencing this problem, a similar outbreak occurred in a hospital in Durban, South Africa.

Investigators interested in this problem have now agreed that the first outbreak of the 'Royal Free disease' occurred in the Los Angeles

County General Hospital in 1934. More than thirty-five outbreaks have been recorded around the world with major ones occurring in Iceland in 1948, Adelaide, South Australia in 1949 and numerous other places, suggesting that this is not a geographically restricted problem.

In the late 1960s scientists were becoming interested in the problem of Royal Free disease when a 'disastrous advance' occurred. Just as investigators proposed the name myalgic (painful muscles) encephalomyelitis (inflammation of brain and nerves), usually abbreviated to ME, as a satisfactory name for the disorder, two psychologists unwittingly but arrogantly brought research into this disease to an abrupt halt.

The two investigators in question had recently experienced a major triumph and were looking for a follow-up. They had been called in to examine an epidemic of painful muscle spasm among young ladies attending an all-girls' school in England.

Interested, indeed expert, in mass hysteria, they were soon able to attribute the painful spasms of the hands and the tingling of the lips felt by the girls to overbreathing; mass hysteria leading to epidemic panic and hyperventilation. Increasing one's rate of breathing when it is not demanded by physical activity soon results in too much carbon dioxide being released from the body. The acid content of blood and tissues falls, nerves become highly irritable and spasm results.

The two doctors asked the Royal Free Hospital for permission to review the records of those patients affected during the famous epidemic. The hypothesis they wished to test argued that those affected would be found to be predisposed to psychoneuroses. In 1970 they published their opinion that the Royal Free epidemic was indeed a marvellous example of mass hysteria and that similar outbreaks in the world would be similarly explained. The confidence of these psychologists was hardly justified when one considers that they did not see the patients and saw no inconsistency associate with the fact that 79 per cent of the patients had swollen lymph glands, 89 per cent had a fever, 45 per cent had paralysis of their eye muscles and 19 per cent were unable to move their facial muscles; all signs that are hard to produce hysterically.

The damage was done, however, and the media seized upon this sensational explanation as an example of how improved medical sophistication allowed modern doctors to understand that personality disorders, not new organic diseases, would provide the new syndromes.

The *Sunday Times* in London and no less a medical authority than *Time* magazine accepted without question the hysteria explanation and is so doing added enormously to the suffering of many thousands of far-from-hysterical individuals afflicted with the chronic fatigue syndrome. The public, many of the patients themselves and countless numbers of physicians, uncomfortable with their inability to understand the disease in organic terms, accepted the hysteria explanation and the syndrome became almost invariably regarded as a neurosis.

The best scientists are similar to the best detectives. They can't throw away major clues just because they distort some preconceived suspicion. Our psychologists surely should have couched their conclusions on a bed of reservations, admitting that there were some clues that didn't fit their hypothesis. Surely their unequivocal diagnosis of mass hysteria should have been more restrained, as the medical records of many of the patients detailed that it was necessary to feed them via a rubber tube inserted into their stomach, so severe was the paralysis of muscles needed to swallow.

Physicians who deal with patients suffering chronic illnesses know, if they are at all perceptive, that psychological problems develop as a result of the frustrations of living with poor health. Often such situations challenge physicians to use both their art and their science to dissect the functional away from the organic. Both elements of the disease process demand treatment—but different treatment. It is in no way surprising that many, indeed most, patients with a chronic fatigue syndrome have some psychological turmoil increasing the misery orchestrated by their basic disease.

The prominence of symptoms such as emotional lability, depression, impaired memory and powers of concentration is consistent. They are, in my opinion, caused by the disease itself and thus do not represent the secondary psychological problems discussed above.

Now the epidemics just described are not epidemics of CFS; rather they are epidemics caused by some unknown agent, probably a virus, which triggered CFS in a few genetically susceptible patients. Most infected people in these epidemics recover their health reasonably quickly, but for an unlucky few a long-term problem, CFS, develops. It is an important point that the symptoms of 'Royal Free disease' with its muscle paralysis are quite distinct from those of CFS. Indeed, we know that most people who develop CFS do not do so as part of any community epidemic at all. Most cases are sporadic or *endemic*. In Western countries, about 1 in 2500 people may develop this disease while everyone around them is quite well.

In fact, CFS is not a new disease and is most certainly not a product of the twentieth century, as some misguided clinical ecologists would have you believe. There are classic descriptions of the disease we are discussing in the medical literature, with a particularly fine one dating to 1869 when a certain Dr Beard described both the overwhelming fatigue and the neurological problems (poor memory and concentration, etc.) and gave the disorder the name neurasthenia. He noted that in his patients there was nothing at all to suggest that a psychological problem pre-dated the onset of their illness, and he was convinced that the problem was organic, not psychological. Thus we can see that CFS is a disease that has been around for a long time and can attack susceptible individuals during an epidemic or sporadically. Such scenarios obviously suggest that, for disease to develop, you need a genetic defect capitalised on by an environmental triggering factor.

In the endemic form, many different foreign (non-self) agents appear to be capable of triggering CFS. This is the reason why I don't like the term 'post-infection fatigue syndrome'. CFS can be triggered by foreign proteins incapable of causing an infection. This is most commonly observed following the administration of a vaccine or antigen to boost the immune response.

At thirty-six, Harry was thoroughly enjoying his family life and his work as the supervisor of a national park when CFS struck. Typical of people who spend their life protecting nature, Harry was softly spoken, ruggedly healthy and at peace with himself and the world around him. One day he was cleaning an area in his forest that had been polluted by some visitors. They had left behind cans and bottles to prove how little they had appreciated the beauty that they had come to explore. While pulling a can from the soil Harry cut his finger, not badly, but possibly, he thought, a stitch would be needed. He drove to the local community hospital, where the doctor considered a bandage would suffice but ordered a precautionary tetanus toxoid booster. Harry had not had such a shot for ten years and the advice was therefore appropriate. Twelve hours after his tetanus shot, Harry was in trouble. He had developed a high fever, shaking chills and and a severe headache. He retreated to his bed. There was no reaction at the site of the tetanus shot, excluding an extremely vigorous immune reaction to the tetanus antigen itself as the cause of the problem. Such reactions do occur if one has too many tetanus shots too frequently.

Harry did not improve for three days and then made a partial recovery. He returned to work after a week but felt totally exhausted. His weariness persisted. Three years later, Harry has not returned to his forest. For him, to walk around his house is to be sentenced to six hours in bed to recuperate. He is still racked with headaches and a mental fuzziness that impairs his memory and concentration. I have observed this type of reaction a number of times and yet we know that, for the vast majority, a tetanus shot is a harmless, indeed life-preserving stimulus to our immune system. A tetanus shot per se cannot cause CFS but it can trigger a chain of events that may lead to CFS.

In the United Kingdom the most common triggers for CFS are

claimed to be enteroviruses. These are a family of tiny viruses that like to live in our intestinal tract (hence 'entero' meaning enteric or bowel). It may be of considerable significance that the particular enterovirus associated with CFS in the UK, the Coxsackie virus, is a close relative of the demons that cause polio. Coxsackie viruses were discovered forty years ago in the feces of two children suspected of having polio. We now know that there are seventy-one members of the enterovirus family, which include not only the polio-producing viruses and the Coxsackie family but also the ECHO viruses that are responsible for a number of diseases. All multiply within the intestinal tract.

Coxsackie is a delightful little village on the banks of the Hudson River in New York State. The villagers regard with some chagrin the fact that their main claim to fame is that it was from local residents that the nasty enteroviruses we are discussing were first isolated.

In experimental animals and humans there is no doubt that Coxsackie viruses can damage both muscles and nervous tissue. These are highly infectious viruses and if one member of the family becomes infected there is a 76 per cent chance that other members will also become infected. Recent evidence suggests that in genetically programmed individuals a particular Coxsackie virus can trigger off the immunological attack on the pancreas that may cause juvenile-onset diabetes.

In the United States, the Epstein–Barr virus that may cause glandular fever and precipitate a number of cancers has long been considered a major trigger for CFS. No matter which side of the Atlantic we review, no matter which agent acts as a trigger (Coxsackie, tetanus, parasites, EBV, etc.), the syndrome is identical.

Most recently, a new candidate has been discovered that might trigger CFS in some patients. It is the sixth member of the herpes family of viruses (all bad news) discovered to infect humans: HHV6 (human herpes virus number 6). The others, to refresh your memory, are EBV, the cytomegalovirus that causes so many severe problems for patients with AIDS, the herpes simplex viruses 1 and 2 (the latter causing genital herpes, the former causing cold sores around the mouth) and finally the chicken pox virus known as varicella.

American investigators found antibodies to this sixth virus in many of their CFS patients. We looked at our patients and found the same thing. The problem is that it is now clear that infection with this virus is ubiquitous; most of our control subjects have also been infected at one time or another. Thus HHV6 may be another potential trigger for endemic CFS but it is not the sole cause, as it does not produce the syndrome in the majority of people that it infects.

In the few years that have elapsed since the publication of the first edition of this book, it is gratifying to report major advances have been made in our understanding of CFS and I hope that you will find the discoveries fascinating and satisfying. CFS is a disease that is about to be forced to surrender its mysteries.

Two seemingly unrelated discoveries provided the conceptual breakthrough that has allowed us at last to begin to understand this disease. The first was the discovery of cytokines and their role in producing an immune response; while the second was the unravelling of the mechanisms associated with the toxic shock syndrome discussed in the chapter on allergies, which certainly highlighted the fact that allergies could exist within the T cell system.

At the beginning of this book we discussed the all-important role played by the hormones of the immune system, known collectively as cytokines (*cyto*, cell; *kines*, chemical manipulators). Once a CD4 lymphocyte, our alarm-sounding cell, has recognised that foreignness is present in our environment, a veritable cascade of cytokines are released from this cell and many others devoted to working in concert to produce an immune response that will kill and eliminate a given invader. As mentioned earlier, those cytokines that deliver messages from one leukocyte (white blood cell) to another are called interleukins, and one of the first released in the evolution of an immunological attack is interleukin 1 (IL1). When this substance was discovered and purified, it was soon realised that this substance stimulated CD4 lymphocytes to get on with the job of stimulating an immune response efficiently. Of more relevance to our story, however, was the completely unanticipated discovery that IL1 is responsible for the fevers that are so commonly associated with infectious diseases.

When we are infected with viruses, bacteria or other organisms we frequently develop a fever; indeed that is one of the cardinal signs of infection, the clue to what is going on. Severe fevers are terrible things to live through as many of you will know from personal experience, and very high fevers can actually be dangerous in young children. One shivers and shakes, aches from head to toe, and feels totally miserable and exhausted. For many years it has been presumed that the invading organisms produced this fever by secreting substances that would affect temperature control mechanisms in the brain, and arguments about the damaging or protective nature of fevers were commonplace in scientific circles.

With the discovery of IL1, which when injected produces fever, our thinking was changed forever by the experiments that then became possible. Modern research has told us that, in moderation, fever is indeed a good thing, enhancing the performance of many of the cells belonging to our immunological army.

The discovery that a normal part of the immune response to infection produces some of the major *symptoms* of infection rapidly led to further work. This has demonstrated convincingly that when we feel ill because of an infection it is because our bodies are caught up as innocent bystanders in a fight to the death being waged by lymphocytes and their partners and the invaders they are trying to eliminate. Certainly, a few organisms can secrete toxins that may injure us. The bacteria responsible for tetanus, for example, may secrete a poison that can induce paralysis, while the life-threatening diarrhoea people develop when infected with the cholera organism is also caused by toxin secreted by that germ. The point to emphasise, however, is that the great majority of micro-organisms that try to take up residence in our bodies don't produce any toxins, and it is our response to these organisms that produces the symptoms that lead us to declare ourselves to be 'ill'. If you have a sore throat because of a viral infection, your throat is sore because cells lining that delicate part of your anatomy are being damaged because they provide the battlefield on which immunological war is being waged.

All the above points were soon confirmed when we started to give patients purified cytokines as part of the therapy for this disease or that. In my own case, it was the clinical use of interferon that re-emphasised the concepts described and linked such observations to a possible cause of chronic fatigue syndrome.

Interferons are cytokines produced by both macrophages and lymphocytes and even some cells that are not an intimate part of our immunological defence system at all. These amazing substances are able, as their name suggests, to interfere with the processes many viruses need to reproduce themselves, and in very large doses are even known to reduce the capacity of cancer cells to multiply. With the purification of the interferons and their commercialisation, we at last had available sufficient amounts of the substance to start clinical trials and, in one area alone, namely the control of the chronic hepatitis that develops in patients infected with either the type B or type C virus, the results have been most gratifying. While most patients infected with either the B or C virus recover completely once their immune system has eradicated the invader, a number struggle with the virus for many years and serious liver damage may develop. During all that time they may be infectious. For one reason or another, in those people who become 'carriers' of hepatitis B viruses, we know that their immune system is just not up to the task at hand. Helping out with interferon therapy cures or improves the problems for many. Apart from being able to directly interfere with the multiplication of viruses, the interferons increase the display on the surface of virus-infected cells of those A, B and C proteins needed to present small fragments of virus to passing T cells. Thus interferons not only directly damage viruses but they improve the efficiency of the immune response directed against them.

Well, what's all this got to do with chronic fatigue syndrome? When we started therapy with interferon, side-effects were noted. Patients would say to us: 'I sure hope this drug is going to help me, for at the moment I feel terrible. It's as if I had a severe bout of flu. I have muscle aches and pains, and a headache, and I feel absolutely exhausted and can't concentrate. Why, I'm even getting my words mixed up!' It became obvious to me that if the patient had presented with those exact same symptoms, but had not had interferon therapy, I would have been likely to make a diagnosis of chronic fatigue syndrome. Thus two clues were suddenly in place: 1) the symptoms associated with infection are usually caused by the response to the organism and not the invader itself; and 2) the symptoms of chronic fatigue syndrome can be induced, indeed perfectly mimicked, by giving people large doses of a number of cytokines including interferon. Now for clue number 3.

In Chapter 8 I introduced the topic of allergies and pointed out that, for many years, when scientists and the public thought of allergies it was hay fever, hives, asthma and rashes that sprang to mind. The term had been restricted to those caused by an excessive production of IgE and its activation of mast cells. The basic problem here is in the B cell system, which produces excessive amounts of IgE. However, Von Pirquet, the originator of the term allergy, didn't restrict the term in that way at all. He didn't even know that there were such things as T cells and B cells, so any excessive immunological reaction that caused harm would fit his definition. As pointed out in Chapter 8, we now know that excessive undisciplined action on the part of T cells can produce disease. Toxic shock syndromes and other reactions to superantigens may have quite horrifying consequences for patients, and present an all too graphic example of what happens when too many cytokines are released simultaneously. We now believe that many diseases result from the excessive production of cytokines and the chronic fatigue syndrome fits into this spectrum.

If 17–24 per cent of us have problems with the way in which we regulate the production of IgE and suffer because of it, would it not be strange if many of us didn't control cytokine release in a less than effective manner, especially when the same regulatory CD8 cells seem to be in charge of both tasks? There is excellent evidence for the fact that poor CD8 function is responsible for excessive IgE production. Many of our patients with chronic fatigue syndrome suffer from severe immediate hypersensitivity reactions as well.

From all the above evolved our hypothesis for the chronic fatigue syndrome. This disease is an example of 'tallergy', altered energy in the T cell system. Excessive and inappropriate production of cytokines such as interferon produce the symptoms of infection and also the chronic fatigue syndrome. Patients relate such symptoms to infection, and thus tell their doctors that they are 'picking up everything that's going around' and believe that they are constantly infected. In reality, they can have all the symptoms without any infection at all. Their immune system is too good, too turned on; and that may explain why, with more than 700 patients studied in our research program, we have seen very few tissue infections among these disabled but basically healthy people. These individuals suffering from CFS are such an enigma because they are so sick and yet at the same time are extremely healthy.

So, according to our hypothesis, Carol, our troubled young flight attendant, was born with a genetic defect that made her CD8 regulatory cells (the Generals) susceptible to damage by any number of viruses or perhaps any very potent stimulation of her immune system. A viral infection in her case may have damaged these regulatory cells and, as a result, other players in the immune orchestra were able to secrete excessive undisciplined amounts of cytokines whenever a foreign substance entered her body—something which happens to all of us every day. In most of us, of course, infectious agents provoke a quiet, efficient response so that we don't even know that the encounter has occurred at all. Not so for someone with CFS. The cytokines they release in higher than normal amounts affect their central nervous system, producing all their symptoms.

Now, for this hypothesis to be true, the muscles of patients with CFS would have to be normal. The chemicals we are talking about might increase muscle twitchiness somewhat but we know that they don't damage muscle directly. Exhaustive studies by my group and others have failed to find any convincing abnormalities in the muscles of patients with chronic fatigue syndrome. In fact, even when patients are feeling exhausted their muscle strength when tested in the laboratory is normal. Now, to understand this apparent paradox we'd better consider for a moment just what 'fatigue' is all about.

If I'm mowing the lawn on a hot Sunday afternoon after having worked all morning in the garden, there will come a point when my body tells me I'm tired, that it's the right moment to sit in the shade of a tree and have a cold beer. My brain, receiving messages from nerves that have been stimulated by chemical changes occurring in working muscles, floods my body with the *perception* that is fatigue. Fatigue is clearly a protective mechanism to warn one not to overdo it. If on that same hot afternoon that I was mowing the lawn a marathon runner ignored extreme fatigue and forced himself to continue to run against the protests of all his biological systems, he could quite literally dissolve his muscles, with the protein so released destroying his kidneys and provoking a toxicity that could be fatal.

The immune system has learnt to trigger the receptor in our brain that declares fatigue, so that when we are infected we rest, and this enhances our immune system's capacity to fight infection. If these chemicals were secreted inappropriately in excessive amounts we could be overwhelmed by a perception of fatigue, notwithstanding that we had done little work with our muscles to provoke such a feeling.

If the muscles of patients with chronic fatigue syndrome are normal, and they are, what about their T cells? In the early stages of the disease, the number of CD8 lymphocytes circulating in the bloodstream is certainly lower than normal and studies are in progress to look carefully at their regulatory function. The evidence that the immune system of patients with CFS is overactive, a natural sequel to poor CD8 performance, is indeed very strong. Markers found on the surface of T cells only after they are activated are found in abundance in patients with CFS and in much higher concentrations than one would find in healthy individuals. We have found a four times higher than normal amount of interferon in the fluid that circulates around the brain and spinal cord (cerebrospinal fluid, CSF) in our patients.

This is particularly interesting, for it's not easy for interferon to penetrate into the brain, and we suggest that its well-demonstrated effects on the central nervous system require it to activate an as yet to be discovered second chemical messenger. But higher levels of interferon in the circulation would explain one of the most consistent observations we have noted, and one that is of help in confirming a diagnosis.

We discussed earlier in the book the phenomenon of delayed-type hypersensitivity: that immune reaction involving CD4 cells and macrophages which take some forty-eight hours to reach a peak of aggressiveness. It is most easily observed by injecting into the skin something to which an individual is sensitised and returning to the scene of the crime forty-eight hours later, when a large red lump will be visible if all is normal. T cells, and especially macrophages, have migrated through the skin to the site of our injection of foreignness and are attacking. Now we know that high levels of interferon interfere with the migration of macrophages through the skin. Normally, interferon is only produced locally at a smallish battlefield site where we don't want macrophages that might be passing by to continue on their way. We want them to stop and help T cells do the fighting. Hence interferon interferes with the mobility of macrophages but not their capacity to secrete infection-fighting chemicals and swallow foreign materials. The inability to make a normal delayed-type hyper-sensitivity skin reaction is referred to as anergy and 89 per cent of our patients with CFS fail to respond normally to the test, which is known as the 'CMI multitest' and is marketed by a company called Merieux. An ingenious device holds seven foreign proteins in little wells that have attached sharp needle-like protruberances. When placed on the skin, like a post office stamp on a letter, tiny amounts of the proteins are injected into the skin and strong reactions should follow forty-eight hours later. They *don't* in patients with CFS in the vast majority of cases. When this capacity starts to return, our patients are invariably on the way to recovery.

You will find in the last chapter of this book a discussion of the fact that severe depression, for example bereavement, can affect T cell function. Many patients with CFS are depressed, understandably enough. It was necessary, therefore, for our research team to compare the immunological changes we are discussing with those found in patients suffering significant depression. We did, and the alterations are entirely different and thus easily distinguished. The T cell abnormalities of chronic fatigue syndrome are not due to the reactive depression that is so common in such a debilitating condition.

Thus, while our hypothesis remains just that, certainly not having been established as fact as yet, there's no doubt that it is looking better and better. Intellectually, it is satisfying to have a unitary concept for the site of the pathology. A disease process affecting just muscles and the brain would not be impossible to imagine, but it's more likely that all the defects occurring in CFS result from changes induced by cytokines in the central nervous system. Indeed, new scanning technology, which allows us not just to look at anatomical detail in the brain but actually biochemical events, strongly supports the concept that patients with chronic fatigue syndrome have biochemical alterations occurring in their central nervous system that could well explain their symptomatology. As X-ray techniques have given way to computer-assisted imaging (CAT scans) and they in turn have yielded to magnetic resonance imaging (MRI), we now have technology involving particles known as positrons that enable us to examine these biochemical changes. Just as powerful satellite cameras can now image from space the chess moves being made by a pair of old men relaxing in a park, our medical cameras can now actually look at the molecular events occurring in our bodies.

We have looked at the genetics of chronic fatigue syndrome by studying families in which three or more members of a given family were afflicted with the condition. There is no evidence for the transmissibility of CFS from one person to another, such as would occur with a viral infection for example, but within families certain members are susceptible. When we looked at the type of A-, B-, C- and D-locus proteins they had on the surface of their cells (you remember that these proteins largely determine how effective our immune response will be), we found that there were similarities between affected family members who had the same A, B, C or D profiles, while such profiles were not shared by unaffected family members. The data strongly support the concept that there is a genetic defect in the immune system of patients which makes them susceptible to the development of chronic fatigue syndrome.

Now, it is still possible that the damage done to the immune system of patients with chronic fatigue syndrome is caused by a yet to be discovered unique CFS-producing virus. If there is such a beast, it's likely to belong to the retrovirus family which causes AIDS. While the search for such an agent represents legitimate research, we certainly feel it is far more likely that it is the host that is unique rather than the organism triggering the disease. A number of the groups have suggested that there may be a persistence, for example in muscle tissue, of inadequately cleared particles of the triggering virus that would directly interfere with muscle enzymes or other vital biochemicals needed for muscle function. As pointed out, there is no evidence to support such a concept and plenty to counter the argument. Others suggest that these particles may not be directly damaging muscles, but may act as stimulators which induce a chronic immunological attack that would damage the normal 'innocent bystander' muscle tissue. Again, the evidence suggests that this is not the case. Such explanations would immediately incriminate the immune system, which should have despatched any such triggering agents to the immunological garbage heap within days of its entering our body.

For completeness sake, I should point out to you a newly recognised phenomenon that may or may not turn out to have significance for CFS. The facts involved are interesting enough in themselves. An unusual form of persistent viral infection may be responsible for a number of disease processes. We know that once herpes viruses enter our bodies they never leave. For most of us, this is not a problem. They live quietly and harmlessly along nerve sheaths or in B cells without disturbing the function of a tissue or the cells they have invaded. This peaceful state of affairs has nothing to do with any inherent benignity on the part of the virus. If the watchful eyes of our immune system falter, these viruses will seize the opportunity to multiply and invade. Shingles is the classical example of such a consequence.

What we are now realising is that viruses may enter a tissue or cell and change its *function*, while our immune system shows no interest. This is a new concept of infection. Doctors and lay people alike are used to the concept that organisms invade and damage a tissue as they multiply and release toxins, etc. The battle that follows, in which immunological forces produce their chemical warfare, temporarily adds to miseries of the invaded tissue and its owner. A climactic battle usually sees victory for our immune system: the invader is rejected and the innocent tissue that hosted the battle slowly repairs itself.

The ingenuity of viruses, however, now presents us with another scenario. In this version of infection a virus dives into a cell and inserts its genetic program into the cell's computer (the DNA of its nucleus), so changing the functional instructions of that cell. We now believe that some viruses may do this without interfering with the mechanisms that protect the outer wall of the cell. This second trick is essential if our immune system is to be fooled. Usually, when viruses invade cells the fact is recognised by our immune system as components that are 'non-self' appear on a cell surface. T cells will destroy such cells and the viruses they contain.

In discussing CFS we are interested in the concept that some viruses, perhaps only in genetically susceptible people, cause disease not by destroying the cells they invade but by altering their specialised function. Subtle invasion of nerve and muscle cells in a manner that could destroy normal function without destroying the cells and evade partially compromised immunological surveillance mechanisms would explain the CFS mystery. Such a concept is hard to reconcile with the observation that non-viable proteins (e.g. tetanus) can trigger CFS.

The preceding few paragraphs are included for completeness sake but we do not believe that there is any evidence to support any of these concepts.

This brings us to an immunological therapy that is potentially the most exciting breakthrough we have had in our attempts to help people with CFS. Immunologists are currently fascinated by the beneficial effects of very large doses of gam maglobulin infused intravenously. Preparations of almost pure IgG extracted and concentrated from the blood of 20 000 or more healthy humans are available commercially.

While the administration of this preparation to patients who can't make IgG is lifesaving, we have been excited by the discovery that many patients with autoimmune disease are markedly improved after very large doses of this preparation. Patients whose immune system has lost direction and is destroying their platelets or red cells, blocking nerve and muscle interactions, eating away at their joints, destroying their skin, etc., have been helped, sometimes dramatically, by an infusion of gammaglobulin.

We are far from certain how the pharmacological doses that we administer work their magic, but we are not short of theories. To me the most interesting observation concerns the improvement in regulatory T cell function that may follow these infusions. Large doses of IgG may well re-regulate a disordered T cell symptom.

In 1986, a friend of mine in New Jersey told me how he had given a large dose of IgG to a patient who, he subsequently realised, had CFS, simply because he thought that he was dealing with an immune deficiency state. A remarkable improvement had followed. We speculated on the possible mechanisms. I decided to try this approach on a young man with a very severe form of the disease.

Jason was nineteen years old and devastated by a weakness that 'words cannot describe'. He was so weak that it could take him an hour to move from his living room to the bathroom. Such an effort would leave him so exhausted that he would need to spend five or six hours in his bed to recover to a point where he could sit up and converse with the rest of the family.

Two years earlier, Jason had been set for a brilliant if unusual career. He was a champion surfboard rider and at the age of seventeen he had actually ranked third in the world. Day in, day out, he spent his time dancing on the tops and bottoms of waves. He was extremely fit.

Disaster struck Jason with a typical 'mono'-like flu with fevers for a week, sore throat and swollen glands and the onset of a weakness that did not leave him. As the months passed, Jason became weaker and embarked on that all too familiar journey of frustration that so adds to the misery of CFS sufferers. Doctor after doctor was consulted to no avail.

Finally an eminent psychiatrist confidently told Jason and his frustrated parents that fear of the pressure of competition had produced a psychological cripple. This was his way of withdrawing with dignity from the pressures of the professional surf-riding circuit on which he had been about to embark. They believed the consultant and fed antidepressant medicines to their now thoroughly depressed son. He did not improve.

We could find nothing abnormal on physical examination when Jason finally arrived at our clinic. I say 'finally' because twice he had missed appointments as he experienced the embarrassment of calling a taxi and then being unable to remember where the taxi was supposed to take him. Only when his parents, both of whom work, left written instructions did he make it to our clinic.

Jason was willing to try the IgG therapy and his response was most encouraging. In the week following a three-day infusion he felt worse, if anything. His muscles ached and we could actually see the quivering as myriad tiny contractions raced along muscle fibres. He had pains in his chest and a feeling of anxiety. Then, 'as if a devil had left my body', he awoke one morning feeling incredibly light; a sensation that his body was floating in a swimming pool swept over him. As he left his bed he felt energy for the first time in three years. Three months later Jason was tentatively challenging the waves and now a year later he feels he is ready for competition. I much enjoyed writing the follow-up letter to his psychiatrist.

We have now treated more than eighty patients with severe chronic fatigue syndrome with this therapy. In a trial in which we did not use any form of placebo, 69 per cent of patients appeared to improve. Realising, however, that the path to scientific hell is paved with uncontrolled trials and anecdotes, we subsequently proceeded to a double-blind placebo-controlled trial; that is, one in which neither patient nor doctor is aware of the nature of the treatment received by each patient. In that trial, 42 per cent of patients were very significantly helped—the first double-blind placebo-controlled trial to demonstrate benefit to patients with CFS.

I am cautiously optimistic that this therapy will result in a double breakthrough in our battle with the CFS problem. Firstly, we will help many patients recover, though it is already certain that not all respond—a fact that demands its own research. Secondly, it challenges immunologists to find out why IgG helps. If we can find the explanation we will surely be closer to understanding the basic cause of the disease.

It is possible that pooled gammaglobulin contains antibodies to a specific virus that is commonly experienced by many who make an adequate immune response to the agent and have no sequelae from the encounter. Such antibodies would therefore be in the pooled blood donated by so many volunteers. Their immunological know-how, in the form of antibodies, may lead to the clearance of the same ubiquitous but unknown virus that has not been handled well by the immune system of a patient with CFS. There is no evidence at all to support this theory. Alternatively, and much more likely in our opinion, gammaglobulin may correct a defect in the immuno-regulatory T cells that then return to the business of getting their house in order.

Dealing with hundreds of patients with CFS brings one face to face with many of the inadequacies of modern medicine. For those of us who teach medicine it is saddening to realise that we have produced a generation of physicians who are so delighted with what they know, and so comfortable with high-technology investigation, that they spend insufficient (if any) time in considering medical science's ignorance of so much of the body's ordered and disordered function.

Modern doctors regrettably prefer to look at the results on a piece of computer paper than to listen to the credible, consistent and reasoned observations of their patients who, after all, live with their bodies. If the blood tests are all normal, the symptoms must be generated from a disturbed psyche.

This attitude on the part of doctors has led to exaggerated suffering, despair and even suicide among victims of CFS. The almost universal reaction of my patients with CFS when I show them their abnormal T cell results is to break into tears of relief. To be believed, to have some proof that they are not neurotic, results in an instant measure of improvement. 'Please, can I have a photocopy of the results?' is an almost universal request.

The other consequence of the intellectual arrogance of some of my colleagues has been the driving of patients with CFS and indeed all incurable and poorly understood diseases into the somewhat dangerous world of alternative medicine. Here, if one is lucky, one may find an innovative, intuitive and scientifically minded practitioner of a healing art that constructively challenges the orthodoxy of modern medicine. Unfortunately, however, one is far more likely to find oneself being treated by a scientifically unsound seller of hope to the hopeless, the easiest of targets for charlatans and the misguided. No group has been more exploited than patients with CFS who, in quite understandable and indeed predictable despair, will try anything.

Patients have flocked to New Zealand to a man who claims to cure CFS by exposing one to a specific sequence of colours. Others have been fed massive amounts of vitamin C, tryptophan, lecithin, macrobiotics, cod liver oil, etc. One American healer claims that CFS can be cured by tapping repeatedly over the thymus gland and summoning, with all one's mental energy, the T cells that lurk within. Patients can spend $3000 or so to go to detoxification units to be purified by enemas, vitamins and exercise. One poor patient of mine recently spent a lot of money purchasing variously shaped crystals that she placed strategically around her bed as instructed, so as to draw upon the ancient and mystical powers of the Egyptian pyramids, which can exorcise the evils that produce CFS.

The therapy and therapists survive only because of the fact that many patients in their desperation experience short-term improvement as the well-known placebo effect influences those anxious to find a cure. Many who are helped are indeed psychologically disturbed patients for whom such way-out remedies are psychotherapy. Many of these patients feel and indeed reported that they had CFS, but in reality this is not the case.

Because of the nature of the symptoms many patients I see who are sure they have CFS are wrong. As we noted previously, the art of physicians as much as their science is needed to distinguish the organic from the functional and to realise that, while the treatment will differ, the suffering with both types of disorders will be the same.

Let me finish with an attempt to settle some of the controversial points about which we now feel certain. It is true that CFS can run in families but almost certainly for genetic, not infectious, reasons. Genetic programming of family members makes them susceptible to whatever is the disease-producing mechanism.

It is true that CFS rarely starts in patients over the age of fifty but definite cases do occur. It can affect middle-aged individuals and can persist well into their old age. It is certainly not true that CFS spares children; I have treated numerous children, the youngest being six years of age. It could well affect even younger children.

CFS is often reported in the media as a 'yuppie disease'. This is not only cruel but inaccurate. The connotation conjured up by the term is that of a successful young executive or professional who finds it all a bit too much and who needs an excuse to withdraw from the rat race. CFS affects people from all socio-economic groups, though the persistence and contacts needed to clear a path through the prejudice and ignorance of many physicians may be more readily available to better educated people.

It is true that CFS seems to affect many more women than men, as is true with most immunological diseases. When a man does suffer from CFS he usually has a very severe form of the illness.

A number of patients with symptoms consistent with CFS claim to be extremely sensitive to the environment and the numerous chemicals found in food, drugs, etc. Is such chemical sensitivity (that, whatever its cause, is definitely not allergic in the immuno-logical sense) an extension of the basic CFS syndrome? Do mechanisms similar to those that affect muscle and nervous tissue interfere with biochemical events that detoxify incoming chemicals? I do not know the answers to these questions but have a completely open mind on the matter. Most people with CFS do not have extreme sensitivity to chemicals, but those who do are even more incapaci-tated than patients for whom fatigue and changes in mental function predominate. Much more research is needed before we can say if this is a separate disease or part of the CFS spectrum.

To summarise, many hundreds of thousands of people through-out the world suffer from a syndrome, the constant feature of which is an extraordinary, almost indescribable muscle fatigue that makes even the most minimal exercise difficult. This syndrome also features neurological disturbances most commonly resulting in headaches, confusion, defects in concentration and short-term memory and emotional lability.

Recent evidence has established the organic nature of the problem. It is associated with a disordered immune system and the possibility that many, perhaps most, patients can be helped by immunotherapy is exciting. That the mysterious mechanisms responsible for this disease will be revealed to medical science in the near future is a more than reasonable prediction.

In the meantime it is essential that we spread this new knowledge throughout the medical and lay communities alike, so that thousands of sufferers of CFS can be given the appropriate sympathy and encouragement—and indeed hope—that may make their suffering bearable as we move ever closer to the definitive cure for this disabling disease.

PART V

ASSISTING THE WARRIORS

11

Some weapons of the immunologist

Around the visitors' quarters at the University where I was working in Dakar, Senegal was one of the poorest 'suburbs' of a poor city. Seven hundred and fifty thousand people lived in tin shanties and mud huts. In this area there was no sewage, and no running water for individual shacks. There were, at frequent intervals, in corners of intersecting unpaved streets, water pumps from which the precious fluid was collected and carried home in all kinds of vessels.

One afternoon I was strolling down such a street, in the middle of which were playing perhaps twelve to fifteen boys of about ten years of age. They were enjoying their beloved soccer, running with endless enthusiasm after the tired soccer ball that bounced at crazy angles from the ruts in the road. No fear of being run over here; goats on the road were more of a menace than automobiles. A noisy, happy and very dusty scene.

As I approached the boys, one of them, a ten-year-old called Ibrahima, kicked the soccer ball to his friends and ran to a corner water pump. With one hand he pumped some water into his other hand and sipped the none too sterile liquid, splashing some on his hot and dusty face. As he was leaning down to enjoy his refreshment a dog appeared from nowhere and, quite unprovoked, rushed at the little boy and nipped the back of his neck. As a result of the bite the skin on the back of Ibrahima's neck was broken and oozed blood immediately.

Naturally, the bitten child screamed. His soccer mates, many of whom had witnessed the attack, fell into a shocked silence for a few seconds and then started yelling loudly as they ran off in different directions; clearly, they wished to distance themselves from that dog as quickly as possible. Ibrahima stood frozen to the spot then bolted up the street, right into the arms of his father, who had come outside with other adults to investigate the cause of the commotion.

Much shouting from the adults ensued and the father disappeared into his shack, to emerge seconds later with a towel in one hand and a large knife in the other. With the towel wrapped around his left hand and forearm he approached the dog responsible for the attack.

Now the dog in question was of course a stray, one of thousands of emaciated, pathetic-looking animals that wander the dusty streets in these parts. Dirty brown fur covered much of his body but a number of areas, particularly on his back, were bare and indeed ulcerated. The dog was a distressing sight. After its 'attack' it had not moved. It stood, head down, looking slowly from left to right, as if it could not make up its mind whether to catch some of the water drops still falling from the pump.

Urged on by the instant crowd now surging all around me, the father slowly approached the hapless animal. I remember thinking that the father's revengeful intentions were somewhat extreme. I knew little of the Senegalese then or I would have realised how out of character such a motive would have been. That the father was desperate to save his son's life never entered my head.

The dog made no attempt to move as the father fell upon it; the animal appeared to be in a trance, in fact. The big black arm partially covered by the towel encircled the neck of the surprisingly placid dog and in a second the large knife had cut the animal's throat. Blood spurted into the dusty street ahead of the animal as the father carefully positioned himself with legs astride the dog's back. The animal died instantly, but before my horrified and perplexed eyes the father continued to saw away at the dog's throat. In seconds his large knife had decapitated the animal. The head was quickly wrapped in the towel that had protected the father's arm and the dog's carcase was left in the gutter to be instantly attended to by a million ever-ready flies.

Throughout this drama the street resounded to yells of fear, advice and congratulations. Someone, perhaps Ibrahima's mother, was washing his neck with what looked like a bar of soap. It was at this point that I was noticed. The father, who of course did not know me, let alone know that I was a doctor, hurried up to me and explained. '*Monsieur, monsieur! Je pense que le chien rage! Avez-vous une voiture? Il me faut porter la tête à l'hôpital.*'

Suddenly the scene made sense. The father was convinced that the dog had rabies, a very common problem in this part of the world. The local population had been taught that an imals that bite must be killed and their head transported '*immediatement*' to the hospital for an examination of the animal's brain. Anxious to help, and fascinated, I took the father and a few supporters to the hospital with the dog's head wrapped in the now very messy towel. Ibrahima, strangely enough, was left behind with his mother.

At the hospital the head was checked in with details about the incident. Father was instructed to return for the results of the pathology test two days later. Muttering that he knew the results would confirm the fact that the wretched dog had rabies, he headed for home while I had myself educated at the hospital.

Rabies is one of the most lethal of infections, but there are measures that can be taken to help people who are at risk of developing this infection after a bite. The problem is that the treatment is somewhat risky, hence the need to be sure of the diagnosis before commencing someone on preventative therapy.

A million Americans, for example, are bitten by animals every year; this is a common problem throughout the world. After every bite from an animal, one must consider whether anti-rabies therapy is warranted. Skunks, wolves, raccoons, mongooses and bats can all be responsible for spreading this disease. In the poorer parts of the world, however, wild dogs are mainly responsible.

Rabies is caused by a tiny virus excreted in the saliva of infected animals. Once it finds itself under the skin of someone who has been bitten, it burrows into the nerves in the skin and then literally marches along those nerves up the spinal cord into the brain, where it can cause terrible damage. It may take twelve days or twelve months to reach the brain; thus the clinical picture following infection varies considerably.

Rabies is lethal; only three humans are known to have survived an established brain infection. The paralysis of muscles needed for swallowing, which is a feature of the infection, means that saliva will accumulate in the mouth and eventually spill out; hence 'frothing at the mouth'. While only five people a year die of rabies in the United States, probably fifteen thousand or more die of this infection worldwide.

In countries where rabies is a problem all domestic dogs should be vaccinated against the virus, as this very much reduces the risks of humans getting the disease. Dogs are more likely than humans to wander unprotected into the woods and be bitten by wild animals. Thousands of proud owners have their dogs vaccinated against rabies every year and, indeed, have them similarly protected against other scourges such as distemper (dog measles)—yet few of those owners would ever stop to think about the extraordinary benefits that vaccines have brought to humankind and animalkind.

Why don't we make vaccines to all the infectious diseases that plague humans? Because getting the agents into a suitable form for introduction to the immune system is not easy. Many viruses are hard to grow in the laboratory in sufficient amounts to produce commercial quantities of vaccine. Indeed, many viruses have defied all our attempts to kill them and yet have them remain good stimulants of the immune system.

Take rabies, for example. This is a difficult virus to culture; until recently it could be grown only in duck embryos. The virus grown in bulk in this fashion is then inactivated chemically. This produces a delicate reaction, however, and there is still a slight risk of developing severe neurological disease after vaccination. This complication rate used to occur as frequently as 1 in every 6000 vaccinations. It is now in the order of 1 in 100 000 with the duck embryo vaccine. An even newer vaccine, made by growing the virus in abnormal human cells, is apparently even less risky and seems set to replace the duck embryo vaccine. However, pain at the injection site, fever and nausea continue to be problems associated with the vaccine. For adequate protection, multiple injections are needed. The duck embryo vaccine, the only one available in Africa, does not give one hundred per cent protection; while the newer vaccine appears to be more efficient as no failures have been reported to date.

Back to poor Ibrahima, nursing a sore neck and hating dogs as he awaited the results of the tests on his attacker's brain.

At the hospital the pathologist called a colleague at the Institut Pasteur, a French research and vaccine-producing institute based in Paris but with branches in many Third World countries. The Institute had the equipment needed for the test.

A piece of the dog's brain was removed and rapidly frozen. While in this state a wafer-thin slice was cut with an extremely sharp blade and the frozen piece of tissue laid on a glass slide. The slide was then coated with a preparation known to contain antibody against the rabies virus. If rabies was there the anti-body would find it. The antibody was tagged with a dye that emits a bright green color when stimulated with ultraviolet light. Green spots in the brain mean virus. The dog's tissue was brilliantly green, so loaded with virus had it become.

Ibrahima was brought to the hospital and examined. He had a fever and a sore neck but seemed otherwise OK. Into the area of the wound he was given an injection of serum containing antibodies to the virus.

The Center for Disease Control in the United States has been collecting blood from volunteers who have been immunised against rabies. This blood would, of course, contain high levels of antibody against the virus. The Center's serum was packaged as hyperimmune antirabies gammaglobulin and shipped around the world. It was, however, in short supply and was therefore precious. It was not to be used unless the diagnosis was clear.

This preparation gives a form of instantaneous protection, a gift from one human to another. In addition to the antibodies, Ibrahima was given an injection of the rabies vaccine. A large amount of killed virus would rapidly stimulate his T and B cells to make a vigorous response to the agent that had almost certainly been injected by the rabid dog.

The ending to this story is a happy one as Ibrahima did not develop rabies and may one day grow to be a great soccer star, thanks to modern immunology.

Passive protection

We must explore a little further the concept of passive protection, in contradistinction to the active protection induced by immunisation.

In 1668, Sir Christopher Wren, very busy rebuilding London after its great fire, was asked to design a needle that could be used in experiments aimed at determining the feasibility or otherwise of transferring blood from one animal to another. He promptly designed the hypodermic needle, which is still in use today.

As I mentioned earlier, Samuel Pepys records in his diaries that a successful demonstration of the needle took place at the home of a doctor in London. Blood was indeed passed from one animal to another. (Presumably the transfused animal did not die, for it is not mentioned, but if it did not it was very lucky as the blood it received would almost certainly have been incompatible.) One of the doctors at the demonstration, Pepys told us, said to the assembled throng, 'I feel this is the beginning of a new era that will see the mending of bad blood by the borrowing of blood from a better body.'

So was born into medicine the concept of passive protection, long used by Nature. Maternal antibody crosses the placenta to fill up babies with antibodies made against troublesome germs that the mother has seen during the months of her pregnancy. This is a gift to tide babies over until they can make their own antibodies. From the last decade of the nineteenth century, passive protection in this form has been used in medicine.

At first, serum from horses was used. Old horses were immunised with substances that were dangerous to humans such as diphtheria and then, after they had had time to make a lot of antibody, serum was collected from the animals. This was then administered to patients at risk of developing the infection. Diphtheria, at the time, was one of the most serious killers. Patients were definitely protected in this way but, as you can imagine, giving horse serum to humans provokes its own set of problems. Our immune systems react to the 'foreignness' that we recognise in these equine proteins.

Today we often use human serum collected from subjects who have either recovered from or have been immunised against a particular infectious agent. Immune serum of this nature is available to help protect us from tetanus, hepatitis B, rabies, mumps, pertussis or whooping cough and chicken pox. You may be surprised to know that we still use some serum containing potent antibodies obtained from immunised animals. Animals supply us with antibodies against diphtheria, those organisms that cause fatal food poisoning or botulism, the venom of the black widow, red back and funnel web spiders, jellyfish and certain snake and scorpion poisons.

Another form of passive protection is needed by the many patients who cannot make antibodies at all; that is, patients with antibody deficiency disease. Blood is pooled from 3000 to 20 000 healthy donors and the serum extracted. It is then concentrated in a form that contains almost pure IgG. This can be given intravenously to patients who need it. Monthly infusions for life of this gift 'from a better body' allow such patients to lead an almost normal life.

Active protection

In the United States, most children receive the full benefits of the best vaccines because there are laws that stop children from going to school unless they are adequately protected and hence will not act as a source of infection for others. In many Western countries, where these vaccines can be afforded, immunisation sad to say is not compulsory. These countries continue to have children and therefore adults who suffer from horrible complications of common infectious diseases.

All babies should begin their assisted defence of self at two months of age with an injection of a vaccine mixture containing diphtheria, pertussis and tetanus antigens (DPT shot). In addition, they should swallow a little polio vaccine. Babies should then receive booster doses of the same antigens at four and six months. At that point the child is considered to be fully protected against these four diseases.

At fifteen months of age children should be given another combination of antigens. This one contains measles, mumps and rubella (German measles) viruses. They will be protected for life from these diseases following successful vaccination. At eighteen months of age, I recommend a further booster dose of DPT and polio and then a final one at seven years of age. Tetanus shots should be given every ten years throughout life.

Diphtheria is caused by infection with *corynebacterium diphtheriae*.

The bacteria penetrate the back of the throat and there may produce a powerful toxin that can paralyse nerves. From the throat this poison may spread rapidly around the body. The bacteria, interestingly enough, do this because they are infected with a virus that makes them do it. So, with diphtheria you get two infections at once. People of all ages who are not protected die of diphtheria—about thirty people a year in the United States, for example. Generally they come from isolated communities where they have escaped the attention of immunologists.

Tetanus, in which a painful spasm and then paralysis of muscles causes death, is produced by the release of a neurotoxin from *clostridium tetani*, a ubiquitous organism found in the soil everywhere and commonly in animal excreta. The organism lies dormant in the ground in the form of spores that become activated when they come to enter a wound. In many Third World countries there is still an unfortunate habit of placing cow dung around the stump of a baby's severed umbilical cord. Many infants die of tetanus as a result. As many as three hundred cases of tetanus can occur in the United States in any one year and 70 per cent of these patients will die. No region of the US is spared.

Whooping cough can, and does, kill infants. Until recently 10 000 cases were recorded annually in the US. With adequate immunisation no child should die of this disease. Severe complications and death usually follow infection of the brain and lungs. As whooping cough takes a severe toll on the very young, immunisation must start as soon as feasible. Recent epidemics among adults in England and Australia clearly demonstrate that, when immunisation is not compulsory, the infectious agent will survive in the community and infect adults immunised as a child but whose immunity is now waning. For this reason, adults in such countries are well advised to have a small booster dose of this vaccine. On the other hand, in countries where the whole community is immunised against pertussis, so little of the infectious agent survives in the community that even the odd person who has escaped vaccination is protected.

Today, paralytic polio is rare in countries where vaccine is freely available. In underdeveloped countries it remains a terrible curse. To note how effective this vaccine is you need only remember that 15 000 cases of paralytic polio occurred annually in the US during the 1950s. Today fewer than thirty cases are reported each year. It is a tragedy and a shameful reflection on the Western world's desertion of their brothers and sisters in the Third World that thousands of children will yet be crippled by this virus. Underdeveloped countries simply cannot afford to buy the vaccine.

In the United States in 1962 there were at least 500 000 cases of measles. In 1972 the number was less than 40 000 cases. In 1974, measles vaccination slackened off; fewer than 60 per cent of children were immunised, and as a result a major epidemic broke out in 1977. Measles can be fatal. Five to fifteen per cent of victims develop secondary bacterial infections and one in a thousand cases develop a potentially fatal infection of the brain. Measles should not be taken lightly. In underdeveloped countries it remains a major killer of children under the age of three.

Mumps is caused by a virus that replicates in glandular tissues. While it is usually mild, complications are frequent enough to make vaccination advisable. Mumps is a serious risk for boys who have reached puberty. Twenty per cent develop a viral infection in their testicles that can sterilise them. Such infections are painful and incapacitating complications. Mumps is a leading cause of meningitis and brain inflammation and is also suspected to be one of the viruses that can cause diabetes.

Rubella or German measles is a mild disease of children and young adults. It would not warrant much attention except that rubella during pregnancy is associated with an extremely high risk of having an abnormal baby. Only by having every-body immunised can the amount of virus circulating in a community be contained and the tragedy of the congenital rubella syndrome eradicated. A vaccine was developed in the United States after thousands of blind, deaf and mentally retarded and/or immunodeficient children were born in 1964 as a result of congenital rubella infection. The virus in the vaccine itself, although not dangerous to children or adults, is dangerous to the fetus and therefore cannot be given to pregnant women.

In answer to the question 'Lord, what must I do to have the perfect immune system?', the answer must be, 'First, pick thy parents very carefully.' Not the most practical of advice, maybe, but there is a message here nonetheless. You want both parents to come from at least three generations of octogenarians. No allergies or immune diseases (especially diabetes and rheumatoid arthritis) and no cancer in the family, please. If you have such parents husband your assets carefully, as you are destined for senior citizenship.

If you do not have such parents, do not despair; much can be done and your fundamental genetic flaws may be fixable. We live in an age where genetic engineering, already so useful for examining the basic defects in disease and having bacteria make endless supplies of insulin and the like, will soon be used for therapy. Genetic information can be spliced into chromosomes, adding a new program to the genetic repertoire already present, or correcting one that is defective. In the first edition of this book I speculated that, since we can splice into a bacterial chromosome the blueprints for making human insulin, we should soon be able to splice into the bone marrow cells of a child making an abnormal hemoglobin the genes that would tell that child's cells how to make normal hemoglobin. This has now become a reality. If there is a further edition to this book, genetic engineering will undoubtedly need to be given the fullest coverage. For now, however, we will turn our attention to other, immediately available strategies.

What is the best way of extending the healthy lifespan of caged rats? The answer is to deprive them of some of the calories they wish to consume; that is, mild starvation. Rats can experience a 30 to 60 per cent increase in their lifespan if you restrict the intake of calories from birth. The same is true for mice who, on such a regimen, look like four-month-old mice when they are actually sixteen months old. As mice only live for two years, you can see the significance of this observation.

In addition to living longer, the animals in the above experiments were found to be more resistant to infection and cancer. Thymic involution, that inbuilt curtain on the immune drama, is markedly delayed in the underfed. Why should this be?

While admitting that we do not have all the answers to this riddle, some interesting facts have emerged. Rats do not over-eat in the way humans do and obese rats are as rare as obese snakes. (There are strains of chickens that become obese; interestingly enough, they have an immunological disease of their thyroid glands.) Animals eat appropriately. Restricting the calories available to rats keeps them lean, of course, but it also decreases some of the immuno-regulatory activity of T cells. These rats can therefore make a more vigorous response to infection, etc. What harmful effects may be associated with this 'therapy' are not certain as we cannot gauge rat well-being very well; certainly no gross abnormalities occur.

While most nutritionists feel that Western people, at least, eat a poorly balanced diet containing far too much fat, you only have to look around you to see that apart from eating a poorly balanced diet we simply eat too much; obese humans are not hard to find. Studies of the immune system of the obese have, in fact, been done. The ability of their neutrophils to swallow and kill bacteria is reduced. The killing power of their T cells is damaged. Frequently they are deficient in zinc and magnesium, two elements essential for normal immune performance. The obese suffer from more infections that tend to be more serious.

Would we live longer, healthier lives if we were minimally starved like the rats? Probably, but controlled experiments with humans to settle this issue are hard to organise, as you can imagine.

On the other hand, humankind's inhumanity ensures that we have abundant clinical material with which to determine the effects of real starvation on the immune response. It is dramatic. In Third World countries malnutrition, especially the loss of calories from good protein sources, rapidly takes immune performance through any stage of heightened adequacy and plunges it into despair.

Antibody capacity is lost first and, with that, defences against bacteria crumble. Gastroenteritis becomes a way of life, pus oozes from infected eyes and skin. T cells remain a little longer, then they also fail. All the magical defence mastery we have discussed at length vanishes. To compound the tragedy food, when and if it arrives, does not correct the defects instantly; far from it. It may take months or even years to return T cell function to normal.

With so many people deprived of food and hence immunological help, the parasites that infest the Third World take over and the human suffering that results is indescribable.

In our time, television cameras depict the horrors of the end stages of starvation well but not perfectly. You can see the suffering and you can hear the exhausted sobs of the starved, but you cannot smell it or feel it. The smell is very definitely one of death: death achieved and death approaching.

The feeling is one of utter despair, no faint glimmer of hope is seen in the eyes of adults and children. No longer do exhausted hands brush the flies away. No longer do failing minds pay any attention to another group of healthy-looking doctors moving in their midst with no real help in their hands.

I had the distressing experience of visiting starving tribes in Africa with medicine and vaccines to dispense, but no food; a useless exercise in frustration. What is so clear to those who get a chance to work in such areas is that the world cannot afford to have millions of people chronically malnourished and disease-ridden. Leaving human sympathy aside for the moment, the loss of productivity, the resultant destruction of potentially arable soil and the spread of disease will cost all of us dearly. It is very much in our own interest to end the cycle of poverty and disease that affects so many of our brothers and sisters.

Specific vitamin deficiencies significantly compromise immune performance. Patients with vitamin A deficiency find it hard to make IgA. The binding power of their antibodies is reduced. Lower numbers of circulating lymphocytes are frequently found. With vitamin C deficiency, protein synthesis is impaired and all the cells of the immune system perform less adequately. In addition, wound healing is significantly reduced. People suffering from a lack of sufficient vitamin B in their diet cannot make good delayed hypersensitivity reactions. They cannot reject grafted tissue normally. This deficiency, of course, is a very common problem among the alcoholics in our society.

Other deficiencies that significantly depress our immunological defences result from a lack of iron, folic acid, zinc, riboflavin, niacin and magnesium. The last three are very important if we are to make antibody normally. Let me hasten to stress, however, that there is no evidence that the taking of very large amounts of any of these nutritionally essential materials improves immunological performance.

If some part of your unhappy anatomy is red, hot, swollen and painful, that part is said to be inflamed. The process producing the changes is called inflammation. Inflammation affects tissues, joints and, indeed, any part of the body and results from the release of chemicals that open up blood vessels in a particular area. The aim of the process is to allow antibodies and cells to move into an infected site. If that is the price we have to pay to overcome a potentially serious infection, well, so be it. But if that inflammation should turn out to be useless, indeed harmful, as it would in an autoimmune disease, we physicians must try to suppress it. The most powerful anti-inflammatory drugs we possess are called steroids and of these the most potent are corticosteroids; perhaps you know them as hydrocortisone or prednisone.

Corticosteroids are produced in the cortex (outer areas, hence *cortico* steroids) of the tiny adrenal glands that sit astride the top of our kidneys. These chemicals are indispensable; without them we die. They are one of the body's prime catalysts, activating many processes ranging from protein synthesis to the coloration of skin. In essence, steroids drive forward a cell's intentions and thus may promote some happenings in the body and *suppress* others. Each morning our brain secretes a chemical that tells the adrenal gland to pour out adequate amounts of these precious hormones.

As you probably know, giving large amounts of hydro-cortisone to patients can produce a miraculous melting away of disease processes caused by inflammation. Unfortunately, large doses given for a long time produce many side-effects. Steroids interact with too many of the body's processes, so the results of their administration are many in number. Steroids used with knowledge and therefore appropriately are wonderful tools for reducing suffering. They can control asthma, help in the cure of leukemia and, most importantly, block inflammation.

Some doctors are irresponsible in their use of these potent drugs. In Italy many doctors give them to patients who are suffering from nothing more serious than the flu. This is a bad idea as steroids can, in fact, minimise the body's fight against the virus. On the other hand there are doctors who refuse to use them at all, feeling that the side-effects are too troublesome. Both approaches are erroneous. If the disease is more dangerous and distressing than the side-effects of the drugs, the tradeoff is reasonable. In reality, many patients can have their lives made bearable, indeed enjoyable, on doses of corticosteroids that produce only minimal side-effects.

Steroids in small doses block the actions of chemicals released from neutrophils (the phagocytic or infection-swallowing cells) and the mast cells and basophils that release histamine and other blood vessel–dilating substances. In very large doses they can be immuno-suppressive in the sense that they damage or even kill lymphocytes.

The major side-effects may be stunting of growth, weight gain (especially in the cheeks, upper arms and top of the back), weakening of bones as calcium is displaced, easy bruising, changeable moods, increased appetite, ulcers, cataracts in the eyes, a higher than normal blood pressure and increased hair growth on the skin. In addition, the adrenal glands become very sluggish when one takes these drugs, for they need not produce hormones themselves. Consequently, stopping the drug after a long period of therapy can be dangerous; slow withdrawal is mandatory.

While steroids in high doses can affect lymphocytes, the antigen-recognising cells of the immune system, we seldom use them for this purpose. When it is necessary to suppress lymphocyte function (never a happy occurrence) we do have drugs that are capable of doing just that. Of the three most commonly used drugs two, cyclophosphamide and azathioprine, are borrowed from cancer doctors who use them to block tumor growth. The third and most interesting, cyclosporine A, is a drug with unique properties.

Before we discuss these drugs let us look at situations where it would be necessary to cripple lymphocyte performance. The easiest situation to come to grips with involves organ transplantation.

A man who is now dependent on someone else's heart cannot be allowed to reject it. He must be immunosuppressed, despite the risks associated with non-specific depression of lymphocyte performance. If he cannot reject the heart that he has been given, he will not be able to reject normally those infections that might afflict him. We immunologists long for the day when we can 'tolerise' such patients; that is, teach them to accept as 'self' those foreign antigens associated with their new heart while instructing them to continue to reject anything else foreign that comes their way.

Transplantation of vital organs is as dramatic a scenario as modern medicine can present, but it is a minor part of medicine, as very few patients are helped in this manner. Much more common are the autoimmune diseases we have discussed already. Take rheumatoid arthritis, for example. At least 4 per cent of the entire population suffers from this disease and occasionally, in the worst examples, we must suppress a patient's immune system.

Raymond was wheeled into my clinic in a wheelchair. A man of thirty-four, married with one child, and a retired schoolteacher, he was thin and miserable from long days of pain and frustration. Five years earlier, while supplementing his income, Ray had a job in a timber yard on weekends. At twenty-nine, healthy, happy and hard-working, he appeared to have a happy future.

One morning he picked up a pair of large wire cutters to remove a metal band wrapped very tightly around a bundle of timber. As he cut the tense band it gave way suddenly and fiercely, with the result that his wrist was cruelly twisted. A painful tear of the ten-dons around the joint occurred. Two weeks later, not only had his hand not recovered, but other joints in his body had become swollen, hot and painful. Ray had developed rheumatoid arthritis, a disease wherein the joints are attacked and destroyed by misguided lympho-cytes failing to recognise the joints as a part of self. In genetically disposed individuals, it is not unusual to have such events triggered by a traumatic episode such as this.

Five years later Ray was a cripple, weak, thin, anemic, chroni-cally fatigued and, for much of his time, wheelchair-bound. He had been treated aggressively by experienced people. Aspirin, gold, steroid injections into his joints, penicillamine and every new anti-inflammatory drug that was marketed had been tried, with little effect. Now we discussed the risks of suppressing his immune re-sponse with cyclophosphamide, a potent but dangerous drug that many of us who deal with the severest form of this disease find useful. I explained to Ray that his T and B cells were actively dam-aging his joints. It was clear that some permanent damage had already occurred but even more damage would occur if the disease was not controlled.

Cyclophosphamide is a drug that kills cells when they try to divide to produce more of themselves. Cell division is an essential component of an immunological attack. The cells that divide most rapidly are the ones most affected. In immune systems the cells that divide most rapidly are antibody-producing cells or B cells; they are inhibited by these drugs.

We went on to discuss the benefits of blocking the attack on his joints with the drugs and, of course, the side-effects that he might encounter. The most serious side-effect is sterility; it was very un-likely that Ray would ever be able to father another child after taking the drug for a few weeks. The rapidly dividing, sperm-producing cells in the testes are killed.

I could see that this was a blow, for he had only the one child and the family longed for a second. Today we would store his semen for future use by artificial insemination. At the time, however, we

were not doing this. After much discussion and time for consideration of all that was involved, Ray decided to take the drug. The
disease was worse than any potential side-effects.

Not all patients with rheumatoid arthritis respond to this drug,
but Ray did. His disease seemed largely to disappear in his first
months on therapy. He left his wheelchair and cried at the joy of
being able to walk freely. Not that he was perfect. Some structural
damage could not be reversed. Ray lost his hair for a few months,
he was sterilised by the treatment as predicted, but he was able to
return to his profession. The psychological benefits of being gain-
fully employed again might even have exceeded his happiness at
having his arthritis subside. He continues to do well, although he
will always need the most meticulous medical attention if he is to
securely walk the tightrope that is suspended between a flare-up of
his disease and a dangerous degree of immunosuppression.

Of all the immunosuppressive drugs the most exciting is the
newest to be developed: cyclosporine A. This drug is produced by a
fungus and is a tiny chemical that packs a huge punch. It has the
ability to stop T cells from secreting interleukin 2 (IL2). You may
remember that IL2 is the pivotal chemical that gives permission for
all other cells in the immune system to attack. This drug has
revolutionised the transplant business as it makes non-rejection of
donated organs almost certain. The drug brings us closer to the
idea of having chemicals that will affect only the cells we wish to
target, other tissues being unaffected. Cyclosporine does affect the
liver and the kidneys and can only be used for three months without
concern for side-effects, leading many of us to switch to other agents.
Intense research is being carried out to produce a drug with similar
effect on the immune system which will not be toxic to other cells
even with prolonged use. One, FK506, looks very promising.

Immunologists can use naturally occurring and potent chemicals
that drive forward or alter immunological responses. We now have
on our therapeutic shelves interleukin 2 (some of which is produced
by friendly bacteria after some genetic trick), interferon, thymic
hormones and a myriad of small chemicals extracted from healthy
T cells. These factors are not specific for any one person and therefore are of great value in modifying immunological responses. We
use these for patients with immunodeficiency, chronic viral infections and cancer.

Clinical immunologists are experimenting with a number of potentially exciting ways of helping patients with immunological diseases. Watch the developments with the technique known as total
lymphoid irradiation. Here, by giving gamma irradiation to all
lymph nodes in the body, we seem to be able to return the immune
system to a fetal-like state in which it may be possible to re-establish

tolerance to self that has been lost and is resulting in serious disease. Antigens that were being treated as foreign may again be respected as self. This treatment is proving particularly valuable in its early experimental phases for patients with multiple sclerosis, rheumatoid arthritis and systemic lupus erythematosis.

Watch also for progress in the food allergy business. At last we are purifying the antigens from food that actually cause the allergic response. Once these are purified, our ability to diagnose and treat the misery produced by food allergy will be very much improved.

As is true with all significant areas of human advancement, science needs its theoreticians as well as its development specialists, i.e. people who can take a hypothesis, prove it and utilise the result. Immunology is no exception. One of the supreme theoreticians of our time was the Australian Nobel Laureate Macfarlane Burnet, who influenced me and hundreds of other young would-be scientists as we learned our craft. When I knew him he had officially retired but was nonetheless only too happy to discuss experimental results with those of us around him. Interpretation of observed data was for him a great game of chess. How many ways could you make that result mean something? How many new experiments could you demand as a result of your life's efforts?

Burnet was a great theoretician who understood autoimmunity before anyone else. He realised that scientific truths would have to be established in slow, often painful, A to B to C fashion but this was not his way. A to L and then on to S was his way; let someone else come along and prove that your ideas were correct and fill in the missing pieces of the puzzle. They would have an honorable second prize. 'Don't cross t's and dot i's,' he told me time and time again.

I first met his good friend and intellectual adversary Niels Jerne at a scientific birthday party to honor Burnet's seventieth year. These men were at that time the giants of theoretical immunology. Nothing pleased either man more than to come up with a theory that challenged contemporary beliefs and then have someone else prove that they were 100 per cent correct.

It was in this spirit that Jerne produced his 'network' theory. In essence what he proposed was this. When we make an antibody to, for example, a part of the tetanus toxoid that might be injected into us after an injury, the antibody does all the things you would now expect of it. But, said Jerne, those antibodies become antigens. Their presence will make our bodies make antibodies to them; that is, anti-antibodies!

Surely this time Jerne had gone too far; our antibodies are self and should not promote a response from any of our cells. Strange or not, claimed Jerne, you will find that we make antibodies to anti-bodies and that such antibodies will provoke a third antibody, etc.

Imagine you are in a boat in the middle of a small lake and you heave a big stone into the middle of all that confined water. Shock waves will race to the shore and back again, causing visible ripples to appear on the surface as the waves collide. Little by little the ripples get smaller until they fade away completely. That is what happens when you throw an antigen into the body, claimed Jerne; waves of antibodies are formed against each other, each new one provoking a little less of a response than the one before so that the process gradually dampens down and disappears.

I would not be telling you this story if Jerne had not been correct. Fascinating to report, however, there is more to this phenomenon than just the rippling effect. Anti-antibodies interact with specific T cells that can regulate the production by B cells of the first antibody. Being able to harness this form of immunological reaction will provide us with exciting therapeutic possibilities. If you had available antibodies to specific antibodies, you could stop the body's production of those specific antibodies. We will look at some examples shortly.

In our ignorance at the moment we just have to accept the fact, now well established, that our immune system makes an exception to its 'no reactivity to self' rule when it comes to antibodies. More accurately, we are reacting to just one part of the antibody when we produce anti-antibodies. That part of the antibody that is antigenic is called the idiotype. This is the portion of the molecule that has combined with the antigen, that is, the portion of the antibody with the three-dimensional configuration that is perfectly moulded to the shape of the antigen: the key (antigen) in the lock (antibody) analogy we discussed earlier. Antibodies to this 'lock' are called anti-idiotypic antibodies. (Figure 19.)

Let's see how we can apply Jerne's discovery. Imagine you are in a clinical immunologist's office in a few years' time. Your problem is incapacitating ragweed allergy. Your immunologist explains to you, as we would today, that you have made an excessive amount of IgE antibody to ragweed. When the two combine on the surface of mast cells and basophils, histamine and other similar agents are released and you suffer hives, hay fever, asthma, etc.

Your future immunologist will add the following good news. We will have to turn off your production of IgE antibody against ragweed, or you will never get better. You are not making enough antibody to the IgE to keep its production moderate. We will give you some anti-idiotypic antibody—that is, antibody to that part of your IgE that recognises ragweed—and shut production down. This will be safe, specific and indeed sensational desensitisation.

Figure 19. Turning antibodies into antigens

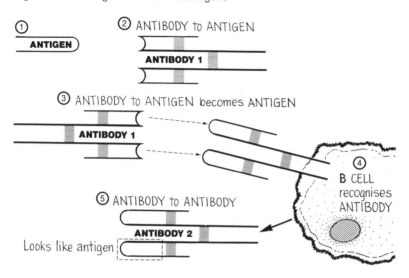

One other use of anti-idiotypic antibodies is already with us. If you think of an antigen and an antibody using the lock and key analogy we can take it one step further. If you make an antibody to the lock it will look like the key. In other words, the idiotypic region of the anti-idiotypic antibody will look like the antigen that started off the reaction in the first place. We can immunise animals and humans with anti-idiotypic antibodies and get the same response that we might get if we gave the antigen. The difference is that the antigen might be harmful. When we immunise people with live viruses (e.g. polio virus) there is always a chance that the attenuating process might not have been satisfactory, and disease could develop. But administration of an antibody against antibodies to polio virus is harmless and yet effective.

These are but a few of the tools of the clinical immunologist currently in use or soon to be developed. It is an exciting area, for I do not exaggerate in saying that 80 per cent of all human suffering from disease could be wiped out with mastery of the immune response.

12

Reinforcements: the mind as an ally

MARTINA was fourteen and thin; better than being fourteen and fat she supposed, but her thinness worried both her and her mother. It was not that she was sick; far from it. She was a likely candidate for her school's track team. Her lack of padding was not due to poor eating habits either. She would outeat her sixteen-year-old brother every time. Everybody joked about her skinny frame and she hated it. She prayed that puberty would make a difference. At least if she developed some breast tissue, that would give her some shape.

Martina was not doing well at school despite working fairly hard and she had come to terms with her own (and everybody else's) conclusion that she was not too smart. Academic achievement or rather lack of it did not worry her, for her ambition, constant now for six months, was to travel the big wide world; the life of a flight attendant was for her. Mother thought she was pretty enough and if she grew too tall for the jumbo jets she might just make it as a model. Skinny frames were great for hanging clothes on.

Martina did, however, have two big worries besides her lack of avoirdupois. Her brother David was taking drugs and no one else in the family knew. She had caught him sniffing some white powder into his nose. She was not stupid, and did not accept his claim that the stuff was medicine.

Her second worry was her mother. Although healthy-looking at the age of thirty-six, her mother had suffered from rheumatic fever as a child and the mitral valve in her heart had been damaged. Something about it was too narrow, Martina had heard many times, and her mother's heart had to pump very hard to push blood through a valve that had become a tiny hole. Twice her mother had undergone surgery to open the valve but each time, after a few years' improvement, it had closed down again. Martina adored her mother and could not bear to think of her pain if she knew how stupid David was being. She was about to have another operation; a new, manufactured valve would be sewn into her heart.

Then, quite unexpectedly, Martina's mother died on the operating table soon after her operation started. A blood clot or something had shot into her lungs and killed her. Martina's father told me later that his daughter screamed denial as he told her the news, and then cried in pathetic despair for three never-ending days before total physical and emotional exhaustion led her into a restless sleep punctuated by body-shaking sobs.

Months later Martina told me how severe had been the shock, how painful the acute sense of loss. She felt cheated, not only because she had lost her best friend and mother, but also because she had had no reason to worry about the surgery and therefore no time to prepare herself for this loss. As a result those first weeks after Mother's death found her racked with despair, anger and guilt.

A sad story, of course, but had there been no more to it than that I would not have subjected you to the details. No, the story and the suffering for this child were just beginning.

Two weeks to the day after her mother died, she awoke to find her fingers and right shoulder painful and stiff. By noon the pain and stiffness were gone but by the same evening the pain had returned and was now in her right knee as well. Two days later she was a bedridden cripple. Excruciatingly painful hot knees, ankles, shoulders and hands robbed her of her mobility.

Doctors examined the child. Tests were done on her blood and some fluid that was aspirated from her knee by a long needle connected to a syringe. A diagnosis was made: Martina had rheumatoid arthritis. The progression from track team candidate to cripple had taken a mere three days.

Five days later, as her joints were improving slightly thanks to continued bedrest and medicines, Martina noted that she was passing a lot of urine. Every hour she would pass large amounts and the thirst that this produced made her drink constantly. After three days of this her thin frame looked like a skeleton with grossly disproportioned joints.

More tests, more doctors and a new diagnosis. Not only did Martina have rheumatoid arthritis, she had also developed diabetes mellitus. Diabetes occurs when our pancreas fails to secrete enough insulin. Insulin is needed to get sugar (energy) into our cells. If the sugar cannot get into cells, it circulates in the blood and must be removed by the kidneys. This they do well, but they must remove a lot of water from the blood to accomplish it, and hence one passes a lot of sweet urine. It is sweet because of the sugar, of course.

Perhaps Martina's psychic torture, racing around her brain in the form of frenzied electrical impulses, upset some delicate control mechanisms that actually operate far away from the cerebrum in distant joints and abdominal glands.

As both rheumatoid arthritis and diabetes are autoimmune diseases, i.e. diseases in which the body's immune system attacks self tissue as if it were foreign tissue, could this immunological turning against self be related in some strange way to a psychic turning against self?

Most experienced doctors could tell you stories similar to Martina's. I could tell you many more myself. I could tell you, for example, of a concert pianist who nearly died of bowel inflammation three weeks after breaking and permanently damaging a finger. I could detail the struggle for breath caused by an acute spasm in the airways of a forty-two-year-old mother who miscarried after six months of pregnancy. This was the closest she had come to fulfilling a now desperate dream of having a child. But instead of more stories let us look at some basic scientific facts, as we see if we can convince ourselves that mind rules body and, in particular, that mind and immune system talk to each other constantly.

Charles Darwin was perhaps the first scientist to clearly enunciate the hypothesis that the mind, our intelligence-gathering and decision-making computer, can instantly and at will summon up a body response.

Darwin was fascinated by fear. Most people have been frightened. I do not enjoy fear myself, but some people love it and indeed will pay money to sit in the dark for two hours to be frightened. Like it or not, however, most people know that fear produces a bodily response or responses almost as quickly as the mind tells us that a situation is scary.

A dangerous situation is recognised by the higher centres of the brain. A car is coming around the corner too fast, the driver will not be able to stop at the pedestrian crossing, we are only halfway across—danger! Now, if our mind computes these dangerous facts and tells us that we are in danger, and yet does not automatically solve the problem for us, we will be struck by the car. We may die knowing what happened to us and regretting for a millisecond that we did not jump out of the way.

Fortunately, however, as Darwin appreciated, survival has demanded that mechanisms be developed whereby the appreciation of danger produces fear and fear produces an instantaneous bodily reaction. Our muscles tense and we *do* leap, most often success-fully, to safety. Fright prepares us for flight. This wonderful mech-anism obviously demands that a message race from the brain to the muscles and other vital organs.

The novelists of course have been describing these biological responses forever. Increased mental alertness in someone being ter-rorised may be related to us as: 'Hunted and desperate, his senses were as acute as those of a cat ready to pounce'. Activation of the nerves of the autonomic (automatic) nervous system that control the tiny muscles at the base of our hair follicles and the muscles that open and close blood vessels may be described as: 'Too late he saw the snake prepare to strike. The hair stood up on the back of his neck while the color drained from his face.'

The result of messages from a frightened mind that affect the nerves controlling sweat glands and bowel contractions may be described as: 'His stomach knotted with fear and beads of sweat formed on his brow as the executioner's gun was raised...'

Fear is good; fear is essential for it does marshal, with incredible speed, body responses that may save our life. But how is it that fear can instantly drain the color from one's cheeks by making super-ficial blood vessels in the skin spasm and therefore empty them-selves of color?

The mind sends messages from the cerebral cortex, the most developed part of the brain, to other parts in one of two ways. Electrical messages can pass along the billions of telegraph wires that connect one vital part of the brain to another. Alternatively, chemicals may deliver messages as one part of the brain releases a substance that will activate some other part of the brain, while not affecting yet another region. We know how rapidly a chemical signal can work: how long does it take for some voluptuous odor to con-jure up a specific memory or anticipation in your brain?

But all this is going on inside our heads and to jump out of the way of that rapidly approaching car we need action in our legs. For some time now we have known that these peripheral responses involve not only electrical messages racing along nerves but the rapid release of hormones.

Hormones are the chemical products of the endocrine system. This system comprises strategically placed glands that produce and store incredibly potent chemicals (hormones) that are released, when appropriate, to make us do something different. When we eat, within seconds the pancreas gland releases insulin into the bloodstream to handle the sugar we have consumed. When a young man's genes tell him it's time to grow hair on his chest his testicles will make and release testosterone and hair will sprout, muscles will strengthen and many other alterations will occur.

Not so long ago it was found that most of the hormones released around the body are controlled by a specific set of regulatory hormones released by the pituitary gland. This gland lives at the base of the brain. Put your finger at the top of your nose and point into your skull; just under the finger (under the bone, of course) sits the pituitary gland.

At the appropriate point in a woman's menstrual cycle the pituitary gland sends a chemical message to the ovary, instructing it to release into the Fallopian tubes some eggs ready for fertilisation. The pituitary then waits for an egg to be fertilised. If it is not, the gland sends another message to the ovary, instructing the uterus to close down and shed the soft, warm and cosy lining built up in the uterus to nourish a young embryo. The woman then has a period: 'the weeping of a disappointed uterus'.

What has all this to do with Martina's swollen joints? Patience, please, for just a little longer.

Recently it has been found that the pituitary gland itself is under the control of other hormones that come from a specific part of the brain called the hypothalamus, which is intimately connected by chemical and electrical links to many of the brain's higher centres.

The glands that have received all the scientific publicity about 'fright and flight' are the adrenals, on top of the kidneys. They produce two very important types of hormone: adrenalin, also called epinephrine, and steroids such as hydrocortisone. They are rightly called 'stress hormones' for their immediate release in times of danger is very important, but we now know that there are many others of equal importance.

Adrenalin makes the color drain from your face, not necessarily because Nature thinks there is an advantage in being pale. The advantage of having less blood flowing through the skin is that more blood flows into muscles; the muscles need blood for oxygen, oxygen gives them the energy needed to jump out of the way of a car, for example.

So far we have discussed fright leading to frantic messages being despatched around the body, with physiological adjustments being made instantly so that we can respond appropriately. But novelists have often noted that this is not always the case . . .

'Marie saw him emerge from the shadows and recognised him instantly as the moon's light bathed his all too familiar face. She froze, terrified, mesmerised, her heart racing. She wanted to run, she wanted to scream, but all she did was look into those cruel eyes as he approached her.'

What went wrong? Where was her hypothalamus when she needed it? Where were those electrical and chemical signals to her adrenal gland? We will never know and it is obviously likely that the monster had his way with her and then strangled the poor neuro-endocrine misfit.

'Too bad,' said Darwin. 'Only the fittest survive and pass their genetic superiority to their offspring.'

Some of us, confronted with situations of terror, respond appropriately; others do not.

Stress in any form—fear, bereavement, anger, etc.—calls not only for hormonal alertness but also for immunological alertness. Suppose at the time we prepare for 'flight after fright' we engage the immunological system, another vital link in the human defence. Some individuals may *enhance* their immune capacity when stressed, while others may damage its operations.

If that is so, then one can perhaps explain what happened to Martina. Mental anguish led to inappropriate, indeed harmful, alterations in her hormonal and immune systems.

There is evidence that the central nervous system and immune system are linked, with hormones playing major roles as messengers connecting the higher centres of the brain to the immune system.

If you ask a biology student, 'Where do you find in the body the ability to "know thyself", the adaptability that allows for responses that are appropriate not reflex, and memory capacity which means that one can learn from experience and improve?', the answer in all likelihood will be 'The brain', with a quizzical look as to why one would ask such an easy question. In fact, the answer should be the brain *and* the immune system. The latter's ability to recognise self, adapt to circumstances and make specific responses as well as utilise memory capacity, bestows without doubt a certain intelligence on the immune system.

When something foreign enters your body, the immune response genes you inherited will determine whether you make an appropriate or inappropriate immune response. When one is stressed, coping response genes determine the stress response that you will make and whether that response is appropriate or inappropriate. Simply put, some people for genetic reasons handle, say, tuberculosis better than others; likewise, for genetic reasons some handle tension better than others. We are exploring the possibility that the genetic knowledge for appropriateness in either situation is in some way linked. We would hypothesise that good coping genes are more likely to turn up in a patient who also has inherited good immune response genes.

We should backtrack for a minute and make sure that a couple of points already made are quite clear. Psychologists refer to an appropriate stress response as coping, in the way that an immunologist thinks of an immune response in terms of inflammation. We should also define how we are using the word 'stress' in our context.

Stress is confusing as the noun can refer to the thing causing the stress (e.g. a situation) or to the response that situation provokes. Throughout, we use the term 'stress' to mean the situation that calls for a response from the person interpreting the situation.

Now scientists can study this subject in humans, and many do, but it is often easier to get at basic facts with animal observations and experiments. Let us look at the evidence, derived from animal studies, that suggests that the mind sends signals to the immune system and vice versa, and that some of these signals arise from a perception of a stressful situation.

If you have read any behavioural physiology books you must know something of the great Dr Pavlov and his equally famous dog. Pavlov knew of an unfortunate man who, at the end of the nineteenth century, made a remarkable recovery from a savage war wound to his stomach. The recovery left the man with some of the lining of his stomach outside his body: bizarre but true. What Pavlov noted was that whenever the man became hungry, even before he began to eat, his now inside-out stomach put forth all sorts of digestive juices as he prepared for his *expected* feast. At dinner time his stomach poured. If he smelled food, it poured. In other words, his brain was somehow getting his stomach to work *before* the food arrived.

Pavlov operated on a dog to give him a similar inside-out piece of stomach and performed some experiments with his laboratory pet that made them both famous. In essence, after much work, Pavlov found that he could 'condition' the dog so that he would make it pour out gastric juices when neither food nor hunger was involved.

If you take an animal such as Pavlov's dog and ring a loud bell every time you expose it to a delicious aroma that would normally get its juices flowing, you can soon get those same juices flowing just by ringing the bell. Whatever message usually goes from the brain to the stomach with hunger now travels the same pathways when a bell is rung. This learned response is called conditioning.

So entrenched in the scientific soul of behavioural psychologists and physiologists is conditioning, that it is not surprising that some of the first and most interesting attempts at demonstrating that the mind controls or at least can influence the immune system came from conditioning experiments. Let me give you a few examples.

If you take an ordinary mouse and inject into it some red blood cells from, say, a sheep, the mouse's immune system will obviously object. Its T cells will recognise the intruders, sound the alarm, and among other things activate the mouse's B cells to make antibodies to the sheep's blood cells. Three weeks later you would not have trouble detecting these antibodies in a few drops of the mouse's blood. All perfectly normal.

Today we have drugs that poison B cells. We use them to treat diseases in which B cells are so disturbed that they become a menace—for example, in some forms of leukemia. Such a drug is cyclophosphamide, which we will call Cy for short. If you put Cy (which is tasteless) in the drinking water of our mouse and give him some sheep red blood cells, he will not make as much antibody as a mouse given plain water. After a couple of weeks the mouse given the Cy recovers and is back to normal. At this stage he would respond quite normally if given a second injection of sheep red blood cells.

Into such a model you can add a conditioning trick. Say you add some saccharin to the water as well as the Cy and then inject the sheep red blood cells. Now we know the water is very sweet; and, of course, the mouse still does not make as much antibody as normal because the Cy in the water poisons his B cells.

Allow the mouse to recover and repeat the sequence. Allow him to recover again. On the third time put only saccharin in the water—no drugs. What do you think will happen to his antibody production? You are right. It is suppressed.

Saccharin will initiate a taste signal that goes to the brain where it is translated as 'it must be B cell suppression time'. That message in the brain leads to a chain of events that suppresses the B cell response and yet there is no poison in sight. Obviously, the clever scientists doing these experiments had to show that saccharin per se had no effect on antibody production, and they did.

Encouraged by these remarkable observations, these sorts of experiment were varied. There is a mouse strain known as the NZB (New Zealand Black) mouse, which is famous in the immunological world because it contracts systemic lupus erythematosus (SLE) almost identical to the strain humans get. After a few months of life, autoantibodies form in this strain of mouse and destroy many of his normal tissues including his red cells and kidneys. The disease can be prevented by giving the NZB mouse Cy from an early age. We now know that the same conditioning tricks described above allow saccharin to minimise the disease while subjecting the mouse to many fewer side-effects than one would produce by continuing to treat him with Cy. You can see the potential use for this approach in humans.

This sort of evidence is not just restricted to experiments performed in this strain of mouse, nor to the use of saccharin. If you take a guinea pig, for example, and graft on to its side a small piece of rabbit skin, what happens?

Healthy guinea pig T cells recognise that the rabbit skin is foreign and in a few days attack in full force with millions of cells invading the rabbit's tissue and destroying it. If that experiment is done but an 'operation' is made of the operation, another example of conditioning is demonstrated—for example, doing the skin graft while playing some music in the room and having differently colored lights flashing on and off. You give the animal an injection of local anesthetic in the area in which you will place the graft, and then wrap up the site in big bandages that make it awkward for the guinea pig to walk. In other words, the guinea pig learns that lights, music, anesthetic and bandages are associated with the placement of a graft on his side.

If you do this three times but on the third time you do not place any rabbit skin on the side of the animal, what happens? There is no skin to reject, of course, but, if you biopsy the skin a week or so later, where the graft *would* have been you find the skin full of angry-looking T cells searching everywhere for a foreign graft that is expected to be present but is not. These little T cells obviously were given a message from the guinea pig's brain to expect trouble.

How could a guinea pig learn that lights, music, etc. mean that a skin graft was to be expected so that messages could be sent from its brain to its T cells urging them to be on the lookout for trouble in a specific area? The answers to such a riddle are not all in, but we are getting close as you will see.

If the mind can influence the immune system, could stress, in general, or perhaps a particular form of stress, damage the immune system of some animals and in this way produce a model for what may have happened to Martina?

The study of the way in which a genetic makeup may make one animal perform better than another under stressful conditions is fascinating. For most of these sorts of experiment we use small laboratory animals which we have inbred to the point where all the animals are identical. That is, we have hundreds of cloned animals all with an identical genetic makeup.

If you take a rat or a mouse and fix it in its cage so that it has little room to move, and you strap electrodes to its tail, you can stress the animal for various periods by delivering very small electric shocks. The shock is tiny but obviously unpleasant.

Numerous such studies have shown that rats and mice become physically ill from this treatment, despite normal amounts of food and water. The physical deterioration noted involves a dramatic decrease in T cell function and a marked increase in susceptibility to infection. But isn't this all wrong? Shouldn't the stress get the animal fighting mad and ready for flight? Shouldn't the T cells be turned *on*, not off?

In some animals the reverse does happen. Certain strains of mice lose weight and hair lustre and have T cell depression for quite some time after the stress begins, but then they recover spontaneously.

Their weight increases and their T cells become, in fact, super-efficient. They have adapted to the stress magnificently.

Other strains of mice, given a similar set of stressful circumstances, simply fade away. This obviously suggests that genetic information can help us perform better under stress. Most interestingly, pre-liminary studies seem to show that if you inject some serum from the mouse that has successfully adapted to a stressful situation into an inadequate mouse, the latter becomes a fighter. If this is con-firmed, can you imagine how valuable will be the blood of the cool, calm, efficient IBM executive who thrives on the stress of his job?

The mouse that roared in the face of stress as described above (inescapable tail shock) is the exception rather than the rule, so it brings us back to the 'how come' question we asked before. Shouldn't stress improve physical responses if Darwin's fright and flight concepts are right?

Psychologists have long thought that the *deleterious* responses to stress that one may find associated with a certain set of circumstances can be markedly reduced if we have room to manoeuvre in the situation. If you can respond to the stressful situation in a positive fashion, in other words if you can do something about the situation, the harmful effects of stress are reduced. Could the ability to cope with danger or, for that matter, with constant pain, etc. be the important factor that determines the effect of stress on the immune system?

Back to the laboratory we go and take two sets of identical rats. We place electrodes on their tails and intermittently shock them slightly at ten-second intervals for three minutes. Both sets get the same shock. One set of rats, however, have in their cages a small lever and when they learn to push this lever with their paw the shocks will stop. The shocks will also stop for the other group but they have no way of controlling the situation; they are not involved in actions that spare them pain.

It is amazing how quickly the rats with a lever in their cage will learn to turn off the shocks and, although stressed by having the shocks start all over again at variable intervals, the animals that can turn off the shocks thrive. Not so the rats who feel the same shocks but are helpless. They lose weight and have their immune system depressed.

Thus it would seem that, for most of us, stress causes the brain to initiate a series of endocrine and immune responses that help us terminate the stress. Successful application of these moves with subsequent lessening of stress is called coping. If it so happens that circumstances make it impossible to handle the situation, many important systems in the body may not function normally and dis-ease may result.

In this context it is important to realise that regardless of whether the circumstances are *really* impossible to handle or just *perceived to be* impossible to handle, the results may be the same. How much stress an individual human can handle without getting into trouble varies considerably, as it does with mice.

Before we talk about studies and observations of the interactions of the human mind and immune system we should look at possible ways that the interdependency of the nervous, endocrine and immune systems could occur. If the sensation of taste can pass from nerves in the tongue to the centre of the brain, which appreciates taste, and then initiate effects that stop B cells in the spleen from making antibodies, then there must be brain-lymphocyte connections.

We are all used to thinking of the brain sending messages down nerves in the spinal cord which will branch off between the vertebrae to connect muscles and blood vessels, etc. to headquarters (the brain) in a physical fashion. You can follow the messages from initiation to reception.

Messages, of course, race back along similar pathways to tell the brain that the desired effect has, or has not, occurred. If you move your big toe right now you have sent a message at incredible speed to the muscles of your foot. This has resulted in your moving your toe and this results in a message being sent back to the brain so that, in fact, you know you have really moved your toe.

That system isn't good enough to connect the immune system to the brain, however, because, as we have seen when discussing our immune system, we are talking about collections of cells patrolling around the body; they are certainly not dancing on the ends of nerves like puppets on a string.

The brain is composed of numerous subsections that control specific functions. Smell, speech, sight and hearing, for example, are all controlled by different parts of the brain. This is why it is possible for someone who has had a stroke (i.e. had damage occur to a small part of their brain by an interference with that region's blood supply) to lose, say, the ability to speak while still being able to comprehend the written or spoken word.

It is possible for scientists who are trying to map the specific functions of various geographical areas of the brain to place a small electrode, via an extremely thin needle, into certain parts of the brain. They may then send an electrical message through the electrode that will stimulate a specific part of the brain or they may damage it and see what happens to the animal when this section of the brain is no longer working.

Studies of parts of the brain in humans can be so precise that stimulation of a specific area will always invoke the same memory. A specific memory circuit has obviously been located in this case.

Using such techniques and others, scientists have studied areas of the brain which may influence the performance of the immune system. Already much has been learned. We know that nerves pass from the brain stem directly to the thymus gland in the neck. You will remember that the thymus is the immune system's 'soul'. These nerve fibres indicate that messages can pass from the brain to the thymus and vice versa. What sorts of signal are despatched along these recently discovered fibres is unknown, but they are not there by chance—something important is going on.

There is a little gland in the brain called the pineal gland. It is very important in regulating sleep patterns and in regulating many other rhythms that fluctuate between night and day. Damage to this gland damages the ability of immunoregulatory T cells to do their job in a way that is as yet poorly understood.

Damage to the hypothalamus, which is so vital for the initiation of hormonal responses, also damages many aspects of immune function, inhibiting the ability of lymphocytes to circulate and regulate their own activity. In addition, those non-specific scavenger cells that mop up the immunological debris (dead bacteria, etc.) are prevented from performing normally by some as yet unknown mechanisms when the hypothalamus is damaged. If you damage the left side of the brain but not the right side you will damage natural killer cell (NK) activity.

In summary, we now know that the brain has many circuits that are linked in some way into the heart of the immune system. That leaves us with the problem of how the interaction occurs. Faced with this dilemma, scientists began to seek evidence that the mind that uses the ability to control the release of hormones could use them or another set of chemicals to deliver messages to the cells of the immune system.

For this to be possible we would need to show that the wall of the lymphocyte, i.e. its outer membrane, is equipped with the necessary receptors for accepting such chemical messages. There is no use having a lot of adrenalin, for example, arriving at the surface of the lymphocyte if the cell has no way of knowing that it is being bombarded with this hormone.

As you have no doubt guessed, the surface of lymphocytes turns out to be bristling with antennae for the reception of various hormones and chemicals. Lymphocytes have receptors for insulin, steroids, adrenalin and a host of other potent chemicals. But lymphocytes and other cells of the immune system themselves secrete chemicals and therefore could potentially send messages back to the brain, if the brain had nerve cells that could read these signals; of course it does. The science of psychoneuroendocrinoimmunology is with us!

This extension of the concept that danger and other stimuli provoke not only neuroendocrine interactions but also neuroendocrine immunological reactions would no doubt have delighted Darwin, who was so interested in the human defence, but there are some potential traps in it for the human species.

I suspect that for centuries doctors have observed 'the fighting spirit phenomenon' and certainly many would tell you that depressed patients are more likely to suffer frequent infections. But suspecting this and proving this suspicion are two different things. Depressed patients may have more problems with infection if the depression itself depresses their immune system, but there could be simpler explanations. Depressed people do not eat as well as others; their standards of personal hygiene can slip. These factors may play a major role in producing health problems.

We are now certain that depression is associated with suppressed immunological functions in humans. Here we run into the difficulties that plague this sort of research: measuring in objective terms a degree of depression is much more difficult than documenting a specific percentage decrease in T cell function. For this reason it is perhaps easiest for scientists interested in the question to study emotional extremes to find out if they are on the right track.

Perhaps the most potent emotion experienced by people is the sorrow that follows bereavement, the overwhelming sadness associated with the loss of someone loved. Characteristically this emotion is not shortlived and therefore such an intensive experience is indeed able to engender hormonal and/or immunological changes. One may expect that clinically significant results may occur. Panic can be even more dramatic than bereavement, of course, but it is so shortlived (you make it or you don't make it) that there may not be enough time for any significant change to occur.

Even when studying something as powerful as bereavement one must remember that, while all intelligent species who can feel are subject to emotions associated with bereavement, in humans and probably animals there is a variation in the intensity of bereavement that is both cultural and individual. Most people are more or less devastated for four to six weeks after the loss of someone loved then they pick up the pieces of their life and march on. Others take months or years to pull out of the depths of their depression, with disastrous results to their social and working lives.

Psychologists cannot, of course, specify an exact time for a normal grief response period, but in their analysis of the individual case they can decide that, yes, this person's suffering is beyond the normal, in fact it is pathological bereavement.

We are not going to discuss those pathological situations. What we will look at is the effect that bereavement, handled normally, has on the immune system of otherwise *healthy* individuals. That is, we will be looking at the sort of emotion you may see in a man who is grief-stricken for four to six weeks after his wife dies, who suffers episodic depression over a period of months as he faces life alone.

Statistical analysis of mortality figures tells us that men, at any age, who lose a wife have a fourteen times greater chance of dying within the next twelve months than if they had not been thus bereaved. What happens to them? Do they try to clean out the electric toaster while it is still plugged in? Do they trip and hit their heads in the parking lot of the supermarket? We do not know. The figures I quoted are just that; statistical facts which are now being carefully researched.

Some preliminary studies have reported that women have substantially less chance of dying in the year after their husbands die than if their husbands had survived. Psychologists argue that most women, at either a conscious or a subconscious level, expect that their husbands will die first; and if they do in fact die first, the wives are prepared—conditioned over the years.

Men never think that their wives will die first and the shock is therefore much worse, especially if they are left with young children to rear. Studies have shown that suppression of the immune system after the loss of a wife is directly proportional to the troubles experienced in handling children now left with out a mother.

Most of the studies of this situation have been restrospective, which introduces problems. One does not really know that a man who is immunosuppressed after a loss has not developed his present problems because his immune system was not normal *before* bereavement. Secondly, historical details, which are often sketchy, might be wrong. Therefore prospective studies are needed and these are indeed under way.

Some of the problems associated with the studies we are talking about can be overcome by looking at depression in animals. Bereavement can be induced in animals, and the effects studied. One model that has received a lot of attention creates a loss and then corrects the situation, thus allowing us to look not only at the effect of bereavement on the immune system but also to repair the damage that has been done to the mechanisms.

Monkeys are very emotional animals and have long been known to suffer physical changes while bereaved. Experiments which sound cruel (and are), but are of vital importance, involve the study of maternal deprivation among monkeys. Baby monkeys can be removed from their natural mothers at an early age and the effect of separation upon both mother and baby studied.

Various conditions can be established. The babies are sometimes given to other mothers who have or have not had their own baby monkeys removed so that some maternal care, if not the correct maternal care, can be supplied. Alternatively, the baby monkeys can be totally cared for by humans. After a period of studying the deprived monkeys the youngsters can be reunited with their natural mothers and the effects of this emotional reunion can be measured.

Studies have shown that maternally deprived monkeys become agitated over a two-week period and then become depressed, the latter being judged by disturbances in their sleep patterns and very decreased activity. Both mother and baby suffer a very significant deterioration in T cell function. Physically reuniting mothers and babies, however, very rapidly reverses the damage and by looking at the data there is little trouble in determining which babies had been returned to their mothers and which had not.

As you would probably expect, something like great sadness may cause the release of many hormones simultaneously and it does not necessarily follow that all the hormones released will affect the immune system. Mapping the hormonal changes associated with a particular emotion would be the first step to asking which hormone or hormones change the immune system. Scientists at New York's Mt Sinai hospital are studying this subject with the help of some remarkable people.

Even if you, the reader, are not a parent, I am sure you can understand the particularly devastating sadness associated with *knowing* that you are about to lose a child.

I have observed, over more than twenty-five years as a doctor, that most people die with a degree of resignation that ensures dignity and speaks well of the basic human realism that can be brought to bear on this one inescapable occurrence. Children certainly are no exception, although they must face death within the limits of their intellectual development.

After explaining the nature of their research and its importance to parents who are about to lose a child, the doctors concerned have invited the parents' help by requesting that blood samples be constantly monitored before, during and after a near-final meeting with the dying child. A thin plastic catheter is placed in a vein in the arm so that blood can be withdrawn at will and unobtrusive electrodes are placed on the scalp so that brainwaves can be measured. From this type of research will come clues to how the brain and the body's chemicals interact with the immune system.

While we are examining connections between the brain and the immune system, we must not overlook an important but as yet poorly understood set of interactions involving left-handedness. Medical and physical consequences are associated with this preference.

First, the good part. Among true lefties (that is, excluding ambidextrous people) there is a disproportionately high number who, because of a heightened appreciation of spatial concepts, are very good at such things as sport, the arts and architecture. In addition, there is a lack of the common mental illness schizophrenia among left-handed people.

But the news is not all good. Left-handed people have twelve times more learning disabilities than do right-handed people, and stuttering and autism are more common. While lefties do not get schizophrenia they seem to be more prone to suffer from manic-depressive psychosis, a severe problem that mani fests itself as the blackest of depressions alternating with manic behaviour. There is a delusionary component to the illness so that, for example, a victim may feel very rich during his manic phase and race around the city buying thousands of dollars' worth of goods he does not need and certainly cannot afford.

In our context, however, we are interested in an association between left-handedness and the early onset of childhood allergies and a number of autoimmune disease such as ulcerative colitis, myasthenia gravis and coeliac disease.

So that I am not besieged with letters beginning 'I'm left-handed and have never stuttered in my entire life', let me stress that most left-handed people have none of these problems (I also know a lot of terrible left-handed tennis players). It is clear that left-handedness per se is not the cause of these problems, though it may frequently be associated with other abnormalities that do cause problems.

When the embryonic brain is developing, some sections seem dependent for normal growth on the presence of more or less of the male sex hormone testosterone. If there is a little too much testosterone then an area of the brain known as the *planum temporale* overdevelops in the right-hand section of the brain and the result is a 'lefty'.

As we discussed in the chapter on autoimmune disease such problems are much more common among women than among men, and it may well be that an imbalance in sex hormone concentrations during fetal development causes not only left-handedness but also the development of less than perfect central nervous system connections to the immune system. This may result in the loss of certain regulatory controls that normally prevent autoimmunity.

Summarising to this point, we can see that the human immunological defence is in the hands of lymphocytes: cells that can be influenced by the central nervous system either directly (e.g. nervous innovation of the thymus) or indirectly (by hormones controlled by the brain). Lymphocytes can also send messages to the brain, so it is definitely a two-way street. The potential for mental conditioning that might strengthen our defence mechanisms is obviously an exciting area for exploration, as is the possibility that higher-centre-generated feelings, such as depression, might damage the immune system of some. Let's look at both ideas, but the latter first.

Let us visit the West Point Military Academy in New York State in any typical year, and take a look at the young candidates for officership who get glandular fever. The correct name of this disease, as we noted earlier, is infectious mono-nucleosis, known as mono. It is a miserable disease and it is very infectious.

In a place like West Point it takes only one or two recruits to come down with the disease after picking up the virus and the whole academy is in trouble. Under dormitory conditions it is easy for the virus to spread and a mini-epidemic will result.

One of the interesting things about infectious mononucleosis is that not everyone infected with the virus (EBV) that causes the disease suffers the same fate. Some have a very mild flu-like illness, while others can be bedridden for six months or longer or even die of complications.

In some people in Africa the virus can trigger off a cancer in the immune system, while in Asia it can trigger a cancerous growth at the back of the nose and throat. A good immune system is certainly needed to handle this virus, which in some respects is a close relative of the AIDS virus.

EBV belongs to a different family of viruses from the retrovirus that causes AIDS, but mono does result in an infection occurring within lymphocytes—B cells in this case, not T cells as in AIDS. We are then left with the distasteful task of killing our infected B cells and just how long it takes our T cells to do this job determines the length and severity of the disease. The point is that EBV virus infection is a great challenge for the immune system.

What would one find if one analysed both the clinical disease (i.e. how sick an individual becomes) and the immune response to the virus, and related these findings to various psychosocial features that might be important at a place like West Point?

This training ground for young officers is full of cadets whose fathers were either graduates themselves or are professionals in the military forces. It seems, on careful examination, that a lot of the young students are there only because their fathers want them to be there. In such circumstances, many have a miserable time of it and do poorly in their examinations.

Studies have shown a clear separation between those who made a very good immunological response to the virus, once infected, and those who did less well. Students who were not happy at West Point and were under a considerable amount of stress because of doubts about their career choice had more symptoms and their immunological response to the disease was poor. There was an equally strong correlation between satisfaction with the establishment and a good response to the infectious agent.

I can give you many other examples, but two will suffice. You will remember NK or natural killer cells. These are the cells that spontaneously attack malignant cells that may appear in the body, and destroy them.

Their action is almost immediate and there seems no reason to imagine that these cells do not play an important role on a day-to-day basis in protecting us from the development of cancer. Their action depends on the presence in the body of the naturally occurring chemical interferon.

We have known for some time that a number of potential cancer-causing chemicals depress NK cell activity and that depressed NK cell activity is associated with increased risk of getting cancer. More recently we have learned that NK cells' performance is very markedly affected by stress. When these cells are activated by interferon, they become somewhat larger than normal lymphocytes and have a granular appearance that makes them easy to recognise. Recently a number of scientists involved in behavioural immunology have begun to call them 'stress lymphocytes'.

Studies have been done among medical students at Johns Hopkins University, while the students were undergoing stressful examinations. It certainly would appear as though candidates who were less well prepared for their examinations and who subsequently did poorly were under a lot of stress. Their stress and failure correlated very well with depressed NK cell activity. These studies are particularly interesting because they suggest once again that the nature of the stressful event and one's ability to cope with that stress determine whether one's immune system performs adequately.

One final example of this sort of thing comes from dental students who were having examinations. Here it was found that students who were suffering from a great deal of stress, because they were less well prepared for the examination, did poorly in their exams, as would be expected. They also had an increased occurrence of upper respiratory tract infections following the exams. No such effects, of course, were noted in students who did well and who were well prepared.

What was so fascinating to the investigators was the fact that secretory IgA, the specific immunoglobulin that protects our mucous membranes and therefore our upper airways, was suppressed in those students experiencing much stress at exam time. It is entirely feasible to suggest that the suppression of this form of antibody response left them vulnerable to upper respiratory tract infections.

A little earlier I mentioned that, apart from the potentially harmful effects of stress on the immune system that clinicians will have to deal with in the future, it is also necessary to contemplate the possibility of *improving* immunological responses by conditions. Some very encouraging results have been reported in recent years.

If you remember our little mouse taking the saccharin and how he could be tricked into suppressing his immune system with just a sweetener, then you will understand why it is that clinicians may want to use conditioning approaches to improve a person's immune response to cancer.

Scientists in the United States used this approach with a group of doctors suffering from cancer. These doctors were ideal candidates for this form of experimentation because they had elected not to receive any conventional treatment. Let me hasten to add that they were not in any way a group of anti-medical-establishment doctors who were seeking alternative medicine approaches to their cancer; far from it. These were doctors, who, because of their lifelong experience in the profession, knew that the cancer from which they suffered meant that they had at best a few extra months to be gained by submitting themselves to chemotherapy. In their minds, any suppression of the cancer would be more than offset by the loss of quality of life caused by the side-effects of the drugs required. For such physicians the chance to take part in conditioning exercises was most appealing.

The physicians were first educated about their immune system, as many of them would certainly not have kept up with the more recent information about immunology that we have been discussing in this book. It was explained to them that they had immune cells with the capacity to kill tumor cells if only they could be activated to do so. The doctors were shown slides and movie films of normal cells killing tumor cells in a test tube, and were asked to concentrate on sending from the brain to the immune system demanding that similar proficiency be developed for the fight against their own cancer.

The physicians had immunological studies done before their conditioning experiments started and, among the immune function studies performed, were ones to look at their ability to kill cancer cells. Needless to say, the studies were repeated during and after the conditioning therapy.

While these doctors did not have their life prolonged significantly by these conditioning experiments, the studies reported clearly demonstrated that they were able to increase the cancer-fighting capacity of their immune systems. Intervention in these cases was clearly too late and studies with less advanced disease are under way. A trial of this approach is under way at the M.D. Anderson Cancer Center in Texas. Again, while the results are preliminary, the initial impressions of the investigators have been very favorable. In this study, it seems that there is a correlation between increased activity against tumor cells and a longer than expected survival time.

Numerous other pieces of the psychoimmunology jigsaw puzzle are being reported and need further investigating. There is at least a doubled incidence of cancer among humans who suffer a long period of depression after loss or separation. There is a particular risk, for example, that men in that situation may develop testicular cancer. Juvenile rheumatoid arthritis, an immunological attack on the joints of children, is much more common among adopted children and children who have suffered through a traumatic parental divorce.

Other investigators have reported that children who grow up in a household where they feel that there is a lack of closeness have a much higher risk of developing cancer later in life. Autistic children who appear to have withdrawn from the world clearly have depressed T cell function.

I could go on and on, but I feel that this review has given you the flavor of one of the most exciting areas of modern medicine.

In closing I must stress that, although there is a voluminous literature on the subject of the mind as an ally, there are few really good scientific studies that have been carried out with all the safeguards that top-class scientists would demand. But these are under way, and there seems little doubt that information of great value will be available to us in the next few years.

In the meantime, it is probably wise for all of us to think carefully about the words of wisdom provided by the American cardiologist, Robert Elliot. In worrying about Type A personalities (whose anxiety and pace of life may lead to early heart attack) he promulgated two useful rules. Rule 1 is: Don't sweat the small stuff. Very good advice. But Rule 2 is even more useful. This rule simply states: It's all small stuff.

Certainly, we can extend the concepts important in controlling heart disease to the control of diseases linked to abnormal functioning of the immune and endocrine systems. Perhaps, therefore, we will leave the subject with some famous reflections on behavioural immunology from that well-known observer of the human scene, Mr Woody Allen. Trotting forth his wisdom in the movie *Manhattan* he supplies the following lines, which clearly demonstrate his knowledge of psycho-neuroimmunology.

Well, I don't get angry, OK?
I mean, I have a tendency to internalise.
I can't express anger.
That's one of the problems I have.
I . . . I grow a tumor instead.

Index